Tundra

A Memoir of Alaska

Georgeie Reynolds

Tundra: A Memoir of Alaska

Copyright 2021 by Georgeie Reynolds

Disclaimer: Names of major characters have been changed.
Events are as I remember them and as written in my field notes.

Artifact illustrations by the author.
Typesetting and cover design by István Szabó, Ifj.
Cover photograph by Dale C. Slaughter.

First edition: February 2021
ISBN: 978-0-9983857-4-7

For Harvey and the Rest of the Gang

ACKNOWLEDGEMENTS

First of all, my comrades from 1977 made this book possible because they changed my life completely. I am forever in their debt and consider them my littermates.

The manuscript underwent ten drafts and was moved along by Linda Stirling's SW Washington/NW Oregon Write to Publish group in earlier iterations and by Zeek's writing group in later versions. In particular, I'd like to thank Karla Von Huben, James Chesky, Jim Rogers, Sharon Harris, Gary Cullen, Jessie McClure, Penny Simpson, Andi Crockford, and Kumiko Olson. Their honest assessments, while sometimes daunting, enabled me to make *Tundra* more focused and honest.

Two professional editors labored over later drafts of the manuscript, changing it for the better. Jamie Garbacik performed a thorough developmental edit and Cali Kopczick a complete copyedit. They turned my convoluted prose into clear language.

Tundra benefitted from the scrutiny of my Alaskan readers and comrades. I'd like to thank my academic advisor, Dr. Al Dekin Jr., for his encouragement, and to Tim Smith and Dale Slaughter. Without their help, my descriptions of helicopters and small planes would not have been accurate. Dr. Slaughter also provided the black and white cover photograph.

To all the people I've met, worked with, and bonded with up north in the tundra, this book is for you.

TABLE OF CONTENTS

PART I
1977

UMIAT,
NORTH SLOPE OF ALASKA, 1977

I pressed my nose against the window of the old DC-3 as it touched down on the dirt runway.

Where is the tarmac and, for Christ's sake, where are the trees?

We taxied to a stop, clouds of dirt and dust obliterating the blue sky.

I stepped down onto the dirt with the others and looked around cautiously while the dry wind blew dust in my face. I reached for my pair of sunglasses.

"Here's home," Malcolm, my new boss, said, standing next to me. A smile crossed his face behind his scratched-up glasses as he bobbed up and down on the balls of his feet.

Looking over at him, I thought he might be getting a kick out of my apparent discomfort.

"That's the Umiat Hilton," he said, pointing to a dilapidated trio of industrial trailers hitched together. Over the entrance, a giant moose rack was affixed to the peeling and faded paint.

Umiat boasted a radio tower, garage, and row upon row of dilapidated Quonset huts left over from World War II. Two of the Quonsets billowed black smoke into the sky. One of the geologists ran over to meet our plane and saw my horrified expression.

"Fuel for the choppers is stored in a few of the Quonsets. Some of it ignited a while ago, but don't worry, it's probably under control. And only *some* of the Blazo ignited. We got plenty left. Hope those old Quonsets don't explode."

I was uncertain what my reaction should be so I said nothing. My eyes felt as big as saucers and I hoped my apprehensiveness about, well, everything, did not show elsewhere on my face. I was supposed to begin my career as an Arctic archaeologist up on the North Slope, but I had my doubts.

I remembered what a soldier at Fort Wainwright had said while hooking me into a harness and a set of ropes as I prepared to rappel down a cliff during the previous week's survival training in Fairbanks. I was having misgivings as I lowered myself over the abyss. The ground seemed so far away. He said: "Lean back. Trust your equipment."

I pushed off and rappelled to the bottom.

Here in Umiat, far above the Arctic Circle where there were no trees, the runway was dirt, and two Quonsets were on fire, I thought of that advice again and put my trust in a different kind of equipment, the common sense and knowledge of strangers, people I had no control over and would have to rely on.

* * *

Four crews of archaeologists and several support people descended on Umiat that day in early June, swelling the local population of about ten to almost sixty. We'd been hired by the federal government to survey a large part of the Slope in anticipation of future oil and gas exploration. Our results would identify areas of archaeological significance to avoid. Teams of biologists had already dispersed across the landscape to identify endangered species with a similar mission.

I had chosen Malcolm's Howard Pass crew during orientation because he had more Alaskan experience than the other bosses, one of whom had never been on an airplane before flying north that summer. Malcolm's crew also had the most people with Alaskan experience than the others. Malcolm, Ron, Tom, and Helen were all survivors of several Alaskan expeditions. The non-Alaskan crowd—Toni, Kelly, and Lucy—had wilderness savvy from other parts of the country. As for me, all I had was book learning, and no field experience to speak of.

Also, Malcolm made a pitch I couldn't refuse—Howard Pass, in the northern foothills of the Brooks Range, was the prettiest area to be investigated that summer.

There were eight of us, five women and three men. Almost everyone looked younger than me and all of them appeared more experienced. I could tell by the way they carried themselves with confidence, knowing what to do at any given moment. Maybe they were scared, too, but I couldn't tell. I only knew *I* was.

* * *

"Okay, gang," Malcolm said, "time for us to offload the Howard Pass supplies from the plane."

Well, shit, what does that mean and how do I do it?

I looked at the others grabbing equipment and food and pitched in, copying their movements closely. I resolved then to do whatever I saw other people doing during the summer in the hope

I would fit in. I focused on the best method of flinging tents, food, stoves, and miscellaneous field gear on the ground.

Malcolm inspected our progress and said, "Alright, campers, I've borrowed a pickup from some of the geologists at the Hilton to take us and our stuff down to the wall tents."

The beat-up old truck lacked paint, muffler, and side view mirrors, but seemed up to the task of hauling us a half mile. We loaded our mountains of gear and supplies into it and climbed into the back. We drove past the smoking Quonsets and a new looking and out-of-place prefab house to an open area where large wall tents had been set up.

I stared at our newly erected base camp at the edge of Umiat, trying to take it all in. There were three wall tents lined up neatly in a row facing others. There was no sidewalk of any kind, just dry, unvegetated dirt, like the runway. At the end of the row of wall tents was tundra with no indication human beings had ever set foot there.

"Okay, here's the Howard Pass tent." Malcolm said, pointing in the direction of one of the tents.

Jesus, where are the bathrooms?

Tom, one of my crewmates, answered this question by turning his back, unzipping, and peeing. I guessed I would have to go behind our tent when nature called.

I helped toss everything into the middle of the plywood floor of the designated tent. I heard yells and hollers from the three other crews—Lookout Ridge, Colville River, and Ikpikpuk— who were arriving in similarly rundown conveyances to set up shop in their own tents. Empty cardboard boxes flew out of tent doors, littering the ground. Garbage was even more prolific outside the two supply tents at the end of our compound. Laughter spilled into the air.

"Home, home on the range," bellowed someone inside the Lookout Ridge tent. Titters followed, then, "Where the deer and the antelope play," from the direction of Ikpikpuk.

"How bout a doobie?" Tom said as he heaved an empty box outside our tent. Dimples showed through his beard as his face lit in a smile.

Malcolm, chewing on his beard, took a deep breath, and said, "Well, I'm not sure it's allowed, but I guess it's okay."

"Home on the Range" was forgotten as Tom rolled some Matanuska ThunderFuck into a slim, tight joint.

Oh boy, now you're talking. Maybe some weed will loosen me up.

Everyone except Ron wanted to partake, so I took a long grateful drag when the joint was passed to me. Kelly made a simple ashtray from a piece of tinfoil, and we both reached for our stashes of cigarettes. I'd had a heavy-duty conversation with her about us both losing her fathers at age five back in Fairbanks and we'd bonded over our loss and our fondness of nicotine.

I began to relax and mellow out.

Malcolm assigned us tasks. Kelly and Ron inventoried survey supplies— pencils, sharpeners, Rite-in-the-Rain notebooks, aluminum stakes, string, line levels, flagging, three-meter tapes, thirty-meter tapes, and compasses.

"Wow, this is quite a bunch of stuff," Kelly said in amazement, taking a puff on her Winston.

Toni, a leggy blonde from Texas, tackled food and cooking gear. She checked off pots and pans, and then handed them to Tom and Helen to begin cooking dinner. The couple discussed which containers and implements were needed for the task. Much clanking of utensils ensued while they contemplated the necessary steps to bring a meal of freeze-dried chili to fruition.

Lucy, from Georgia, also a leggy blonde, counted sleeping bags, sleeping pads, and backpacking tents, a relatively simple task. "Good," she said, "somethin' I can do," in a pronounced southern drawl.

"Okay, Georgeie," Malcolm said, "count the cameras and rolls of film. Write down the cameras' serial numbers on this sheet of paper."

"Yes, Malcolm," I said, thankful to contribute something to the crew's welfare.

"When you're done," he added, "find the bug dope and hand it out."

I felt honored to be assigned this exceedingly important chore. I guessed the Army surplus bug dope would become important to our physical and emotional health in the upcoming days.

"Okay, Tom and Helen," Malcolm continued. "Time to fire up the propane backpacking stoves to see if they're working. Assuming they are, boil some water for our freeze-dried food. Take all the supper fixins outside, okay?"

"Yes, master," Helen said with a doff of her red knit cap. She bowed deeply at the waist. I noticed she was bundled up to a greater extent than the rest of us. Perhaps it was because she was tiny with not a lot to spare on her bones.

I followed Malcolm, Tom, and Helen outside to observe how propane stoves were lit. After pumping the fuel-filled stoves to build up pressure, Helen lit both of them with scary sounding whooshes, but there were no explosions, as I'd feared. I'd always been afraid of sudden loud noises and flashes of light due to early terrifying experiences with thunderstorms when I was a kid, a phobia that followed me into adulthood.

It took a very long time for the water to boil. Malcolm rocked back on his heels a few times, a worried expression on his face. He chewed his beard again, a nervous habit, I now realized.

In a barely audible voice he muttered, "If it takes this long to boil water here with no wind, how the hell are they going to work in gale-force winds out in the Pass?"

If anyone else heard his grumbling, no one seemed concerned at all.

* * *

"How about some appetizers? I know you're getting hungry from the weed," Tom said magnanimously, as if he were about to pass around a tray of caviar. Ron retreated into the tent and brought out a box marked "Pilot Bread," a can of strawberry preserves, and a jar of peanut butter, diving into them with great ceremony. "Come and get it," he said. Like a triangle on a farm, his cry brought everyone racing outside.

"What is this?" Lucy asked, eyeing the navy and white box with a juvenile-looking sailor on it.

Lucy and I had never seen pilot bread, a kind of hardtack disc about four inches in diameter and pasty white.

"This is pilot bread. Everyone up here eats it," explained Helen. "In every cabin from Juneau to Barrow you'll find shitloads of the stuff. You can't get by without it. Lasts forever. Doesn't get soft. Doesn't get moldy."

Sailor Boy Pilot Bread, Sunny Jim Strawberry Preserves, and Jif Chunky Peanut Butter went well together. One piece of tooth-cracking pilot bread spread with chunky peanut butter and jelly was a hors d'oeuvre. Three such hors d'oeuvres were a meal. We would not starve, but we would not quite eat like kings.

Guys," Malcolm pleaded, "Don't dive into the chocolate bars or the nuts! We'll need them later and we don't have that much. Our supply of goodies will only last so long."

He yelled this just in time to stop Ron from opening a bag of peanut M&M's.

Hell, I guess that means no breakfast bars either.

* * *

We sat outside our tent in a circle around the stove, just outside our tent and stared at the stove. Tom had kept it lit after the water boiled for warmth because in early June, it wasn't summer yet. I was thankful for my new down vest.

I was also gratetul for the new walking stick I'd cut from the woods a couple of days before in Fairbanks during our training week. I practiced the art of carving designs into the bark and, of course, I carved my initials in it first.

Malcolm had told us that a stick would come in very handy in the bush. "You can lean on it when you take a break and you can walk uphill more easily, he'd said.

I'd taken his advice to heart, and here I sat in Umiat carving zigzags into it, kind of like doodling. Also, it gave my hands something to do when I didn't know what to do with them.

The ground I now sat on was dusty and my new jeans were already dirty. I only had two pairs with me and the project would last twelve weeks. I wondered about how I'd keep clean that long.

Our repast that evening included crunchy and indigestible freeze-dried peas to compliment the freeze-dried chili.

"Peas, carrots, and corn look the same before and after you eat them. You can't digest em. I've tried for years. They're like eating Styrofoam" Helen said seriously.

I smiled. Ron changed the subject.

"So, Georgeie, where'd you go to school," Ron asked.

"George Washington University in DC," I answered, feeling like an alien dropped into the middle of someone's home planet. Perhaps the crew saw my three legs and eight eyestalks. My urban lifestyle was not going to serve me well here.

Heads nodded, offering no particular feedback beyond "Uh-huh."

Short and stocky with wild brown hair, scruffy beard, and huge blue eyes hidden by Coke-bottle glasses, Ron said he was a grad student at Brown and had a photographic memory. I hated him immediately for that skill.

"I've been up here a few summers already—on the pipeline and at Healy Lake with John Cook. Will write my dissertation on one of my favorite sites, Aniganigaruk, to the east of here. Has a couple of components. Found it on the pipeline. Or I may write up some of Doug Anderson's stuff from Onion Portage."

He farted loudly.

"At least you left that one outside," Helen said in mock disgust. She sighed. They'd worked together before.

"Just you wait. You were saying, Georgeie?" Ron said, redirecting the attention back to me.

"I just got my MA at GW. Bob Humphrey was my advisor," I said.

The Alaska crowd looked up. There was an audible "hmm." I had made a few points.

11

Yeah," I continued. "Bob hopes I can visit his sites on the Utukok."

A few "ahhs" followed, with a couple of nods of approval. Now I had even *more* credentials. "I'm Bob's only student to follow in his footsteps to Alaska," I continued. For the coup de gras, I slam-dunked, "And in the fall, I'm going to the University of Connecticut to study with Mike Fitzsimmons," dropping the name of a famous Aleutian and Siberian expert.

"Wow," Malcolm said, "I hear he's hell on wheels. Be careful!"

A premonition of bad things crossed my mind. I discarded them.

"Your turn, Lucy," Kelly said.

"Well, I just graduated from the University of Georgia," she said in a soothing voice. I judged her to be three years younger than me.

"I've only been on a couple of projects down in the southeast. I'm real excited to be up here with y'all." She pushed her blonde bangs back and looked into her coffee cup. The guys stared at her classically striking face, but she didn't seem to notice. "Not sure what I'll do next year. Maybe work on a master's degree. Don't know. What about you, Kelly?" she asked and took a sip of her instant Folgers.

"I'm from Colorado," Kelly said. "I've worked on a lot of projects, like Chief Jo. That was a big one. Lasted a few field seasons. It was so hot! Thought I'd die. Drank tons of water and peed all day." She laughed and shook her head at the memory.

Her tone seemed animated and upbeat as she described various discoveries and adventures. I thought of her as a superior being with her ease at coming north. I offered her a Marlboro. She accepted.

12

Malcolm cut our "getting to know you" conversation short when he asked Helen and me to wash the dirty dishes at the creek.

"Yeah, sure," I said, grateful to show off a skill of any kind. I had no experience in the wilderness, but I could wash dishes.

"I can tell you're a tenderfoot," Helen said as we walked down to the stream, "but you're on the best crew."

"It shows that much?" I'd wondered if my inexperience was that obvious.

"Yeah, you look uneasy. But we'll keep you safe and you'll do great."

Helen was the first person to ever tell me she'd keep me safe. I thought about this and hoped the safety net she and the others offered would give me the sense of security I wouldn't have alone. I hoped a feeling of belonging would grow.

We set the dishes and pots down on the gravel bar that hugged the edge of the clear, cold stream.

"This is Dr. Bronner's," she said, pulling a large plastic bottle covered with writing from her daypack. "It's biodegradable and you can wash your hair, wash dishes, and brush your teeth with it. Comes in peppermint, almond, eucalyptus, lavender, and vanilla. Made by Rabbis in some desert place in Israel."

"Sounds cool," I said, thankful for some inside information.

The air smelled fresh and the free-running stream sparkled. We performed our chore in silence, except for Helen's soft humming of a Beatles tune. When we finished rinsing the dishes, we dried them off with our bandannas and started the brief walk back to the Howard Pass tent, both humming Tom Paxton's "The Last Thing On My Mind."

In this stark, new place, the mundane activity of washing dishes grounded me. I looked forward to washing more dishes the following day.

* * *

Back in the Howard Pass tent, the crew fidgeted with gear, packing it neatly into backpacks and duffels. We had been encouraged to leave what clothing we didn't need right away in Umiat, knowing we'd take turns flying back to base camp for R&R during the summer. I surveyed my meager wardrobe and determined there was nothing I could leave behind except the clean new pair of khakis I'd bought at Eddie Bauer in DC.

I watched Malcolm sewing a tear in his well-traveled daypack with dental floss.

"Shit," he said, sucking his thumb after stabbing it with a needle. "I can knit, I can crochet, but I can't sew worth shit."

"Don't worry, boss," Tom said, "There's plenty of women folk here who can sew. It's what they do. Look at my lovely wife."

"Bite me," Helen said. "Not only can I fix this rip, but I can kick your ass into next week. And I'm a crack shot, too, don't forget."

"So sorry, your worship!" came Tom's answer, along with a hug.

They stuck their tongues out at each other at the same time, making all of us laugh.

"What have I gotten myself into?" Malcolm whined. "Who gave me these children?"

The banter continued until Toni looked up and said, "Hey, I hear a party." She got up from the floor where she had been sewing a tear in her jeans and opened the door of the wall tent. "I smell weed."

"Oh, yeah?" Lucy said, bounding over to the front of the tent.

"Hey, how cool is this?" Tom said, sticking his head out of the door.

Commotion emanated from all the tents. Excitement was no doubt growing in the four project tents at the prospect of dope, booze, and fraternization.

Maybe I'll loosen up some more.

The crews and visiting officials on hand to inaugurate the new project were assembling in front of the Colville River tent, passing liquor around in Styrofoam cups. Corey from Lookout Ridge brought a pipe full of aromatic hashish and someone's chocolate chip cookies sent from home. Someone from Ikpikpuk poured scotch from a plastic container into eager cups. A government honcho from Fairbanks sat in a director's chair, legs crossed, sipping a gin and tonic and smoking a cigar, as relaxed as if he were in his own living room. More bottles of booze and various instruments appeared as if on cue.

Sam, one of our two helicopter pilots, walked into the thick of the crowd. A chorus of cheers and hoots rose as he unpacked a fiddle and handed the case to the person next to him. He spit some Copenhagen snoose on the ground, wiped his mouth on his sleeve, then played the opening chords of the "Orange Blossom Special." People began to clap and some started to dance.

"Hey, gimme your cup, Georgeie—here's some vodka," Kelly said, reaching into the middle of the melee and pouring straight booze into my cup. There was no ice, of course, because there was no refrigerator, and the available water was too precious to waste on alcohol.

I took a deep swallow and lost some of my shyness.

Ian, the crew chief from Ikpikpuk, caught my eye, smiled, and winked confidently. I felt myself blush. Looking relaxed, he held a cigarette in one hand and a cup of booze in the other. The epitome of tall, dark, and handsome, he was also as funny as he was attractive—we'd shared many off-color jokes back in Fairbanks and had had each other in stitches. I still couldn't imagine he found me attractive—there were other women more beautiful and statuesque than me floating around the party, ripe for the picking. I didn't stand a chance, and yet...

Around two in the morning, Rick, the diminutive head of the project from DC, clapped his hands together and called for silence.

"Listen up," he began in an official voice. "Welcome! It's gonna be an exciting summer. We want you to have a great time, and safety is our top priority. Many or you are heading out tomorrow real early, so you have get at least a few hours of sleep before you leave Umiat. Come on, let's go. Move em out."

I was just sober enough to feel anxiety return with a vengeance but blitzed enough to think things would sort of be okay.

Before heading back inside the Howard Pass tent, I paused to take in the landscape one last time on this, my first night north of the Arctic Circle. Beyond the wall tents, the brown tundra and distant blue mountains dazzled in the sunlight and the breeze was fresh on my face. Between our party and the civilized town of Fairbanks were a silent mountain range, some spindly trees, an untold number of bears, and 330 miles.

* * *

I returned to the relative comfort of the tent and found a spot by the back wall where I would be out of the way and could observe the others. Our tent was large enough to accommodate all of us on the floor of thin plywood that flexed whenever more than one person walked. I grabbed a sleeping bag and sleeping pad, rolled them out, and lay down on top of them.

"Take your stuff sack and put your clothes inside so you can use it as a pillow," Kelly advised me from her nearby spot.

She stripped down to her red long johns and filled her stuff sack with elements of her vast collection of clothing.

Okay, I'm gonna strip down to my undies in front of everyone and act like I do it every day.

I did as Kelly suggested, but my pillow was not as plump as hers because I had fewer things to stuff it with. Her immense wardrobe dwarfed mine.

My crewmates snuggled into their sleeping bags. Some read; others wrote letters; still others slept. I looked around and felt fairly secure in their self-assurance, at least for the sun-filled night.

I dreamt about my hometown, Rye, New York, so far away. I was walking past the village green and the library with high school friends on a warm spring day right before graduation. We stopped at Rip's Deli, next to the Olde Preppe Shoppe and across the street from my stepfather's pharmacy, and ordered chocolate sodas. My stepfather knew Rip; he knew everyone downtown. He'd told mom and me about the time he'd seen Rip's wife chasing him down the street with a frying pan. Passersby had stopped and stared. Wish I'd seen it.

I dreamt about walking from our house on Forest Avenue to Apawamis where I'd meet Nancy and walk to school. I'd graduated only eight years before I came to Alaska, but it seemed like a hundred years ago. The grass was hyper-green in my dream and smelled of spring. I had no cares at all.

* * *

I woke up the next morning with mixed feelings of dread and excitement, and an urgency to pee. Today, we'd fly out to Howard Pass. I stayed in my sleeping bag as long as possible. Most of my bravado from the previous night had evaporated and I felt unsure of my near-term future and my ability to cope with wilderness life.

Last chance to turn back. But you can't back out. It's too late! Get your shit together.

With a sigh, I grabbed my plaid shirt, jeans, and Sorel boots, and ran out the door to find a private spot behind the tent to pee and take a few deep breaths. My morning ablutions complete, I lit a Marlboro and stumbled back towards front of the tent only to realize I'd been the last person up. I hadn't noticed the crew boiling water due to my disorientation, my dream of a simpler time, and my need to pee.

"Georgeie's awake! Feeling a little hungover?" Ron asked, handing me a cup of freeze-dried coffee.

"Uh, what?" I managed.

"When we get to our first camp at the foot of Ikhlhuk Mountain, I'm going to make us sourdough pancakes for breakfast but that takes time and we need to hurry up this morning," Malcolm said. "The sourdough starter's old, like twenty years old, from my days Alaska Peninsula days working for my advisor, Don Dumond. He brought the sourdough up from Oregon."

Wow, Dumond. I'd read the name many times at GW.

"Sure seems like you've been up here a while," Toni said to Malcolm.

"Yeah, you could say so, I guess. Came up in the early 70s from U of Oregon. I worked on the pipeline in the 70s, too. Fun times. Don't know if I'll get a PhD. Don't need it for my job. The government doesn't reward you for getting more degrees than you need."

Although I'd heard that Malcolm was fearless in the wilderness, he could hardly be described as macho with his nerdy glasses, disheveled appearance, and fondness for crocheting booties, not to mention making sourdough pancakes. He oozed quiet confidence. No one would make fun of his crocheting.

The Quaker Instant Oatmeal box was passed around. I took a packet, opened it, and poured it out into the bowl from my Girl Scout mess kit. I watched, surprised, as Toni and Malcolm took their spoons and dug out hefty wads of peanut butter. They plunged the rich, calorie-laden scoops into their steaming hot cereal bowls.

"Ooohh, peanut butter. I love the stuff." Toni said enthusiastically. "Peanut butter in oatmeal is the best."

Brown sugar, maple syrup, peanut butter, nuts, and raisins mixed deliciously with my apple cinnamon oatmeal. It was a big meal, and oh, so good. Oatmeal and a few cups of black instant coffee were plenty. My hangover began to dissipate.

* * *

The morning people—Malcolm, Toni, Helen and Tom, and Ron—quickly finished their oatmeal and continued getting their gear together. Tom and Ron headed out to the creek to wash dishes. Kelly, Lucy, and I, decidedly *not* morning people, were slow to function. In the tent, I listened to the others prattle on about lichens and other uninteresting topics as I continued to drink coffee and think about repacking my daypack and backpack.

"Want a smoke?" I asked Kelly.

"Sure."

I lit our cigarettes with my Bic lighter. Sharing felt good and the cigarette soothed my jitters. I listened as others recounted field stories while getting ready. I didn't have any tales yet, so I talked about growing up near New York City.

"I grew up outside of the City," I said.

"What City," Kelly asked.

"New York City, of course."

"How would I know? I've never been east of the Mississippi."

"Well, I've never been west of Pittsburgh, so we're kind of equal," I laughed. "Rye is, or was, home," I said, a frown crossing my face. "DC, where I went to school, is also home. Lotsa old buildings there, lotsa history."

"What's so cool about New York?" Kelly asked, mystified.

"Babkas, bagels, and buildings," I replied.

Our chat was cut short when Malcolm, having grabbed a pencil, notebook, and a roll of maps, rejoined us outside.

"C'mon, gang, I'm going to talk to everyone about going into the field, and to answer any questions."

My lack of confidence and dread of the unknown resurfaced. Yet, there was a glimmer of something more positive percolating up through the fear—cautious excitement mixed with a little hope.

Malcolm yelled to the other three crews finishing breakfast and soon, all of us were assembled in front of the Howard Pass tent.

Malcolm had been chosen to plan the day because of his considerable Alaskan field experience. Rick and the other crew chiefs—Ian, Mitch, and Andy—had played a small part in planning the project apparently but had pretty much deferred to Malcolm.

As Malcolm began speaking, Ian winked at me like he had the night before. I was intrigued but unsettled. I had not missed his wedding ring. It glinted in the bright sunshine as if to emphasize his unavailability. I returned his gaze briefly then stared at the ground.

Why does he have to be so attractive?

I knew I wanted him. Actually, I'd wanted him the day I met him.

"Listen up, campers," Malcolm began. "Howard Pass is going out first because we're the farthest away. Sam will take us out in four loads. When he's done, he'll rest up while Al takes out Ikpikpuk, forty miles to the northeast of the Pass and nearer to Umiat."

Ian grinned from ear to ear at the mention of his crew. Ikpikpuk meant "big asshole" in Inupiaq, someone from the Hilton had told me, probably because it was low lying and swampy, with scant topography. It would be hell to slog through, and not an area I wanted to experience. Ian had chosen it to prove his masculinity; at least that's what one of his crewmembers, Lynne, had guessed.

"It will take about eight hours to get two crews out if the weather holds. I'm sorry, Lookout Ridge and Colville River, you'll have to wait until tomorrow."

Members of both crews grumbled.

"On day three, when everyone is safe in their remote camps, our wonderful helicopter pilots, Al and Sam, will take turns caching

Blazo on a Colville river sandbar near the center of our study area. It will take a couple of days to build up the fuel cache, but our safety depends on having enough Blazo for emergencies. Sam and Al stay in Umiat all summer. When one is flying, the other one is resting, so we have a pilot available every day. Sam, Al, do you have anything to add?" Malcolm asked the pilots.

"Now I know you had some helicopter safety lectures in Fairbanks last week, but let me go over the most important facts," Al began, sucking on a cigarette. His finely chiseled muscles recalled a perfect sculpture, rippling underneath his tight T-shirt. The reflective aviator glasses added to his attractiveness. I thought of Michelangelo's masterpiece, David.

"Not to scare you guys," he continued, "but all helicopters, even this lovely Bell 206 Jet Ranger, are dangerous. The most important thing is to never, *never* walk towards the front or the back of the helicopter when the rotors are turning. You could lose your head. Second, when we set the chopper down, do *not* get out until the rotors have stopped turning, or one of us has told you it's safe to leave. As for loading and unloading, follow our orders *exactly* to balance the load. And I promise you that I will *not* fly around the way I did in Nam. No hot-dogging. Well, Sam, what did I leave out?"

Sam, a shy man if ever there was one, drawled softly, "Just listen to us and y'all will be safe. And no smoking around the chopper." He spit some snoose on the ground.

"Any questions?" Malcolm said.

There was silence as everyone reflected on this latest lesson in Arctic survival; at least I thought we were all having thoughts like mine.

"Alrighty, you heard it from the horse's mouth—now let's get going and load the Jet Ranger for the first load," Malcolm said.

I inhaled quickly and exhaled noisily through my mouth.

Kelly, Toni, and Malcolm helped Sam load the 206 with supplies and food, while Tom and Helen, Lucy, Ron, and I watched and shot the breeze. My turn to fly would come soon enough.

Sam supervised strapping backpacks and duffels onto the skids, securing them with bungee cords, and then inspected the storage compartments and the two spare seats crammed with equipment.

Satisfied, he stepped back from the chopper, reached into his pocket, retrieved a bag of Redman chewing tobacco, and inserted a wad inside his mouth *'twixt cheek and gum,'* as the label on the bag suggested.

Al was off to the side, chatting up Carol from Lookout Ridge.

"Okay, guys, hunker down," Malcolm said when the chopper was ready. He unrolled the Howard Pass quadrangle map and motioned us over.

"I'll find a flat spot near Rough Mountain Creek, close enough to carry water to camp, and well-drained enough so we're not camping on soggy, wet ground. We'll be sheltered by the mountain, here," he said, pointing to a spot on the map, "but not so much that we won't get a breeze if it gets warm in the next week or so and mosquitoes come out. We'll have good visibility along the creek, too. We'll be able to spot any bear, wolverine, or yeti if I can find just the right spot. Got that?

"We're going about 140 miles to the southwest—that's along the northern face of the Brooks Range. It's about an hour away, so look for the helicopter in about two and a half hours. Georgeie, you and Lucy come next, so get your shit over here and be prepared to load the next bunch of equipment and supplies on board when Sam gets back."

I listened intently as if my life depended on it, and it did.

Malcolm chose the highly experienced Toni to fly out with him on the first load. She adroitly climbed over several daypacks and wedged herself in next to a pile of duffels and two-man tents. Malcolm climbed up front next to Sam, holding his notebook and maps. The rotors started to turn. Those of us left behind stepped away, turned our backs to the chopper, and held on to our hats as the chopper rose and began to kick up dust and dirt. The scene reminded me of the TV show M*A*S*H. When the whirlwind stopped, we turned back and waved. The 206 grew smaller against the blue sky and was quickly lost from view. The whirr of rotors still hung in the air.

I thought about Malcolm and Toni leading our expeditionary force into the vast tundra, glacial lakes, and snow-capped mountains, and began to doubt my capabilities again.

They're both so competent. And me, well...

The knot in my stomach tightened.

Ron interrupted my thoughts, "Let's go down to the Umiat Hilton for some real coffee," he suggested. "Last chance for a while."

Hearing no arguments, the six of us set off, hands thrust in our pockets, kicking the dirt.

* * *

In less than ten minutes, we reached the Hilton, the heart and soul of Umiat with its mess hall, showers, and living quarters for staff. In the antiquated mess hall with its Formica-topped picnic tables and gurgling coffee urn, the cook had left pieces of chocolate cake out from the night before. Tales of the cook's marvels traveled fast in our little world, thanks to our engineer neighbors at Geophysical Services Inc (GSI), who lived in the prefab house next to us. Aromas wafting from the Hilton smelled better than those from your mom's kitchen.

We eyed the cake with its thick frosting, knowing we were supposed to stick with our own freeze-dried food, already paid for by the project. Perhaps we could sneak a piece of cake and no one would know.

"They won't even miss it," Lucy said, her eyes fixated on the confection.

She grabbed a napkin and a piece of cake with her fingers since the cook had forgotten to leave out a spatula. I poured myself a glass of whole milk to go with the cake. When would I see chocolate cake and real milk again?

At that moment, a short, bearded man dressed in white entered the mess hall from the recesses of the kitchen, wiping his hands on his apron. I judged his age to be about thirty. His blue eyes sparkled and his thick black hair seemed to be slicked back with Brylcreem.

"What have we here?" he said, walking over to us. "I'm Dick. You like my cake? Help yourselves. You must be some of the archaeologists. Think of my cake as a welcome gift from the Umiat Hilton."

"Thanks, Dick," Ron said. "It's wonderful."

"Like home," Kelly murmured.

"Well, eat your fill, mateys, there's more."

"Well, we're not supposed to, and we ship out in a couple of hours," Tom said.

"It's no problem how much cake you eat. I won't tell."

Tom rolled up the shirtsleeves of his plaid flannel shirt, scooping up a large slice. I was more entranced with the many muscles and sinews of his forearm than the cake for a moment.

"Take a napkin, for Christ's sake," Helen said, and handed him one.

"What would I do without you, my wife?" Tom fluttered his eyes.

"I'll shove that cake into your mouth!" Helen said, her soft almond-shaped eyes laughing.

"Yes, boss." Tom saluted.

I was fascinated by the cook, an affable little guy. I had heard through the grapevine that although his name was Dick, he was referred to, always, as Dick the Cook, a combination father confessor, shrink, and best pal—the bush camp equivalent of a bartender. I'd look for him when I came back to Umiat for R&R in about ten days.

The Howard Pass crew sat in the mess hall shooting the breeze over the whine of the generator that kept Umiat running twenty-four hours a day.

"When I was on the pipeline," Ron said, "we flew around a lot in helicopters like Sam's. We lost power once and had to auto-rotate down. If the blades can keep rotating, you won't crash, you just kind of slowly lose altitude until you're on the ground, hopefully on a level spot."

Tom added, "Oh yeah, when we were working on the north coast near Wainwright last summer, we got caught by the weather and were flying fucking blind in fog. I'd rather be in a chopper than a fixed-wing in fog because you can go a whole hell of a lot slower and lower. But there's nothing much you can do if you don't see the mountain in front of you in time. You just kiss your ass goodbye. It doesn't much matter what you're flying."

I cringed, peered into my coffee, and added auto-rotation, mountains, and fog to my list of worries.

After a while, Kelly looked at her watch and said, "We should mosey."

"Bye, Dick!" Helen yelled. "Thanks for the eats."

"Thanks, Dick," I said.

"Bye," he yelled from behind the counter. "You guys and gals be safe."

We downed the last of our cake, grabbed some cookies, and headed back towards the tent camp. It started to drizzle. The air felt colder, too.

"Time to put on your rain gear, George," Kelly advised.

I liked Kelly more and more. Apparently, she had taken me under her wing, fledgling that I was. Dutifully, I took my spotless Eddie Bauer rain pants and jacket out of my brand new, first-ever daypack and suited up like the others, then heard the unmistakable whirr of a helicopter. Sam must have gotten back ahead of schedule. We picked up our pace and reached him just as he was shutting down.

"I made good time," he said hopping down on the ground.

"How come?" Lucy asked.

"Well, the chopper isn't near as heavy empty so I didn't have to stop to refuel," he answered, looking at his sneakers and spitting his chew on the ground.

A small throng of people from the other crews gathered to watch us stuff the chopper like a sausage. When the six of us had packed in as much as possible, we stood back while Sam did a cursory inspection. Satisfied, he declared the sausage well stuffed. The small crowd clapped and cheered. We were ready to go.

I thought about my friends in DC and my family in New York. They would be, well, the word escaped me. Horrified, maybe. My mother would clutch at her throat and my stepfather would begin his nervous, tuneless whistling. My friends would think what I was doing was too risky. Insane. *They* sure wouldn't be climbing into a helicopter at the edge of the known world. Not on your life. What if something went wrong?

But they're not here, I am. I'm getting on the goddamned helicopter!

Lucy waved at our comrades and climbed into the co-pilot's seat easily. I tried to haul myself up into the back seat next to a duffel full of food, but I was having trouble finding a foothold.

"Georgia," Sam said quietly. "put your left foot on the step halfway up the back strut, then haul yourself up."

"The what?"

"Here," Sam said, putting his hand on the step.

"Oh."

Christ, how stupid. They all think I'm an ass.

I thought I wouldn't be able to haul myself up into the copter, especially with a bunch of people watching, but I did, however ungainly my ascent appeared to be. Sam hopped up into the pilot's seat. Settling into the back, I realized he'd called me Georgia instead of Georgeie, but I already liked him and didn't care.

Because the floor of the helicopter was Plexiglas, I could see the ground beneath my feet. My boots floated above the dirt and gravel, making me feel disconnected from the real world. The rotors started to turn; the hum grew louder. Sam turned around to see if I had buckled my harness correctly. He gave me a thumb's up and pulled back on the collective.

The ground slipped away beneath my feet and the dirt formed little tornadoes as the chopper's rotors picked up speed. People on the ground turned their backs and held on to their hats. Entranced by the world below, my field of vision grew larger with each foot of altitude. A small creek glinting in the sun meandered off to the southeast, disappearing into the distance. Stunted trees and bushes accompanied it on its journey.

A couple hundred feet above the ground, I could see an endless brown carpet of tundra rolled on to meet black mountains dotted with pristine snow. Cold and unpleasant-looking ponds dotted the landscape.

So stark So alien.

Rain streaked across the Plexiglas windshield and the air grew colder. I grabbed my wool knit hat out of my daypack, along with the only pair of wool gloves I'd brought with me.

I twisted around in my harness to watch Umiat recede in the distance. A few people, including the rest of the Howard Pass crew, milled around where we'd lifted off. I envied those inhabitants of the last outpost of civilization. The Quonset huts that had been on fire the previous day had stopped smoking. I had forgotten all about them. Umiat was not going to become a grease spot after all.

We soon flew over a big river Malcolm had identified on the quad map as the Colville. It flowed swiftly to the northeast, with sedge grasses hugging its margins.

Standing on a gravel bar in the middle of the river, a moose with huge antlers drank from the clear water. If I were to be set down here by myself, there would be only two prominent things on the landscape—me and a thousand pounds of moose. The thought alarmed me. The moose looked up as we approached, then fled.

Jesus, look at that bastard run!

I stared, transfixed, into the distance. Eventually, I heard the pitch of the rotors change and felt the helicopter bank, then drop down to just above the ground. The effect of the ground moving quickly up to meet me was both terrifying and wonderful.

Ahead of us, Malcolm and Toni waved at us in their vivid yellow rain gear. The rain gear stuck out against the brown and black of the land.

CAMP 1, ROUGH MOUNTAIN CREEK

The helicopter set down and Sam cut the motor. At his signal, I cautiously hopped onto the spongy ground as if in a dream. Drizzle fell gently on my raingear. Steep black mountain slopes streaked with snow looked cold and forbidding against the brown tundra.

* * *

An image of my mother and stepfather eating dinner and watching the news in our den back in Rye floated into my mind. They were eating Mom's meatloaf on tray tables and talking about the price of gas and the state of politics under the Carter Administration.

My father's death continued to haunt me twenty years after the fact. Memories of that abandonment kept me insecure and distrusting of people in general, and men in particular. I was certain fate would strike again and my stepfather, twenty-five years older than my mother, would die soon, and I'd be plunged into more uncertainty and sadness.

I pushed these familiar thoughts from my mind as scenes from a different life. This was my reality now, but the cobwebs were never far away.

* * *

Toni and Malcolm had already set up the large cook tent. "There's coffee," Malcolm said nonchalantly, as if welcoming me into his house in Fairbanks.

I ducked into the tent to find a spoon sticking out of a Folgers instant coffee jar, poured some hot water and instant coffee into an ugly Melmac cup, property of the government, and rejoined the group. Lucy, quick on my heels, brought out coffee for Sam and herself.

We stood in a circle in the light drizzle, drinking the coffee and taking in our new surroundings. I wouldn't have touched instant back home, but here it tasted good in the cold. The cup warmed my hands. Malcolm unwrapped a chocolate bar and offered it around.

Sam didn't have raingear. He probably hadn't thought he needed it for the few minutes he'd be outside. His black jeans and beat-up leather jacket suited his grizzled white beard and dirty baseball cap, but his shyness and soft voice exposed a gentle nature. I judged him tough on the outside and soft on the inside.

"Good flight, Sam?" Malcolm asked.

"Uh-huh. Weather's closin' in. I gotta go get the next batch sooner rather than later. Who do you want to come out next?"

"Ron and Kelly. Will we get Tom and Helen today?"

"Yeah, she'll be good for another four or so hours. Al may have some trouble getting the Ikpikpuk crew out, though."

"Well, we better unload the chopper so you can get on your way."

Offloading completed, we waved Sam goodbye. The 206 roared to life and kicked up an impressive amount of dirt. The sound of the rotors spinning at top speed reverberated from the nearby mountain slopes. Sam disappeared from view and the sound gradually faded away.

Silence engulfed me like fog.

There's nothing out here. Nothing.

My ears soon began to adjust to the subtle sounds of the wilderness: the gurgling of Rough Mountain Creek; the breeze making a soft rustling sound against the tent flap; and the soft patter of rain on the ground.

I slowed my breathing, calming myself, but anxious thoughts would not go away. I lacked the inner strength to banish them.

I hope I don't die up here.

I remembered *The Golden Book of Archaeology* my mother giving me when I was about six years old. I'd been fascinated, and especially liked the part about the Mayans in the jungles of Central America. The book hadn't contained anything about Siberia or Alaska, though. I'd developed that interest later in college. Alaska's remote, raw, and cold nature was as foreign to me as the Mayans had been twenty years before.

* * *

A little while later, Toni and Lucy volunteered to make a second water run, grabbing two empty plastic Jerry jugs each.

"Hey, guys," Malcolm yelled after them, "Take the shotgun—just in case! It's loaded and the safety's on."

Then, to me he said, "Have you ever set up a tent?"

"No," I replied, rubbing my gloved hands together in the brisk air.

"We need to set up all the tents by the time the rest of the gang gets here and before it really starts to pour."

Finding a flat spot, Malcolm retrieved a tent bag from under the bright blue supply and food tarp. He dumped a bag of parts on the ground, and counted the pegs, ropes, and poles.

"Let me show you, Georgeie. First, we burn the ends of the rope so they won't unravel, insert a short piece of the rope into the grommets, and tie a knot in each one."

He sealed the ends with his Bic. A pungent aroma filled the air as the plastic in the ropes began to melt.

"Do you remember how to tie a bowline?"

"Not really."

I watched him, trying to follow his hands. He was right-handed, and I was a lefty, but I kind of got the hang of it. He had some rhyme about a rabbit and a hole, but I never remembered it. I managed to learn a left-handed version after a few tries.

"Okay," he continued in a steady voice, "next we put the poles together and stuff them into the tent sleeves to form the frame, like so."

Slowly, I secured the rain fly to the top of the tent, pulled it taut, and placed tent pegs through each fly and guy line. When Malcolm and I finished placing a large piece of plastic called Visqueen beneath the tent, we pushed the tent pegs into the ground.

"Good job, Georgeie, now put up the others, and I'll find a place for my tent."

I set about my task with a tentative feeling of confidence.

Malcolm selected a strategic spot for himself, close to a rock outcropping overlooking the creek, and sheltered by a low, hummocky rise.

"I claim this spot as my personal kingdom," he said, brandishing a tent stake, and began to erect a tent the size of the cook tent for himself.

He saw me looking at him quizzically as he put up the large tent and said, "Hey, this is one of the perks of being the boss. I get the other big tent for my archaeology library and me. I know we'll all enjoy reading archaeology on weather days—you know, when it's too cold, pouring down rain, or we're caught in a blizzard." He smiled.

I began to assemble my tent about ten feet away from Malcolm to be close to my new security blanket. I could have connected the guy lines between us like an umbilical cord.

"For God's sake, don't put your door facing mine, and move over that way a little," he said, patiently.

I felt my face flush with embarrassment.

Malcolm looked at me and softened, "I know this is all new to you, but I need my privacy, and so do you. You'll be happy to have time to yourself. Take it from me."

"Of course. You're right," I said, warming to Malcolm's kind voice.

"One last thing," he said, raising his voice over the increasing wind, "get sleeping bags and pads from under the tarp and throw two of each inside the tents so they don't blow away."

"Uh-huh. Will do."

The tents up and pads and sleeping bags distributed, I headed over to the cook tent for a break and some chitchat. Lucy and Toni had returned and were boiling another pot of water. Pilot bread and peanut butter had magically appeared.

They began comparing notes about their experience with poisonous plants. I felt as green as the poison ivy they were discussing. I knew nothing about the subject, so I just listened, glad to hear that poison ivy didn't grow up north.

"Howdy, gals," Malcolm said, entering the cook tent. "How you all feeling? Okay?"

"Good. A little cold. It's not like Texas," said Toni, pulling up the neck of her hand-sewn parka.

"Good, Malcolm," Lucy said, cupping her coffee. "It's a little much to take in. So beautiful. It's like *The Sound of Music* up here. Lotsa mountains and a few wildflower buds."

"Georgeie, how about you?"

"Wow, I don't know. I feel like I've been dropped onto a different planet. Like this is *The Twilight Zone* or something."

"You'll be fine. You'll feel more and more at home every day." He reached over to touch my arm reassuringly through my rain gear, sweater, shirt, and long johns, and looked at me with a reassuring smile.

"You'll see. By the end of the summer you won't even recognize yourself."

"Thanks, Malcolm, I sure hope so."

"Are you happy with the campsite, Malcolm?" Toni asked, her green eyes looking intently at him.

"Yeah, I am. Actually, it's a great place for an archaeological site."

"How come?" I asked, curiosity winning out over shyness.

"Well, if *we* think it's a good spot to camp, probably people in the past thought so, too."

I was amazed. "So that's how you find a site—you look for a good place to camp?"

"Well, that's part of it," he replied. "It's more scientific than that, but finding a decent campsite is a good start."

"What did they make their tools out of up here?" Lucy asked.

"Oh, let's see, lotsa sedimentary rocks like chert and chalcedony. They're smooth and easy to work with, you'll see, and they come in lots of colors so they're easy to find. The best stone is obsidian, or volcanic glass. It's usually black, and you can see through the edges because it's translucent. You can cut yourself on a piece of it because the edges are so sharp. Highly prized stuff. Not local, so traded for. Very valuable!"

Malcolm's voice was punctuated by the sound of the chopper. We piled out of the tent into the drizzle to watch Sam land and shut down. Ron and Kelly climbed out.

"Wow! What a cool place!" Kelly said, looking around and breaking into a dance.

"Well, you're a happy camper," Malcolm said, laughing.

"Shit, yeah, "Kelly laughed, prancing around like a high school cheerleader on uppers.

"You picked a great spot to camp," Ron added.

When Kelly finished her jig, she reached into her shirt pocket and brought out her pack of Marlboros. I was about to reach for mine when Kelly extended her pack towards me.

"Hey, thanks," I said as I inhaled the cigarette smoke, grateful for this civilized gesture.

"Now, you guys," Malcolm, a non-smoker, said. "Be really careful smoking in the tents. There's plastic in the fabric. If you start a fire, the tent will go up in flames and you with it. If you're lucky, the fabric will just stick to your face and you'll be disfigured but not killed. Either way, I'll have a lot of explaining to do."

Kelly crinkled her nose like Elizabeth Montgomery in *Bewitched.*

"Try not to get yourselves killed just yet. We start work tomorrow and Uncle Malcolm needs *you*!" He pointed at us with an air of authority.

I wrinkled *my* nose like Elizabeth Montgomery in *Bewitched*.

Sam got back in the helicopter and took off. I looked up at him spiraling to a safe altitude and flying off towards Umiat. I felt a twinge of anxiety. Umiat was secure, warm, and comfortable. There were walls and ceilings and urns of coffee back there, and there were none of those things here.

* * *

Ron excused himself to go "tighten the tent pegs" as he euphemistically called taking a leak. A couple of minutes later, I heard him yell, "Hey, we're not the first ones here!"

We headed over in his direction. He finished zipping his fly and stared at a spot on the ground, stock still, like an English Pointer or an opossum.

"Ooh! An obsidian flake! Isn't it pretty!" Kelly said, looking down at the artifact.

"That's what it is! Good job, Ron. We have our first artifact of the summer," Malcolm said. "Have you ever seen a flake like this, Lucy, Georgeie?"

"No, Malcolm, we don't have anything like this in Georgia."

"Nope. Un uh," I added.

I gawked at the small stone. It looked like a shiny pebble to me. I would have missed it completely.

"See how smooth and shiny it is?" Ron asked. "Artifacts are easy to find when it's overcast and it's rainy. They shine."

"Yeah, they glint," Toni added.

"This is the real deal," Malcolm said, "shiny and smooth surfaces, and see the jagged edge? It was probably used to cut something, like a piece of hide. It's called a utilized flake, meaning a piece with a worked edge that shows it was used at some point."

He picked up the flake and handed it to me.

I turned it over in my hand, looking first at the smooth sides and scrutinized the edges.

"Do you know how old this is?" I asked.

Ron answered quickly before Malcolm had a chance to open his mouth: "It's just a flake. Could be any age. Could be 200 years old or 10,000 years old. Flakes are the most common artifacts we'll find."

Malcolm saw an opening while Ron was taking a breath: "Like Ron says, it's an ordinary flake, a byproduct of making a tool; detritus from a larger worked piece. We can usually date a projectile point by its shape, but not a flake. The cool thing, though, is the material. The closest obsidian source is Batza Tena, on the Koyukuk River, about 200 miles to the southwest of here. So, the cobble this flake came from was probably traded for and then carried back here."

I found the topic interesting, but even more interesting was Ron's need to compete with Malcolm. I filed the observation away in the back of my brain in case it meant something important.

Each of us examined the flake, holding it up to the sky to admire the sharpness and translucence of its edges. Malcolm dug into the supplies under the tarp and pulled out a roll of bright pink flagging tape and a coin envelope.

Jesus, Malcolm's prepared for anything all the time.

"Ron, put a piece of flagging on the ground next to the flake, then put the flake into this coin envelope."

"Aye aye, Malcolm."

"Tomorrow, we'll survey around camp to see if there is more stuff nearby and I'll show you how to record the artifacts we find on the site."

"Okay, Malcolm."

"I'll keep the artifacts we collect in my big tent in paper bags marked with their site number. I brought a few textbooks and articles, too, so we have a kind of library."

The breeze had picked up a little and the drizzle felt colder. My thoughts drifted from our camp and the excitement of the find to the penetrating dampness.

Ron handed the completed envelope back to Malcolm.

The now-familiar whirr rotors became audible as the 206 appeared in the sky. Tom and Helen popped out explosively after the chopper landed and the rotors slowed.

"Far out!" Tom said excitedly.

Helen jumped up and down, but whether from excitement or cold, I wasn't sure.

"Look what we found," Malcolm said, handing the coin envelope to Helen.

Helen opened the envelope, depositing the flake in her hand.

"Obsidian? On our first day? Holy shit."

"This calls for a quick smoke from my stash," Tom said, grabbing the flake from Helen and turning it over in his hand.

"Okay, Malcolm?"

"Well, I don't know. It's probably against some regulation, but, okay, be careful!" He wagged his finger at Tom who handed the flake back to him, then reached into his daypack, pulled out a baggie containing already-rolled joints, took his Bic lighter from his chamois shirt pocket, and lit up. The eight of us stood in a circle in front of the cook tent, passing around our celebratory joint, as well as the equally celebratory flake.

* * *

The eight of us squeezed into the cook tent for dinner. Kelly and Lucy sat at the front of the tent, reaching outside to stir the spaghetti boiling on the Primus stove. Once it was done, Lucy got up, dumped the water outside, poured out a can of tomato sauce over the spaghetti, and ladled it onto our plates.

"This is so bitchin' cool," Tom said. "Our first night out and we're not eating freeze-dried shit. My compliments to our chefs!"

A chorus of "bravos" and "yays" split the outside silence like a thunderclap.

"Would you like more of this good spaghetti?" Lucy asked me.

"Why yes, Lucy, I sure would," I answered.

She handed my bowl to Kelly who sat nearer to the pot. Kelly, her fiery red hair peeking out of her cap, her green eyes flashing in the stove's light, handed me back my dish.

"Here you go, Georgeie. Pretty good, isn't it?" she said, smiling at me.

* * *

Because all eight of us were in camp, none of us could have our own tent. That would change when we started rotating back to Umiat for R&R, but for the next several nights, I'd have a tent mate. Lucy and Kelly had already decided to "sleep together." I felt left out, disappointed, and also intimidated by my de facto tent mate, the overly competent and detached Toni of the perfect handmade parka.

I sensed little empathy from Toni flowing in my direction. Perhaps she thought me too incompetent and green to be part of the team. I thought of a few topics to chat about—granola recipes, shooting rabbits, and what fun Texas might be, but since none of these subjects interested me, I let her take the lead.

Tall and blonde, with the longest legs in the world, I felt dumpy next to her. As I'd listened to her during the little time I'd known her, I realized she was one of the most experienced campers on the project, with years of backpacking, hiking, and shooting under her belt. I had never met anyone like her. She awed and scared me at the same time.

When I approached the tent, Toni already had her gear for the next day laid out neatly at the front of her side of the tent and her boots placed just under the rain flap with the insoles resting on them so they would be completely dry and relatively odor-free in the morning. I watched as she took off her sweater, shirt, pants, socks, and panties, and tucked them into her stuff sack. She even took the time to fold them precisely. Being naked with someone she'd only known for a week didn't seem to faze her. She crawled into her sleeping bag and grabbed her copy of Michener's *Hawaii*.

She looked up from her book.

"Hey, George."

"Hi, Toni," I said, taking off my outer clothes and snaking down into my sleeping bag in my baby blue long johns. I didn't think I could take off my underwear in front of another woman, so I didn't even try.

I took a deep breath. "So, you're a Michener fan?"

"Yeah, I guess so. My boyfriend gave me *Hawaii* to read while I'm up here because it's such a long book, and we'll be out here for three months, or something like that."

"Yeah, I know. Have you ever been in the field that long?"

"No, not like this; well, maybe a month or so. Back in Texas, we'd mostly get dropped off by truck at the beginning of the day and brought back to town at night. No, nothing like this."

"No grizzlies in Texas, I guess."

"Nope, not a one, but the cockroaches in the motel they put us in on this one project were huge!"

"Oh gross. I hate roaches. I'd get one once in a while in my apartment in DC. The worst part is the sound they make when you step on them. That, and how fast they move."

"We used to catch them with tweezers and hold them over the gas stove in our rooms and watch em fry. At least you knew they were real dead. Well, goodnight, George," she said rather abruptly.

"Night, Toni."

I was glad for the quiet. I needed time to think. Although my shoulders and Toni's almost touched, I experienced a welcome sense of privacy.

Because I was afraid of grizzly bears and other unknown terrors, I found myself relieved to be in a tent with the cool-as-a-cucumber Toni. I firmly believed she could shoot a grizzly between the eyes at fifty yards.

I wrote an initial entry in my new field notebook:

June 10. First day out. Cold and light rain. Don't know what to make of this new place. Nowhere near anything. All of us made it out today. Ron found a flake that had been utilized some time in the past. Called a utilized flake. Was obsidian, too. Very valuable. Makes the find important.

After a brief moment of inner reflection and overall amazement at my first night in the tundra, I fell asleep with only my nose and the top of my head sticking out of my sleeping bag.

* * *

I woke up as Toni unzipped the tent door and headed out. Worried I was the last one up again, I wiggled into my clothes and leaned out of the tent flap.

Visibility was almost zero. I was dumbfounded. Fog completely enshrouded all but a couple of tents. The landscape had become a surreal white.

The helicopter will never find us. I'm dead for sure.

Then I heard laughter coming from the cook tent, and my curiosity was piqued. I lit a cigarette and walked over to join the others. There was a pause in the conversation as I entered the tent.

"I think Georgeie is going to be our late riser this summer," Ron said in a voice too cheerful for my mood. Surprising myself, I said, "Bite me, Ron."

A chorus of laughter rose from the gang. In what seemed like a joyful Greek chorus, they chanted, "Bite me, Ron" in unison. The refrain lasted a full minute.

"Okay, okay, I get the point," Ron said defensively. He took his dirty white handkerchief out of the back pocket of his jeans, blew his nose loudly, and wiped his glasses with it.

"Ron, you know we all love you," Toni said, rolling her eyes.

My God, Toni has a sense of humor!

In the space of an hour, everyone had eaten their fill of oatmeal, Spam, Pilot Bread, and coffee. Tom and Helen gathered the dishes and took them to the creek to wash.

* * *

"Okay, campers, let's get this show on the road," Malcolm said, looking at his watch. "Meet me in front of the big blue tarp in five minutes."

We piled out of the cook tent to get ready for work. As I brushed my teeth by the creek, I wondered if I could keep up with the others. I'd only camped out once, and that had been within commuting distance of New York City. I hadn't liked Girl Scouts camp very much, but I still had my mess kit, and I'd brought it along for my wilderness adventure I walked back to our tent, then hurried over to the tarp carrying my yellow daypack.

"Here's what we're going to do today," Malcolm began. "We're going to take it easy. We'll survey our campsite—we already know there's a site here. We'll see how much more we can find. Alrighty! Let's hand out the survey gear," he continued buoyantly. "Each of you gets a real honest-to-God number two lead pencil, a roll of flagging tape, a couple of steel stakes, a three-meter tape, some coin envelopes and paper bags, a black magic marker, and a brand-new six-inch Marshalltown trowel. Ron, would you dive in there and get the box of survey supplies and hand this stuff out? Toni, would you help?"

"Sure," Toni replied.

"Love to, boss," Ron said.

"Tomorrow, we'll split into two groups of four. Each crew will get a Nikon camera and film, a compass, a 1-to-250 quad map, plus a ball of string, a thirty-meter tape, a line level, and a file for sharpening trowels. Who wants to carry these today?"

Malcolm looked at Lucy and me, the greenest of greenhorns, and smiled.

"I volunteer for the ball of string and the line level," Lucy said.

"Toss that woman a ball of string and a line level," Malcolm said to Ron.

I volunteered for the file and thirty-meter tape, not wanting anything with moving parts I could break.

"Coming right up, Georgeie. Oops, I forgot—we *all* get to carry an Army surplus entrenching tool. Would you dig into that box on the left and dig them out, Kelly?"

"Uh-huh," she said, not sounding enthusiastic.

"I don't want no stinkin' entrenching tool," said Tom.

"Too bad. No one else will carry yours for you," Malcolm replied.

"Yes, master," Tom muttered. He did his best imitation of Igor—bent over, limping, one arm hanging slack. Perhaps he thought he could convince Malcolm he'd just had a stroke. It didn't work. Tom shoved an entrenching tool into his daypack.

"We'll carry both shotguns today. Tomorrow, both teams will carry a loaded shotgun and extra ammo."

I pictured a grizzly mauling me, lunching on me, and taking the best parts home to the cubs.

"Now go pack a lunch, fill your canteens, and remember your rain gear. You should probably take a knife, a bandanna, your walking sticks, and your bear whistles, too, if you haven't already packed them. See how exciting this is, and how lucky you are?"

I took a deep breath. How much would all that weigh? I would definitely save room for smokes and, if I'd had one, a flask of vodka.

* * *

The fog slowly lifted, revealing the tundra glistening with dew and the base of nearby mountains covered with a dusting of snow. I paused, taking in the primitive untouched beauty of the surrounding terrain. The first hints of green already dotted the landscape, although the temperature still said winter. I grabbed my raingear and met the others back in front of the tarp.

We walked away from the middle of camp to an open area. "First thing, we'll practice compass bearings. These Bruntons are pretty complicated. Some of you'll pick up the technique right away and others maybe not. This is not the simple Silva most of you have used in the past," Malcolm said.

"First, set the declination, which is between 22 and 24 degrees because we're so near the magnetic pole. We'll set it at 23 degrees. Come look." He opened the Brunton to reveal its parts. The innards resembled the gears inside of a fancy watch.

"Then, align the sighting arm with the sight over the mirror and point it at the object you want to shoot and make sure the compass is level. There's a level incorporated into the compass face, see? Then you see where the needle points, and that's your heading."

And the music goes round and round, woh-oh-oh-oh-oh-oh, and it comes out here, I thought, remembering a song from the old *Perry Como Show* I'd watched with my parents before my father died.

"And remember, kiddies, hold the compass real, real steady to get it level and to line up a point accurately. Going through all these steps while it's raining and when the wind's blowing, hoo-hah. Good luck with that."

We took turns with the two Bruntons we had, but the end of compass reading couldn't come fast enough for me. I knew this would not be my forte.

"Okay, now that we've all mastered compass reading, we're going to learn how to survey so we can find sites. We'll walk down to the edge of the terrace we're camped on, stand five meters apart, and walk north for half a kilometer, flagging any artifacts we see. All right, let's go. Move em out."

"Why meters?" I asked.

"We use metric for all field data," Malcolm said, "like the rest of the scientific community around the world. Any more questions? Okay, let's go!"

And so, I took my first official step as a field archaeologist, not knowing exactly what to do or what to look for and oh, so grateful my smoking buddy Kelly was next to me.

After several steps of concentrating on the uneven ground, sparsely covered with lichens and little tufts of what looked like some kind of fake, deformed grass, I saw a small piece of rock that looked out of place. I picked it up.

"Kelly, look at this," I said, showing her the rock.

"That's just a pebble," she said, turning it over. "It fooled you cause it's fairly smooth, but it's not really anything. And, George, put your hat on. You lose most of your heat through your head."

"Uh oh, I forgot," I said, taking my red baseball cap from the back pocket of my jeans.

"There you go. Now, let's find you something really cool." She continued looking for goodies, the ends of her red curls dancing in the breeze.

Let down a bit but still excited for the day, I resumed my search. The first find of the day, however, belonged to Toni.

"Hey! Here's something," she yelled, taking off her daypack to retrieve a roll of flagging tape.

"Let's see," Malcolm said, walking in her direction. "The rest of you, stay where you are and if this is the real McCoy, I'll bring it around."

Taking the object from Toni, he turned it over in his hand, licked it free of dirt, and held it up to the sun.

"Yup, that's a keeper. Good job, Toni. Mark it with some flagging."

When Malcolm brought the artifact over to me, it looked different from what I'd spotted. Its smooth surface was an odd, reddish color that it stood out against the dullness of the earth. I ran my finger over the rough edges. Someone in the past made that flake and used it for something.

"Ahh, I see, Malcolm. I get it. It's kind of like yesterday's flake," I said, marveling at the treasure.

"Good. You'll find something today, I know you will," he said reassuringly.

By the time we had walked several swaths back and forth through our campsite, five more flakes were found. All locations were carefully marked with flagging tape.

"And now, kiddies, here's how we're going to finish with our site. Forget about the five-meter swaths and everyone wander around near the flakes in case we missed anything. That way, we'll look at the places *in between* the places we've looked."

I approached this event with the enthusiasm of an Easter egg hunt but found nothing.

We were ready to record our first site, limited to a few flakes, but exciting to me because it was *my* first site, too.

"Next step. I'll put in a stake at one end of the site," Malcolm said, walking over to Ron's initial flake nearest camp. "Now, I'll take an aluminum tag and mark it XHP-001 because it's the first site to be recorded in the Howard Pass quad—ever! I'll put the year on it, too. This is the datum, one of the points where we measure in all the artifacts and the site boundaries from. I'll set the other datum at the far end of the site. We'll collect the flakes at our first site, just so we know how to record them, but God knows we can't haul every site back to Fairbanks. Gotta be selective. Only the good stuff. Diagnostics.

"Ron, you, Toni, and Helen will record the artifacts by distance and bearing with the thirty-meter tape. Kelly, you and Lucy will take site photos. Georgeie, I have a special task for you; one I think you'll like. Draw a site map and take some descriptive notes like vegetation, setting, and so on. Ask Tom to help you."

Tom opened my notebook to a page with graph paper. I noticed a small, jagged scar on his right cheek, just above his beard, but decided not to ask him about it. I hardly knew him, but I resolved to ask him later in the summer.

"Put the datum here," he said, pointing to the bottom of the page. "North is always at the top of the page. Draw a north arrow. And we need a scale. I think one little square can equal one meter. That should do it. Okay, we'll wait for those guys to call out locations. We're ready!"

Toni attached a thirty-meter tape to datum A and Helen attached a second tape to datum B. They walked the flake nearest datum A.

"Flake one, 5.2 meters from datum A, 7.1 meters from datum B."

"Artifact two, a retouched flake, is 4.2 meters from datum A and 14.7 meters from datum B," Ron said authoritatively.

As Ron called out more coordinates, I wrote them down in a column on the page opposite my map.

"Now, place the points on the graph paper. Ten boxes is ten meters, so find where the coordinates intersect on your map."

"I think I got it."

Feeling creative, I marked the finds on the map, then drew symbols representing short grass and scrub, and a dotted line around what we, well, what Tom, thought might be the site boundary.

At the top of the page, I drew a rather ornate north arrow and penciled in mountains, hills, and Rough Mountain Creek. Just for fun, I drew a tent next to the stream.

"Nice, George. Good work," Tom said, slapping me on the back. "You're a real artiste!"

I got a little thrill when I in placed my initials, GLR, at the bottom of the map along with the date. My fledging role as part of the archaeological survey of 1977 was now documented in black and white and would become part of the permanent record. Malcolm said he liked my map and that meant the world to me. Maybe I'd find a niche as the crew's site illustrator.

At the end of our investigation, we returned to camp and sat outside the cook tent to eat lunch, discussing the site and what it might mean.

"There's not much we can tell about it," Malcolm said, "There's just a few surface flakes. Not too exciting. But we know someone was here at least."

"Perhaps aliens made the flakes," ventured Helen, looking down at the ground, not cracking a smile.

"Or Incas," said Kelly.

"Or maybe I made them yesterday when you weren't looking," Tom said.

"Oh, for Christ's sake, Tom!" I said, feeling somewhat full of myself.

There were titters all around.

"Alright, you greenhorns, enough levity. Let's go explore some more." Malcolm had the final word.

* * *

During the afternoon, we unfortunately had to survey a tussock field next to camp. Tussocks were mean bastards, annoying and unstable balls of grass and dirt attached by only a few roots to the underlying earth, kind of like a loose tooth hanging by a thread. You could not walk over or around them because they were dense and wobbly. You could *not* walk a straight line through a tussock field. We stood five meters apart and walked slowly, trying to catch glimpses of artifacts hiding in the depressions between the balls of grass.

"This sucks," I heard Kelly say to Helen.

I had never heard of tussocks before, although the long-time Alaskans had mentioned them in passing back at base camp and in Fairbanks, usually with the word fucking attached as a prefix. It was especially tough going that first day because we were walking uphill as well as trying to navigate our way without falling.

Ron, walking next to me, was almost immediately out of breath, as was I.

"Let's wait for Georgeie and Ron," Malcolm said, stopping to look back at us huffing and puffing. I badly wanted a smoke. Ron blew his nose loudly. Once we had caught up to the others, Malcolm gave the signal to trudge on.

"Have you noticed that when we catch up, they start walking again? They get to rest, and we don't," Ron gasped, catching his breath and walking at the same time.

"Uh-huh, yeah," I answered, leaning on my walking stick and still short of breath.

Maybe I should think about quitting smoking.

"How the hell do you find anything in this fucking mess? How can you see anything?" Helen bellowed, referring to the tussocks.

Then suddenly, "Shit!" I roared.

I had sunk past my right ankle, overtopping my boots, in frigid water between two of the fiendish grass balls. They closed around my legs like a malevolent creature.

Malcolm looked over at me and seemed to read my mind. "This is stupid. I don't care what we're supposed to do, we'll never find anything in the tussocks, and we'll all end up with sprained ankles."

"Yippee!" yelled Kelly. "I hate those fuckwads."

"Those what?" I asked.

"Fuckwads! It's a word we made up on a project in New Mexico! Can apply to many things, and it sure applies to these bastards."

"I like it!" Malcolm said. "Before we call it a day, let's hike up to that lowest terrace instead of doing more of this shit in the boggy stuff."

More hiking? My ankles hurt and my socks were wet. I thought longingly about my roll of moleskin back at camp as blisters formed on my heels.

* * *

When I got back to my tent, I ministered to my feet, then headed on over to the cook tent.

We had freeze-dried beef stroganoff that night. Ron and Toni heated the water at the door of the cook tent while the rest of us had an hors d'oeuvre of pilot bread and Tillamook cheese.

In conversation, I learned that Tom, Helen, Ron and Malcolm knew everybody who mattered in archaeological circles up north and liked to tell stories about them.

"Remember when Roger stuck the pen in his forehead by mistake?" Tom said.

"Sure. Ink was running down into his eyes. One of his grad students had to hand him his own handkerchief," Helen laughed.

"Wish I'd been there to see it, but I was making a living that day," Malcolm guffawed.

"And I was back in Rhode Island so I missed a lot of Roger's missteps," Ron added.

The rest of us listened along to their renditions of exploits, good and bad, about Roger or Jean or John or Mike or Ed or Bob. It didn't matter that Toni, Kelly, Lucy, and I didn't know these people; it was gossip, and we were getting the inside scoop. I quickly understood that many facts were rumors or embellishments, and that in the tapestry of Alaskan storytelling, you couldn't tell exactly where fact and fiction met. Even if you could, the line between fact and fiction fluctuated.

"How long you guys been up here?" Kelly asked Tom and Helen.

"Born up here!" Tom replied. He stroked his raggedy brown beard.

"Yeah," said Helen, sweeping a lock of dirty blonde hair from her eyes. "We met at the U in Fairbanks in an anthro class and got married five years ago." She wiped her nose on her tan shirtsleeve.

"We're gonna become teachers in the bush. Probably down along the Yukon or Kuskokwim somewhere, maybe Bethel or Aniak," Tom added. He put his arm around Helen and gave her a soft peck on the cheek.

"We like wilderness living. Used to it. You like our nifty white tent? Ours is more comfortable than your government crap," Helen said.

"You got a cool tent," Malcolm said, "but we got good ones, too, don't forget."

"Ours is a little bigger so we can screw in it. If you hear groans, stay away!" Tom said boastfully.

"Oh, gross," Kelly said.

Lucy wrinkled her nose and munched her pilot bread. Tom's comment made me miss my boyfriend in DC whom I really didn't like that much. We had had good sex, though.

* * *

The next day, the weather dawned cold, sunny, and breezy. Malcolm divided us into two groups to survey along either bank of Rough Mountain Creek.

"We're going to walk east on either side of the creek, one crew on the north bank, the other on the south. We'll stay in sight of each other, but you *must* take a loaded shotgun and a walkie-talkie. Helen, Kelly, and Georgeie, you're with me on the north bank. Lucy, Ron, Toni, and Tom, you're on the south bank. We'll check in with each other by walkie-talkie at two pm. Then we'll see where we are and how much farther we want to go."

I hoisted my heavy daypack onto my shoulders, happy in the knowledge that I'd be with Malcolm and Kelly. Helen seemed pleasant in a backwoodsy sort of way and she'd been sympathetic to me in Umiat, but I hadn't really sized her up yet.

Malcolm took the shotgun, thank God. I thought it way too cumbersome, dangerous, and heavy to carry, but I knew I'd have to take my turn. I wasn't the best choice for handling the huge gun. My left handedness made it almost impossible to release the safety. I'd have to reach around below the stock with my pointing finger to press it. Shotguns also made a deafening noise, and I had a phobia of loud noises. I hated guns, fireworks, thunderstorms, and kids with balloons.

We walked down to the bank and followed a well-defined game trail running along its edge until Malcolm saw our destination in the distance, a large, flat terrace devoid of vegetation on the south slope of an unnamed mountain. We lurched through a tussock field and finally reached the closest part of the terrace. Flakes of all colors and sizes caught my eye.

Excited with my discovery, I yelled over the breeze, "Ooh! Look at this stuff."

"Let's see," Helen said, running over. "Will you look at all those? Malcolm! Kelly! Over here."

I had counted about fifty flakes in the immediate vicinity of my feet. Brown, red, black, gray, and tan, they stood out against the dull brown ground.

My first discovery!

"Wonderful! Georgeie gets the prize for first site of the day," Malcolm exclaimed.

Extremely proud of myself, I took a bow.

"Let's walk the length of the terrace and back again, keeping about five meters apart like before. Then we'll do a more informal walkover to catch anything we might have missed. Put some flagging down, Georgeie. Then, we'll come back here to record the site."

We examined the entire terrace, finding several concentrations of flakes. They seemed to be separate groupings, at least on the surface. Just to make sure, after the scatters had been flagged, Malcolm had us get our entrenching tools and dig test pits to a depth of fifty centimeters unless we hit permafrost.

"Put the test pits ten meters to the west of each scatter," he said.

I had not seen an Army surplus entrenching tool before arriving at Howard Pass. I disliked it immediately—it was a bastard to use. Perhaps two feet long, there was no way you could dig a hole without stooping. I hit frozen ground almost immediately. I could see ice crystals embedded in the soil, so I touched a patch of them and confirmed the soil was as cold as hell.

We found nothing more at the site for all our efforts. Malcolm declared it a "surface site consisting of five major flake scatters, possibly a chipping station." I wrote this term and its meaning in my notebook, resolving to ask Malcolm more about it later. The flakes were fun, but there was no obsidian, and no tools like points or scrapers, or even modified flakes, just a bunch of plain old flakes.

Malcolm took a stake from his pack, tied an aluminum tag around it, wrote XHP-002 and the date on it, and ceremonially set the datum point. We mapped and photographed the site as we had the first one back at camp. I enjoyed plotting the flake scatters on graph paper and embellishing the map with various details.

"Now, gang, make sure you note the different kinds of materials in your notebooks. It's mostly chert, but there's some chalcedony and jasper, too. The jasper is the red material, Georgeie, see?"

"Uh-huh."

I drew a couple of the larger utilized flakes. My drawings, along with the photographs, map, and written descriptions, captured the nature of XHP-002.

The walkie-talkie crackled to life.

"This is Brass Monkey calling Malcolm. Brass Monkey calling Malcolm. Whatcha got over there? You forget our check-in time?"

"Oh, shit, it's four o'clock," Malcolm said, grabbing the radio. "Sorry, Ron. We're finishing up recording a site now. Lots of flakes but not a whole lot of other stuff."

"We found the same thing over here. Found two sites. We're heading back in now."

"Sounds good to me. We'll be right behind you. Malcolm over and out."

"Brass Monkey, clear."

"What the hell did he say?" Helen asked. "Brass Monkey? What?"

"Ron's being cute again," was all Kelly could say.

"All my children..." Malcolm sighed and shook his head in mock despair while gathering up his survey gear, stuffing the equipment into his daypack, and hoisting it on his shoulders. Sniggering at Ron's walkie-talkie handle, we headed in for the day.

* * *

I felt drained by the time we reached camp. My feet begged for new pieces of moleskin, but I discovered something *really* bad had happened. My only sweater was gone.

Oh, shit. Oh, shit. Shit. What am I gonna do? Shit. Fuck.

Warming up during the walk home, I had taken the sweater off and tied it around my waist. When I ducked into my tent to take off my boots and put on sneakers, I realized it was gone.

A gift from my mother and stepfather from a trip to Scandinavia, the thick wool sweater always kept me warm. Wearing it was like wrapping myself in the comforts of home and the knitted red and gray reindeer design reminded me of Christmas. It was the only sweater I had with me. I felt like an ass.

Shit. What'm I gonna do when it gets really *cold?*

I'd have to borrow some clothes from someone. Forgetting the moleskin, I headed to Kelly's tent, called her name, and stuck my head through the front flap. Her expression grew alarmed when she saw the fright in my face.

"What's wrong? You look really freaked out. Here, have a Marlboro."

Ducking inside and taking the cigarette, I sheepishly told her about my predicament. I could have cried from the shame and frustration of it all.

"Could happen to any of us. I brought plenty extra. How'd you like this bright red wool turtleneck?

I hugged Kelly so hard I could feel her body heat through various layers of long johns, shirts, her sweater and my down vest.

"Thanks. You're a lifesaver," I blubbered gratefully.

"Hey, it's okay. We have to watch out for each other up here," she said soothingly.

"Oh, yeah. No joke."

I relaxed, took a deep breath, and thanked her again. As I left, cigarette dangling from my mouth and red turtleneck gripped tightly in one fist, she yelled after me, "Put your hat on like I told you!"

My state of upset left me so drained I crawled into my sleeping bag right after dinner and fell asleep before Toni even entered the tent. Toni would have given me something to wear, too, I was sure of it, but she was off wandering around the camp during my crisis, and I felt far more comfortable admitting a weakness to Kelly.

* * *

The next day, Malcolm split us into two groups each day and made sure all of us had a chance to work with each other.

I thought about my sweater and my situation in general as we surveyed a terrace: *These guys are so together. They know everything and I know so little.* But, during my woolgathering session, I had a further thought—maybe I could count on the others to help me in other dangerous situations. They knew their shit.

I'd never depended on anyone for my physical wellbeing before, except my mother after my father died. My friends back east wouldn't know what to do. As for this adventure, none of them would've signed up to begin with, likely thinking it a needlessly risky proposition.

On the other hand, my skills increased daily. I began hitting my stride, although my stride was not that long so early in the summer.

I watched, asked questions, and tried to learn as much as I could. Laughter even escaped my lips from time to time.

* * *

When Al flew out the following day to take the first pair of us to Umiat for R&R, he brought with him a large supply of candy and breakfast bars. Malcolm had complained before we'd left Umiat about the stingy supply of chocolate and other high-fat and rich-in-calorie snacks. We were still in the coldest part of the summer and would suffer from a lack of energy food that could keep us warmer.

After screams of ecstasy on our parts, as well as Malcolm's okay, Tom ripped open a box of Hershey bars. We stuffed the wonderful chocolate into our mouths as fast as we could. The box was soon gone. Kelly and Ron had already packed their sleeping bags and put a change of clothes in their daypacks. Badly wanting a shower and my hair a greasy mess, I told Lucy I wished we were going instead.

She answered sympathetically, "Hang on, girl. We're next. Just think about that shower and real coffee."

Kelly and Ron, dressed fairly neatly, looked almost clean. Ron wore a faded denim shirt I'd never seen and had combed his hair. Kelly wore cleanish jeans and a western shirt suitable for downtown Denver. I think she had on lipstick, too, her face radiant with the anticipation of a good time. I'd miss Kelly, even though she'd be back in two days.

We watched Al lift off, head northeast, and disappear. I felt a twinge of panic and abandonment, familiar feelings since the age of five.

* * *

At the end of the workday, on the slog back to camp with Tom and Helen, I spotted a familiar gray and red object caught in the brush next to the creek.

"Oh, my God! My sweater!" I shouted. I wept in disbelief and delight, then ran over, shook off the moisture, and hugged it like I would have the family dog. Relieved and happy, I sang the rest of the way back to camp. When we reached the cook tent, Tom rolled a celebratory joint, and offered it to me first. I accepted. Over dinner, my happy mood continued, and everyone seemed to feel my relief.

Another surprise awaited me in camp. When I headed over to my tent I found Toni moving out.

"Where're you going?" I asked, hoping I hadn't done something especially annoying.

"I love you, George, but now that Ron and Kelly are gone, we can each have our own tent, and I need my privacy so I'm moving into Kelly's tent."

"Oh, yeah. That's great. I forgot," I answered, thinking of the extra room I'd have in the tent.

Elated, I welcomed the solitude and extra space. Lucy now had her tent to *herself* with Kelly gone, and Malcolm had his tent to *himself* without Ron. Tom and Helen, constant companions since before their wedding, continued to enjoy their shared, conjugal space. Everyone slept well that night, and all was peaceful in Howard Pass.

* * *

Our last day on Rough Mountain Creek, June nineteenth, was a bad one. The wind blew harshly, and gray storm clouds filled the sky, threatening rain. The temperature had dropped down into the high thirties. I had no idea what the wind chill might be.

Malcolm, Lucy and I, leaning into the gusts with great effort, worked our way along a side drainage. Toni, Tom, and Helen went up the nearest slope of Ikhlhuk Mountain. I wore long johns, jeans, felt liners inside my boots, a flannel shirt, my wonderful sweater, Kelly's turtleneck, a down vest, wool hat, and gloves. Over all the layers, I wore my raingear for wind protection. Still cold, I figured I'd warm up during the day.

On the grueling walk, I regretted my lack of a parka. I'd thought my down vest and raingear would be enough, but they just weren't cutting it. Finally reaching a low terrace, we took off our daypacks, threw down our walking sticks, and grabbed the field gear we needed to record two flake scatters glistening at us on the ground. I took off my clumsy work gloves to dig out my notebook and pencil.

"Lucy, would you dig a couple of test pits?" Malcolm yelled over the wind. "Where you put them is up to you, but keep them near the datum. You and I'll measure in everything and you can draw the site map, okay Georgeie? Then, we'll giddy up out of here since it's getting colder. Uh oh, I just felt a raindrop."

"Just felt another one. I'll hurry up with those test pits," Lucy said, grabbing her entrenching tool.

I attempted an answer, but nothing came out. The wind whipped me around, deeply penetrating my thin raingear. Oddly, I had stopped shivering.

What did Malcolm say? I should rest a while.

I plopped down on the frigid tundra trying to concentrate. "Malcolm, I don't want to draw the site map today, and I need to find my gloves," I said, sounding drunk to myself.

Malcolm stopped rummaging in his daypack, walked over hurriedly, and peered into my face. He took off a glove and touched my cheek with the back of his hand.

"Oh, no. she's ice cold and her eyes aren't focusing" he said, "Help me get her up, Lucy. She's got to walk around to get warm. She's hypothermic."

"Oh, my God," Lucy said, coming over to me.

By this time I felt naked inside my clothes. The wind penetrated my many layers, stinging like tiny daggers.

"Okay, now do some jumping jacks, Georgeie," Malcolm barked.

I tried to stand, my legs like rubber. Confused and tired, I finally got up with some help from Malcolm and Lucy, but jumping jacks weren't even a possibility. I stood and swayed, my hands tucked into my armpits.

"Alright, we're marching back to camp *now*. No recording the site. Screw it. Take the walkie-talkie out of my daypack and call Tom. Tell them it's a weather day and we're going in as fast as possible," Malcolm said, wrapping his rain jacket around me and staring into my face.

Lucy, shivering, took the radio from Malcolm's daypack and called the other crew.

"Crew two, this is crew one. Do you read me?"

"Is it time for a check in already?" Tom's voice crackled through the radio.

"No. We're heading back in. Georgeie's beyond cold and the weather's getting worse. Malcolm says for you guys to come in, too."

"Okay, the wind has already blown some rolls of flagging tape away and it's howling up here, and sleeting. Okay, Tom, over and out."

"Lucy, out."

"Georgeie, give Lucy your daypack and follow her. We'll get you back to camp ASAP," Malcolm said, his voice tense, his expression grim. "I'll bring up the rear with the shotgun."

Malcolm pointed me in the right direction, but I stumbled a few times before I found my footing. My feet were bricks. My bare hands were frigid inside my gloves, even folded into my armpits, and my ears were frozen solid despite the wool cap. Lucy carried my daypack.

"You all right, Georgeie?" Malcolm yelled.

"Uh-huh," I mumbled, shielding my face from the stinging sleet.

"Okay, girl, let's sing something," Lucy yelled. She chose "I've Been Working on the Railroad" and began to belt it out. Malcolm joined in, but I was using all my energy to march and stay focused. I couldn't really hear much over the wind anyway.

After what seemed like a long walk in outer space to me, we reached the cook tent.

"Lucy, help me take off her outer layers of clothing. Yeah, strip her down to her long johns. Good, now shove her inside the sleeping bag," Malcolm said, his tone worried.

"Got her, Malcolm," Lucy said. She and Malcolm poured my limp body into the sleeping bag, then filled a stuff sack with my clothes and put it underneath my head for a pillow. I began to shiver.

"That's good, Georgeie, you just lie there and shiver for a while and get warm while we fix you some cocoa," Malcolm said, looking down at me and smiling a somewhat optimistic smile. He put my hands inside the sleeping bag.

A blast of frigid air hit me as Tom, Helen, and Toni barreled through the tent door, gusts of wind propelling them inside. Toni zipped the tent door closed as fast as humanly possible. Freezing drops of rain plopped down on the tent flaps. Winds snapped the flies and guy lines loudly.

"For Christ's sake, Georgeie, what mess have you gotten yourself into now?" Tom joked. "Let's get that Primus stove going and get you fixed up."

The stove lit with a whoosh. I was vaguely aware everyone was now sitting cross-legged around me. I was a low table at a Japanese restaurant. When the water finally boiled, Lucy handed me a cup of cocoa. The warmth of the cup soothed my still-freezing hands. Apparently, Malcolm thought I wasn't responding quickly enough. "Drink the cocoa now, George! You have to!" he shouted.

Okay, okay, I'm drinking. What's the fuss? I thought fuzzily.

I barely had the strength to lift the cup to my lips, much less talk.

"Wiggle your toes, Georgeie," he demanded. My toes moved stiffly in the sleeping bag. "Okay, good."

After I rested my cup on my sleeping bag, Tom grabbed my hand and put it back in the sleeping bag. "Still pretty cold," he said, "but the color's coming back to her face."

I lifted my head a little, looked up and smiled at him, then lay my head back on the stuff sack and rested.

Am I in some kind of danger? I asked wordlessly.

Not fully grasping the situation, I let Helen feed me peanut M&M's like peeled grapes. Toni and Lucy chatted at the front of the tent. Tom and Malcolm watched me intently.

"These Primus stoves are shitty," Malcolm fumed. "I knew they would be. You can hardly boil water on them inside a tent. We could have been in some really big trouble today."

Lucy nodded; her gloved hands wrapped around a mug of coffee. "That was pretty ugly out there in the wind and sleet," she said, "but we made it because we're a good team and you're a good boss." She touched Malcolm's arm gently.

"We need those big, old-fashioned, heavy-ass Coleman stoves," Malcolm continued. "We can't be freezing out here in the process of trying to warm up, for Christ's sake. I'll put a note on the next helicopter going back to Umiat and make Rick order Coleman stoves from Fairbanks. I won't take no for an answer. You tell him, Lucy 'If I don't get them in a week, I'm pulling us out'."

"We'll be okay, Malcolm. We'll get what we need," Lucy said soothingly.

"And guys, I'm sorry about today," he said, his voice trembling, "That was a big mistake. We should never have been out in this weather. It's too cold and too wet and too windy! What the hell was I thinking?" He sounded like he would cry.

"It's okay, Malcolm," Toni said from the front of the tent. "We made it and we're fine."

I knew then I'd had a close call and had been the focus of extreme worry.

Every couple of minutes, someone would look down at me to be sure I was all right and tuned in to my surroundings.

67

"I'm here. I'm listening," I'd answer weakly, finding the conversation fascinating, although not completely following the words. I grew sleepy, sensing the danger had passed, and my friends were beginning to unwind and relax. I rested in good hands.

"Oh, look, she's dozing off," someone said.

"She must be exhausted."

"And I bet she was scared."

Warmth enveloped me. My new friends had taken care of me.

Someone gently took my cup away and placed my hand back inside the sleeping bag.

I drifted off to the whisper of "She's a trooper, isn't she?" in my ears.

Nothing could harm me now. Content and secure for one of the few times in my life, I slept while they kept watch.

* * *

After twelve hours of sleep, I woke up alone in my own tent, in my own sleeping bag. Fuzzy memories of the previous day began to come into focus as I stared up at the khaki green Army surplus clothesline that ran along the inside of the tent ceiling.

Holy shit. Did that really happen?

Familiar sounds and smells of camp life brought me back to the present. I wiggled out of my sleeping bag and into my clothes, amazingly none the worse for wear. I had weathered a traumatic event but found myself incredibly resilient at twenty-five.

Yesterday had been cold, unbelievably windy, rainy, and menacing. I could have died. On the other hand, today was sunny and warm, and promised adventure and fun—it was my turn to go to Umiat.

I made a superficial attempt at combing and brushing my greasy hair, unwashed for over a week, then hurried off to the cook tent.

Gleeful almost to the point of giggling, I ducked inside. A round of applause greeted me as I sat down with the others. My nose quivered as it smelled frying bacon.

"Well, look who's up! You look really happy for someone who almost died yesterday. How're you feeling?" Toni asked.

"Not too bad, I guess. That was close, wasn't it?"

"Yeah. Christ, we were all scared shitless," Tom said. "Jesus, don't do that again!"

"I have no intention of ever being that cold again in my entire life."

"And neither do we. Now, drink some coffee and eat something before you fly off to never-never land," Malcolm said, slathering a piece of pilot bread with peanut butter.

I lit a Marlboro, sipped a cup of instant coffee, and extended my plate for bacon. Helen, the cook that morning, gave me several slices.

Malcolm stared at me, looking for residual signs of distress I guessed, and, finding none, continued, "Are you going to behave in Umiat?"

"No way. Lucy and I are going to paint the town red," I said, my face lighting up.

"Girl, we're going to take us a long hot shower first," Lucy said, a beatific smile on her face. "And we can do our laundry at the same time, you know, in the shower stall, like we all are stomping on grapes."

"Great idea!" I said, "And then it will be lunch time and we'll have real food, real everything."

"That Dick the Cook is a wizard with his fine chocolate cake."

"I love him, Lucy, I truly do. I may propose marriage."

"I guess I'll take a hike with the other folks in on our rotation. We'll have fun. I hear the Red Spot on Umiat Mountain is only a mile or so north."

"Not me, I'm going to sit in the Hilton, read my book, drink coffee, smoke, and shoot the shit with Dick the Cook."

Tom gave me a pat on the back.

"Georgeie, do whatever makes you happy. You're still recovering from your ordeal," he said, his brown eyes examining me for signs of stress.

I paused in an unanticipated moment of self-reflection, the reality of yesterday hitting me in the gut. My voice trembled. "Guys, thanks for taking care of me yesterday. I didn't know I was so out of it. I've never been that far gone, and you guys saved me. I don't know what to say."

Toni stirred her cup of Tang.

"George, we care for each other up here because we have to, and because we want to," Malcolm said, grabbing my hand and looking far calmer than he had looked the day before. "You just happened to be the first one and we got to practice on you," he added easing the tone of the conversation.

"Thanks, Malcolm," I said quietly. We gave each other an awkward hug, balancing our breakfasts on our laps and keeping a firm grip on our cups of coffee.

"I may cry," Tom sniffed and wiped away crocodile tears.

Helen rolled her eyes.

"I'm going to miss you all even though we're only going away for two nights," I said, "really."

"We'll miss you, too, Georgeie," Malcolm said. "Now you guys go get ready for your trip."

* * *

The 206 landed right on time—not that time was strictly measured in Howard Pass. Kelly was sitting up front with Al, probably flirting with him. Ron more than amply took up a window seat in the rear. After the chopper shut down, Kelly and Ron hopped out and down onto terra firma. Kelly held a plate covered in saran wrap. Al, as handsome as ever in a black leather jacket and tight Carhartts, shut down the engine and stepped down onto the tundra, his shoes making a squishy sound.

"Hey, guys. Here's some fresh brownies. Dick the Cook baked em this morning," Kelly said.

A collective "Ooohh!" arose from the crew.

"Jeez, thanks you guys. Let's take em along for lunch today. Thanks for not eating them already," Malcolm said, relieving Kelly of the plate and giving her a hug.

"They'll be gone in half an hour," Helen said. "They won't make it til lunch."

There would be plenty of brownies in Umiat. There would also be guys to flirt with and bearded faces to kiss. I raised an eyebrow in anticipation of wrongdoing and fun. I hugged everyone goodbye except for Ron. When I turned to hug him, he roared, "Get away from me! I'm clean, and you're filthy."

"I'm sorry," I replied in mock shame and climbed into the passenger the chopper.

Al made a final check of the hatches and doors, climbed into the pilot's seat next to me, and fired up the rotors. The chopper whined as we slowly lifted off. Camp shrunk in size while the universe around me grew to include the imposing landscape that went on forever. That universe would soon include Umiat. My anticipation grew exponentially with each mile.

Once we leveled off, clouds like cotton balls dotted the sky. Al flew over or around the smaller ones instead of straight through. A feeling of magic filled me as we soared up one side of a cloud and down the other. Lucy missed the fun—she had fallen asleep in the backseat.

"Hey, Georgeie," Al's voice came crackling through the headset, "There's a bear down by that thaw lake at about two o'clock."

I looked down to spot a honey-colored grizzly and two cubs walking slowly across the tundra towards a nearby hillside. The breeze caught the mother's fur and changed the color slightly from golden to dark brown and back again.

"She's a big one," Al said, "I'd hate to run across her and her cubs without a shotgun."

I shuddered at the thought of killing something so beautiful, but I knew the danger involved. This wasn't a zoo, and, without a gun, I would be no match for a bear. I'd be dead, dead, dead, and quickly, I hoped.

My thoughts turned to our handsome pilot. I asked him where he was from.

"I live in Homer southwest of Anchorage when I'm not flying. I make enough money during the summer to loaf the rest of the year."

"Where'd you learn to fly?" I asked.

"Nam. I hated Nam. After my tour of duty, I went back to Homer."

There was a break in the conversation. I didn't think Al wanted to talk about Nam anymore.

I stared at the tundra, coming alive and green in the Arctic spring. My mind wandered back to my twelve-year-old self, studying a *Look* magazine I'd picked up from our coffee table. I'd never heard of Alaska before and knew nothing of earthquakes, but the photographs of the devastation caused by the Good Friday Earthquake of 1964 had left a lasting impression.

"Were you in Homer during the big earthquake of 64?" I yelled.

"Yeah. I'll never forget it. I had just driven back from Anchorage and pulled into the driveway when it hit. 'Holy shit,' I thought, 'What the hell is this?' Houses shook and the trees started to sway. Then it started rockin' and rollin'. And the noise! The earth made a cracking sound that scared the shit out of me. My girlfriend ran out of the house and I yelled for her to get in the car. All the neighbors were outside by then, some of them screaming. It was *so* fucking scary. You didn't know when it would stop, if it would get worse, or how many aftershocks there'd be. We were already halfway up Diamond Ridge behind town when the shaking stopped."

"Why'd you go up there?" I asked.

"The quake was so bad, we knew there'd be a huge tidal wave, so we had to get up high. Most of the folks in Homer ended up on the ridge. When the tsunami finally hit, the waves were ten feet high. Homer Spit almost completely sank—houses, boats, businesses—gone. But no one was swept out to sea because we were all up on high ground.

"But Seward lost its railroad, most of downtown, and its fishing fleet," Al continued. "It's on Resurrection Bay, which is kind of like a fjord, just perfect for a tidal wave. Anchorage was hit bad, too. Lots of houses slid into Knik Arm, but only 150 people died in the whole state. That's it. Not many people up here to be killed back in 64."

"Jesus, God," I said, not knowing what other reaction could sum up a situation like that.

I concentrated on the tundra and peaks after our conversation lagged. The mountains, still covered with snow, offered no hint of danger, nor any comfort. They were as silent as the tundra.

I'd already learned the Arctic teemed with life, but that life could be quickly extinguished. Alaska could be bountiful, and it could be cruel. The day before, I had almost died. Today, I was on my way to the pleasures of Umiat.

My reverie ended with the sensation of slowing rotors. In the distance, I could make out a group of green tents and six rag-tag people jumping up and down, hollering, shouting, and waving. We had reached the Ikpikpuk camp. I'd forgotten we were making a stop at tussock central to deliver their mail.

All hands raced for the chopper after the rotors slowed, anticipating mail from home. Lucy and I stayed on board while mail and some supplies were off-loaded.

And there *he* was, standing in front of the chopper, looking intently at me through the Plexiglas. I'd forgotten about Ian while out in Howard Pass, but quickly remembered our playful flirting in Fairbanks, as well as his skill in telling filthy jokes and his fondness for folk songs.

Tall and dark, with intense brown eyes, a delightful dark beard, and a hawk-like nose set against pale skin, he had already winked at me at least twice—maybe three times. I stared at his chest hairs peeking out of several layers of clothing as he waved to Lucy and me. "Ladies," he smiled, tipping his broad-brimmed field hat.

I felt a twinge of excitement as our eyes met. Regretfully, I wrote him off once again as unavailable. Then, he winked at me. It was unmistakable.

I studied my hands, encased in Monkey Grip work gloves. I looked at the monkeys cavorting on the back of the gloves, then looked up and met his gaze.

He's off-limits! Forget the bastard. It's just your imagination, anyway.

Involuntarily, I winked back.

Ian removed his fedora, held it in front of his chest, bowed ceremoniously, and then turned back to whatever he had been doing before we arrived. He was perfect except for that wedding ring.

Thankfully, we lifted off before we could continue our flirtation. Al and I chatted, while Lucy roused herself to look out of the window.

Umiat's many rows of silver Quonsets, lined up with military precision and sparkling in the bright sun, appeared in the distance. To me, they shimmered like Shangri-la on Christmas Day. None of them, I noticed with relief, were on fire. Our white wall tents with yellow roof tarps beckoned me, as did the decrepit Hilton with its mess hall and showers. Someone stood fishing in a nearby creek and a battered C-10 was parked on the airstrip. Several bearded men wearing rubber boots and orange vests were unloading it. Umiat looked like a bustling metropolis compared to Howard Pass.

My hair is so gross.

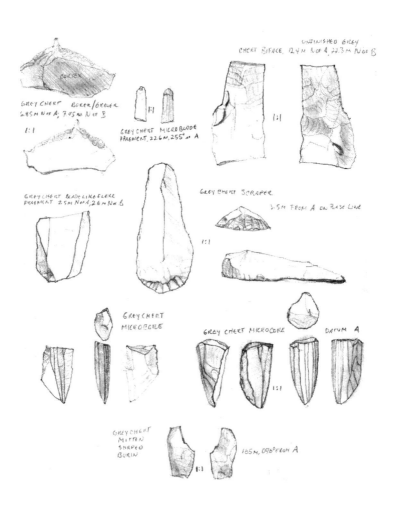

GREY CHERT BORER/GRAVER
2.85M N OF A, 7.05M N OF B

1:1

GREY CHERT BLADE LIKE FLAKE
FRAGMENT 2.5M N OF A, 2.6M N OF B

1:1

GREY CHERT MICROBLADE
FRAGMENT, 22.6M, 255° or A

UNFINISHED GREY
CHERT BIFACE, 12.4M N OF A, 22.3M N OF B

1:1

GREY CHERT SCRAPER

1.5M FROM A ON BASE LINE

1:1

GREY CHERT
MICROBLADE

GREY CHERT MICROCORE

DATUM A

1:1

GREY CHERT
MITTEN
SHAPED
BURIN

165M, 096° FROM A

1:1

UMIAT

We set down at the edge of the plywood tents. Linda, the supply queen, welcomed us home, flipped open the chopper's compartments and began offloading gear. Lucy and I grabbed our belongings and headed over to the Howard Pass tent. "Free the Howard Pass Eight" had been written in black magic marker on the plywood door.

"How funny is this?" I said. "Someone is reliving the 1968 Democratic National Convention."

"They sure have an offbeat sense of humor," Lucy said.

"Well, we're one too many to be the Chicago Seven, aren't we?" I asked rhetorically.

I looked at the two cots in the tent and some odds and ends piled in the corner. Not quite comfy looking, but who cared? It would be a welcome change from sleeping on the ground. The luxury of swinging my legs over the edge of even a makeshift bed, bending my knees, and placing my feet on the floor was something to look forward to, maybe even savor.

"This makes me happy," I said, unrolling my sleeping bag on one of the cots.

"Me, too," Lucy said, sighing contentedly.

We hurried out of the tent and headed towards the Hilton for a home-cooked meal prepared by that magician, Dick the Cook.

Lucy suggested we be friendly and knock on the other tent doors on the way. She knocked on the Colville River door. A deep voice on the other side of the door said, "Just a minute." I distinctly heard a zipper being zipped, always a favorite sound. Ross, a big beefy guy with brown hair tucked under his blue baseball cap, opened the door. He seemed genuinely happy to see us.

"Hey, folks," he said.

Leslie, the other Colville River camper on our rotation, peeked out from behind Ross. I quickly saw she was almost as beefy as Ross. She whined about something inside the tent, but I didn't quite catch what it was. We were probably not going to be best friends.

When we knocked on Lookout Ridge, we got no answer, but saw Debbie and Corey ahead of us, talking to Mike and John from Ikpikpuk. We caught up to them and walked towards the Hilton, past the dusty rows of Quonsets, the control tower, and the airstrip.

Together, we trooped up the front steps and entered the mess hall. Fresh coffee perked in the urn. Next to the urn and a stack of now-familiar Melmac cups was a plate of still-warm chocolate chip cookies. Ross and I raced to them and fought over who would get the first one. Ross elbowed me out of the way and won.

The Lookout Ridge contingent, Debbie and Corey, introduced themselves with a round of "heys" and "howdys."

Leslie and Ross had thought ahead, bringing soap, towels, and clean clothes with them. They would be first in the two showers down the hall and had obviously been coached by their crewmates who had preceded them on rotation from Colville River. I could have kicked myself for not having my stuff for the shower with me, but no one in Howard Pass had told me the race for the showers would be so competitive.

Leslie got up and disappeared down the hall with her bag of toiletries, a cookie, and a cup of coffee. Ross, giving Leslie a head start for privacy's sake, I assumed, said he wanted to find an Early Man site, "You know, they think there's a bunch of really old sites scattered between Alaska and Siberia, some Pleistocene-aged. Damn, I'd like to find a site with a Paleolithic hand axe," he said rubbing his hands together. "Maybe a fossilized man about half a million years old. Shit fire, I could retire now. And I'd be the Chair of Anthropology at Harvard."

"We all have that dream, Ross," Mike said.

"All right, I'll be happy with the first American Neanderthal."

"You're the first American Neanderthal," I quipped, surprising myself.

"Bah humbug!" he said, feigning hurt feelings. He disappeared down the hall toward the shower, whistling as he went.

"I know you folks are dying for a shower, but I'm not going to take one all summer," Corey, a grad student at UAF, said. "Dirt keeps the mosquitoes away, and I've stopped smelling myself anyway. I'd rather be dirty than eaten alive by mosquitoes."

Perhaps he saw me admiring his matted, greasy blond hair after he took off his ancient wool cap and ran his hand through his hair to keep it out of his eyes: "My hair always looks like this anyway."

One of the few Alaskans on a crew other than Howard Pass, Corey said he was putting himself through school by drawing artifacts. His steely blue eyes, I noticed, were fixated on Lucy. He would look at her, then stare into the distance as if thinking important thoughts, then gaze back at her with increasing absorption. I wondered whether Lucy would go for a guy encrusted in a layer of dirt who attracted the flies of Umiat.

Debbie, Corey's companion from Lookout Ridge, came from California where she was a grad student at UC Berkeley. She may have been a natural blonde, and had a certain sophistication I thought I lacked, the carefree attitude of a Californian. I could visualize her in a skimpy bikini on a surfboard or strutting around as a cheerleader and assumed every man on the crew wanted to sleep with her.

Corey referred to her as Butter Butt in conversation. The name stuck all summer long.

"Why Butter Butt?" asked John.

"I slipped on some grass and fell on an open tin of canned butter just outside the cook tent," she said. "Everyone laughed, of course, and it *was* funny, but we were all relieved I didn't cut myself through my jeans. As it was, I reeked of butter and had to wash my jeans in the stream so I wouldn't attract a bunch of bears. Drawing blood would have made me even more desirable to every grizzly within fifty miles."

At the mention of blood, a nerve-racking thought occurred to me: *What about when I have my period? And what do I do with a Tampax? Somebody must know.*

Dick the Cook sauntered out of the kitchen to get himself a cup of coffee. "Hey, guys, welcome to Chez Dick. I bet you're happy to be here."

This was a rhetorical statement, but we answered more or less in a chorus, "you bet," "and how," "you can say that again," and "boy, howdy," all at the same time.

Ikpikpuk Mike took this opportunity to take his dirty bandanna from around his neck, wipe his face with it, and then wipe the table in front of him where he had spilled some coffee. He reached for a cookie crumb with a thumb and forefinger, his nails caked with dirt.

Dick the Cook, looking somewhat horrified, said, "I know you guys have been out in the middle of God knows where, doing God knows what, for God knows how long, with no one to yell at you, so I'm telling you—*wash your hands!*"

Mike spoke on our behalf: "We'll wash anything you want us to, Dick!"

We rushed down to the lavatory en masse, trying to push through the door at the same time to see who could wash up the fastest and get back to the mess hall to grab more cookies.

I washed my hands with well-used Octagon soap in the one long communal basin, then looked into the mirror.

"Oh my God! I'm filthy!"

"It comes off, gal," Lucy said reassuringly.

My eyes then focused on the rest of the lavatory behind me. Okay, so we all used the same basin, but I was startled to see an unknown man walk in, unzip his fly, and walk behind a partition to my left. Another man quickly exited a stall, but not before I got a glimpse of a strange-looking toilet and heard it emit an unfamiliar sound. The smell made my nose want to pinch itself closed.

What is this shit?

Corey obviously saw confusion and horror on my face.

"Those are destroilets. They incinerate your shit. You don't flush em, you stand up and you can look down and see a flame come partway up the toilet as you pull up your pants. They're the way to go up here in the permafrost, no pun intended. No septic tank, no sewage lagoon, no flushing. No shit lying around on the tundra. No shit having to be hauled away to Fairbanks in plastic trash bags."

The other newcomers and I stared at Corey in disbelief. If we had been a group of characters in a cartoon, the group caption above our heads would have said "HOLY SHIT!"

The man who had noisily peed behind the partition and zipped up his fly walked out behind us. Unfortunately, it was quiet and shy pilot Sam. I was mortified and turned away, but not before he saw us. He beat a hasty retreat into the hallway.

I entered a stall, dropped my jeans, and sat down. This would be another adventure of sorts, an experiment in northern life. The seat was warm because flames shot part way up on a regular basis. I imagined on a cold day, this would be a good place to read a novel in comfort, except for the smell. I did my business and stood up. I heard a whoosh and watched in fascination as a flame shot up to within a foot of where my butt had been.

They'll never believe this at home.

Afterwards, feeling newly dirty, I made a second pass at my fingernails, this time with Lava soap. I wiped my hands on several paper towels and was about ready to leave when I remembered my friends from the Colville River crew a few feet away in the showers.

"How's the water?" I asked, anticipating my turn under the wonderful hot water.

"Wonderful!" came the answers, one from Leslie, the other from Ross.

The voices sounded very close together. Apparently, both showers were behind the same opaque plastic curtain on a plain, wooden platform. My questions were plentiful: *Did they get undressed together? What if I'm in there and a guy comes in to take a shower? Should I undress in the shower?* I would find out soon enough.

* * *

Because we'd been given the go ahead by the project to take showers and eat real food at the Hilton during R&R, Dick the Cook's lunch, consisting of leftovers transformed into chili and his widely praised corn bread with jalapeno peppers, were greatly anticipated. My mouth watered as I smelled the savory aroma. I took my place in the chow line, grabbed one of the cheap porcelain plates, filled it to overflowing with chili and cheddar cheese, and balanced two large pieces of cornbread on the plate's edge.

OJ and Ellie Smith, the managers of Umiat, and their adult sons, Jay and Ray, sat down with us. The rest of the table quickly filled with roustabouts. I kept pace with our tablemates, eating three plates full. It didn't matter what leftovers the chili consisted of, it wasn't freeze-dried and wasn't accompanied by wind and rain. Best of all, I could sit down on a bench, put my meal on a table, and not have to balance it on my lap hunched over in a tent. I had never tasted anything so good.

Dick the Cook hauled five-gallon drums of chocolate, strawberry, and vanilla ice cream from the walk-in freezer, then rooted around under the counter until he found jars of chocolate and butterscotch sauces and cans of mixed nuts. He placed the containers and several large serving spoons on the counter. The day was warmish by North Slope standards, in the low fifties, I guessed, and I eyed the ice cream with anticipation.

"Okay, folks, come and get it," he said, folding his arms across his chest and chewing on a toothpick. He wore a satisfied grin, undoubtedly knowing sundaes would make everyone happy.

The first spoonful of chocolate and vanilla ice cream lingered on my tongue, then melted. I closed my eyes to appreciate the moment. Lucy's first spoonful of strawberry ice cream covered in nuts made her sigh.

Jay and Ray, both redheads in their early twenties, seemed to be savoring their chocolate ice cream with chocolate sauce. They began chatting us up. Their parents had left the table and I assumed they now felt free to flirt with us, or at least try to make an impression.

"Between the two of us, we can fix all the trucks and small planes here," Ray said. "No one else except Dad can make that statement. If you needed a part and we weren't around, you'd have to call over to Prudhoe or up to Barrow or down to Fairbanks. Then the part would have to be flown up here in a chartered plane. You'd have to wait days if they were out of parts." He took a gulp of milk. Jay twirled his spoon into his chocolate sauce.

"Uh-huh," I said, marveling at the logistics involved to replace a worn part or get in a supply of gasoline in remote Alaska.

"Ray and I look after the Hilton, the airstrip, the radio tower, and whatever needs fixin," Jay said. "We report the weather to radio and TV stations in Barrow, Fairbanks, and Anchorage. That's the most important thing we do."

"Yeah, and a lot of times we're the coldest station reporting," Ray added. "Mom and Pop run Umiat all year long, and Pop's got a big game business on the side. He flies all over the Slope in a Cessna that can carry two people and gear, max. In the winter, the plane's on skis, and if the customer wants to land on a lake in the summer, he puts floats on it. Pop runs a tight shop and Mom keeps the books, does the laundry, keeps the Hilton sparkling."

"Mom and Pop never rest," Jay said.

"I guess not," Lucy murmured.

Perhaps Ray and Jay could read the astonishment on my face, because they launched into more tales of life at its most tenuous. We were an audience of two at their mercy. Lucy and I leaned in to catch every word.

"When it's sixty below, you don't go outside except to record the weather. Nothin's flyin' in or out. Rubber tires deflate from round to square because the air is so dense, so you're stuck wherever you are until the weather changes. And if you don't have enough food in your emergency stash, you can kiss your ass goodbye!" Ray said.

"We stock enough canned goods and frozen food here to last us a year, kind of like Mormons. And the amount of dough we lay out for fuel before winter sets in is astronomical. I can't even count that high," Jay laughed.

"About four winters ago, a news crew flew up for a story on Umiat. I tell you what we did," Ray said, "we took them outside for a demonstration of sorts. Jay got a steaming cup of coffee and brought it outside."

"Yup, I did," Jay said. "And you know what? I threw the coffee in the air and it froze! Yup, every last fucking molecule of coffee froze in mid-air and clinked when it hit the ground."

"That can't be true," Lucy said, startled.

"Yeah, it is," Ray assured.

"Really!" I said.

Unfortunately, O. J. sauntered back into the mess hall and cut short our conversation.

"Boys, come help me and your mother offload the Piper Cub that just flew in, and then I want you to go over the engine with a fine-toothed comb. It's been making funny noises. Needs a lube job, maybe, before it can fly out."

"Okay, Pop, we're coming!" Ray said. They hurriedly got up and threw their dishes into the rubber basin next to the coffee pot for Dick the Cook to wash later in the day.

"You know, Lucy," I said, "I can't grasp all this information, so let's get our stuff and take that shower," I said. "Maybe it will clear my head of cobwebs. Christ, sixty below. Really?"

"Well, they should know, I guess," Lucy said tentatively.

We ran back to the Howard Pass tent. I grabbed the bandanna holding my toiletries and Lucy pawed through her daypack, grabbed shampoo, soap, toothbrush, and toothpaste, and tied them up in a towel. "Don't forget your dirty clothes and stuff sack," she said. "No one will know we're washing our clothes in the shower instead of paying to use the Hilton's washing machine."

We could have used the old dinged-up old machine, but OJ and Ellie charged five dollars a load. The little cash we had would be better spent on ordering booze and dope from Fairbanks. Stomping on my clothes in the shower and applying Dr. Bronner's seemed the financially sound alternative.

"Yeah, you're right. They'll never know," I said, growing more excited with each step bringing us closer to luxurious cleanliness.

When we reached the lavatory, the guys from Ikpikpuk were almost finished. Lucy and I stood out in the hall waiting our turn.

"I just broke up with a guy," she said. "It was casual. I'm looking for someone new and different now."

"Corey lusts after you," I said.

"I had no idea," she said. "I'll check that boy out. What about you?"

"I'm dating a guy from work," I answered, then caught myself. "Well, I *used* to work nights with him in the *US News & World*

Report newsroom. It's not serious, I mean, it *wasn't* serious, and I'll tell you what—I finally get that you can have sex with a guy and not be in love with him. Joe's fun, has a great sense of humor, teases me, and has an orange cat named Zero. I kind of miss him, but he wouldn't fit in up here. He wouldn't even want to come here. I don't think I'll get back with him in August. I'm going to grad school in Connecticut anyway."

"After my dad comes up to see me at the end of the summer, I'll go back home and visit my family in Georgia. Maybe even see Tommy," Lucy said.

Envy engulfed me for a moment at the mention of her dad, but I ignored the feelings to listen to what else Lucy had to say.

"But, after that," she continued, "I don't know. There are some excavations in the southwest this fall run out of U of Arizona, so maybe I'll sign up for one."

"Maybe I'll come back here," I mused, "but I'm locked into a year at UConn, and my advisor will probably get me out to the Aleutians next summer. That seems like a wild place, too. Hope I'll be up to it. And Joe seems kind of dull now. He wouldn't understand this kind of life. I can't imagine *any* of my friends being comfortable up here."

"Yeah, I know what you mean, Georgeie."

From the inner sanctum of the lavatory, Mike yelled, "Next!"

We dashed inside and over to the shower curtain, yanking it back, certain the Wizard of Oz would be casting spells on the other side. Instead, lovely steam wafted out from the two recently vacated stalls. The humidity opened my pores and I felt nearer to heaven than I'd felt in ages. I breathed deeply, put my clean clothes on the rickety table between the two stalls, stepped into one, threw my dirty clothes on the floor, and turned on the water.

Anyone coming into the lavatory would have heard moans, groans, and sighs enough to convince them there was hot sex going on in both showers. I felt like a snake shedding its skin as I scrubbed off the dirt I'd accumulated. My hair was so dirty I had to soap it up three times before it stopped feeling greasy. Only after scrubbing and massaging my scalp for fifteen minutes did my hair feel squeaky clean.

"How you feeling, girl?" Lucy asked.

"Beautiful," I shouted over the rush of the water.

"Me, too!"

We laughed loudly.

During my long and delightful shower, my fingers began to look like prunes. I reluctantly turned off the water, grabbed my towel, and began drying off, knowing the hot water tank couldn't be *that* large. My old jeans, underwear, and shirt were still at the bottom of the shower. Dirty brown water flowed from them and circled the drain. I picked them up and wrung them out. They were still filthy, but not as filthy as before. Lucy stepped out of her stall. The space was so tiny our rear ends bumped together while we finished toweling. With clean clothes on, I felt like a new woman. I turned around in our confined space.

"You're so clean!" I said, looking at Lucy.

"And I hardly recognize you. Is that the Georgeie I know?"

"God, I feel good," I said, smiling. I felt happier, and more satisfied and content than I would have thought possible. The only memory that came close was a distant one, when my father pretended to be afraid of me when I'd wrapped myself in a sheet like a mummy for Halloween. I remembered giggling, then laughing uproariously, not realizing he'd abandon me forever the following year.

I grabbed my things, opened the shower curtain, and slipped down to the row of sinks. Putting my now semi-clean but wet clothes next to one of the sinks with my stuff sack laid gently on top of them as camouflage, I looked in the mirror again.

At first, the image did not register. My skin looked rough and reddened from scrubbing. With my uncombed hair a mass of tangles, a Medusa's head stared back at me. I looked at my severely chapped lips, peeling nose, and the hundreds of freckles I'd never noticed on my face before and touched my cheek in disbelief.

I'm clean and I'm wild looking. The new me! I like it.

* * *

After hanging my clean wet clothes from a bungee cord strung between nails in the Howard Pass tent, I strolled through the rows of Quonset huts and down to the airstrip, my newly arrived copy of *The Source* tucked under my arm. A friend in DC had sent me the book, thinking it would appeal to me as a nascent archaeologist because of its storyline of a dig in Israel. The thick paperback had arrived in the first batch of mail earlier that week and became my constant companion.

* * *

Lucy, Corey, Mike, and John began their trek to the Red Spot on Umiat Mountain, but I craved time alone to ponder my new, although temporary, life. The sun shone high in a cloudless sky, its rays glinting off the chrome surfaces of a small fleet of rusting yet somewhat serviceable fixed-wing aircraft. A warm breeze gently blew through my newly clean hair. It was a perfect day—cloudless and idyllic. I took a deep breath and exhaled. I felt calm and relaxed, and like I kind of fit in, but not completely.

After a short walk around the airfield, I headed over to the Hilton to read and have a cup of coffee. In the mess hall, Dick the Cook stood washing up dishes for dinner, whistling as he scrubbed. The aroma of roasting beef wafted out of the industrial-sized oven. Coffee percolated in the giant urn on the counter.

"Hi, Dick," I said.

"Hey, Georgeie. How's you doing this fine day?" he said, his jaw working overtime chewing gum.

"Great," I said, and then told him about my recent hypothermia bout.

"Happened to me once," Dick the Cook said. "Scariest day of my life. If it hadn't been for my hunting partner, I'd be dead."

I liked him immensely, but never found out his last name. Since most people referred to him as Dick the Cook, that was his full name to me. There may have been other men named Dick, but there was only one Dick the Cook.

He had a self-confident air, although it did not seem to come from a sense of importance, but from all the people in Umiat who treated him with affection and respect. A field cook commanded reverence, especially one that didn't have an assistant, simply by being the one who fed the masses. He was the most important person in Umiat, except for the Smith family.

I studied his neat jet-black hair and beard, blue eyes, paper-white skin, and freshly scrubbed hands. He was dressed in an immaculate white uniform of starched pants and a short-sleeved shirt, with an open pack of Pall Malls bulging through one of the breast pockets. His was dirty, greasy work, and he had a reputation to uphold, so he dressed spotlessly.

He took off the grease-spattered apron wrapped around his middle and flung it onto a mountain of similarly dirty aprons and towels at the back of the kitchen.

"Ya know," he said to me, "I have my pride, so I change aprons after serving each meal. Need to look tidy for the folks here. Ninety-nine percent of the grease ends up on the apron. Not sure where the other one percent goes."

That afternoon, I observed various pilots and mechanics come in for a cup of coffee and greet him. "Hi, Cookie," they'd say, "What's for dinner?"

Dick the Cook recited the evening's menu.

"Oh, boy!" one of them said, "Roast beef! Aw, jeez, thanks Dick!"

A couple of the roustabouts took handfuls of cookies, grabbed their coffee, and went to sit at the rear table, maybe to talk about recent conquests. Dick the Cook and I continued our chat.

"I like Wednesday roast beef night. You just throw the beef in the oven with some garlic smeared on it and forget about it. I enjoy ladling out the oh juice, too, and watching a guy's face light up."

"Oh juice?" I queried.

"Yeah, you know, the gravy, the drippins."

"I get it, Dick."

"You have to eat good in a camp like Umiat for morale's sake. A bad meal can ruin your reputation, and I have a great one, so far. Don't want to ruin it."

Dick the Cook took the end of a paring knife and cautiously picked that morning's cereal from between the gap in his front teeth.

When I asked him where he was from, he told me he was born and raised in Oregon, surrounded by small towns and tall fir and cedar trees. I asked him how long it had taken him to get used to the treeless tundra.

"Oh, at first it was odd," he said, "but I've been up here for so long now it's the trees that seem strange, kind of claustrophobic, when I go home."

"How long has it been since you've been home?" I asked.

Dick the Cook couldn't say precisely, but it was probably sixteen months. I was incredulous. "The money's good up here," he explained.

"But," I asked, "isn't it boring up here in the winter when nothing is going on?"

"Cold and dark, yes, boring, no. Winter's when all the seismic exploration takes place. Umiat is jumping all the time. We're a hub for oil and gas companies. See, seismic companies can't take their cat trains out in the summer because they'd sink into the tundra. They wait until everything is frozen solid, assemble their equipment, and head out."

He stopped wiping the counter with a rag and looked out the window.

"But you can still see their tracks in some places because sometimes the ground isn't quite frozen or the machinery is too heavy," he continued, throwing the rag onto his pile of dirty aprons. "The tundra doesn't really bounce back. The tracks fill with water, then freeze and then thaw the following spring and get deeper. It's a mess. Maybe they'll come up with something less damaging one day, but not this year; that's what you see out there, those tracks."

"Jeez, Dick, that's horrible. Can't they just fill the tracks in?" I asked.

"Not really. That would leave a bigger mess. The tundra's really fragile."

I'd noticed ruts left by huge vehicles out in the bush, usually in low, boggy areas. There weren't that many, but the ruts I saw scarred the tundra and filled up with water. From the helicopter, the tracks glistened like snakes that had just shed their skins. I didn't know if there was a way to repair the damage, but I knew the tracks would get bigger over time, and that saddened me.

A guffaw went up from the back table. Someone had just described his girlfriend's anatomy, I guessed.

"God damn," I said, "and you know there'll be more and more companies up here looking for oil. That's why *we're* here—to tell them what to stay away from. I'd like to tell them to just go away."

"Ain't gonna happen, Georgeie," Dick the Cook said, opening the oven to admire his roast beef.

I let him return to the tasks at hand, while I picked up my book and spent most of my rotation ensconced in his mess hall, enjoying the creature comforts of home, plowing through *The Source*.

* * *

After breakfast the next day, Dick the Cook began to tell me a little about his personal life. The odd thing was, I hadn't asked him anything at all. Maybe he just wanted to talk.

"My girlfriend is not the mother of my kids. Their mother, my wife, Donna, died in a fishing accident eight years ago out of King Salmon. It was hard on the girls for a long time and I blamed myself. We moved to Anchorage for a couple of years and I worked in some downtown restaurants, real nice ones.

"A couple of years ago, when I visited Oregon with the girls, I met Sheree. She's beautiful, and she loves my kids, and, God Almighty, I love her. She hit me like a ton of bricks.

"But the money is up north, and Umiat isn't a place I'd take the girls to—no schools, no health clinic, bad company. So, they're in the Lower 48 with Sheree, living in a small house I bought with North Slope money. They go to school, have a lot of friends and a dog-named Trooper. Sheree works in the library and goes to PTA meetings. I just need to save some more money to join them for good."

"Why don't you marry her?" I asked, fascinated.

Dick the Cook paused. "I lost one wife. I don't want to lose Sheree. I don't want to be left alone again, I guess. If I keep things loose, maybe it'll all turn out okay."

His candor took me by surprise. Dick the Cook loved Sheree and wanted to be with her, but he also seemed to need emotional distance from the uncertainty of life, or so I gathered. That made sense to me. I'd built up walls as insulation against loss and death, and so had he.

At that moment, I felt close to him. But as much as I enjoyed our growing friendship, I knew it was temporary like most relationships on the Slope, and I'd never see him after the summer.

* * *

Sometime after lunch the next day, I turned back to my book. Seated comfortably at the table nearest the coffee urn for the rest of the day, I picked up *The Source*, again marveling at the book's thickness and amount of detail. Each chapter began with a passage set in the present about an excavation in Israel, then a longer story about each level of the site with an artifact from that time period illustrated by a simple line drawing. Why, as an archaeologist, had I never read this before?

I was captivated. Dick the Cook rattled pots and pans, but I hardly noticed.

I read through the afternoon, then drowsily walked back to the Howard Pass tent with Lucy after a dinner of chili dogs, wilted salad with bottled dressing, and canned cherry pie with melted slices of Tillamook cheese. I continued reading in bed. A blowout party at GSI had been cancelled when their shipment of booze failed to show up, but I felt content to read, then fall asleep.

* * *

The next morning, I got up, stretched, put my boots on, and stepped outside after whispering in Lucy's ear, "It's time to wake up, sleepyhead."

She stirred and I left her to wake up in peace. I stepped out of the tent just as Linda happened by. Our food and equipment supplier, she had an unglamorous job that didn't take her beyond Umiat. She seemed friendly though, so I joined her on her walk to the Hilton for breakfast.

"Where're you from, Linda?" I asked.

"Washington, across from The Dalles on the Columbia."

"What's that like?"

"It's really pretty there. One minute you're looking at really big fir trees downriver, then grass and scrub upriver. It changes really fast. I'm in the trees, but I can see high desert across the river."

I couldn't picture the scene but enjoyed listening to her.

"My cabin is really neat—it has running water and a wood stove. I want to become a forest ranger, but I need to finish my BS at Washington State University when I have enough money. By the way, we call WSU WAZOO—rhymes with kazoo. Makes it a happy-sounding word."

Changing the subject, Linda asked me what I was doing in the fall.

"I'm going to start grad school at UConn."

"The Yukon?"

"Oh, no, the University of Connecticut back east."

"Everyone here will think you mean you're going to school in Canada, you know."

"Jeez, I would never have thought of that. There's a prof there who's worked in Alaska for forty years. He's really famous and I'm really nervous about studying under him, but I guess I'll be okay," I said, hoping it *would* be okay.

"I don't think I'll ever be able to afford an advanced degree, but you never know, maybe I'll strike it rich someday."

"Hey, maybe we'll find gold this summer."

"And hide it from the others. Deal?"

"Deal."

We arrived late at the Hilton and were relegated to seats at the back table with OJ and his sons and a few of the grease monkeys. I placed my cup of steaming hot coffee across from Jay and then went up to the mess line.

"Save my place!" I shouted.

Breakfast was always a treat—eggs cooked to order, bacon, sausage, pancakes, French toast, warm syrup, rolls, and pastries. I collected my order for scrambled eggs and heaped my plate with as much bacon and pancakes as it could hold before returning to my spot, past my archaeo-friends to the hired hands table. Two of the airstrip workers were having a lively conversation about fixing things. Ray and Jay were contributing their opinions.

"You know, you can fix anything with duct tape. Like even electrical cables, piping, rain gear, tents, and even ducts, you name it," Worker Bee One said.

"Shit, you can duct tape a small plane together," Worker Bee Two said, fiddling with the suspenders of his Carhartt overalls.

"Hell, you can fix a DC-3 with duct tape!"

"And WD-40 will loosen anything—switches, rusted lug nuts, and screws. Makes for a dandy lube job, too."

There was a moment or two of silence after the mention of a lube job. I cleared my throat, then chomped on a slice of bacon.

"Let's not leave male and female screws out of this," Jay chuckled. He looked at me. I felt uncomfortable, not sure what he meant. Linda looked down at her plate. Not wanting Jay to get the better of me, I just smiled and ate my butter-loaded pancakes.

"Well, little lady," Worker Bee One said, "How you like it up here?"

He stroked his scraggly beard, picked a few crumbs from it, then ate them.

"I'd never been west of Pittsburgh until a couple of weeks ago, so I guess it's okay," I said kind of sheepishly.

Jay and Ray and the Worker Bees roared with laughter. Al, a couple of tables down, overheard this exchange.

"So, how do those big buildings back east seem to you now, New York?"

"Really far away, Al," I replied, feeling a faint twinge of homesickness. Okay, so I *did* miss New York and DC.

"Well, don't you worry, gal," Worker Bee Two said, "We're all going to take real good care of you. We won't let you get too homesick."

I blushed just a little, but no one noticed the red through my sunburn.

Lucy finally arrived, grabbing coffee and pancakes before she made her way to the back table. Al followed her with his eyes and our tablemates collectively sat up a little taller.

"How are all y'all this morning?" she asked in her attractive southern drawl.

"I'm fine now that you're here," Worker Bee One said, giving her a wolfish once over.

"That's so nice of you. Would you please pass me the butter?" she asked, seemingly unaware of the men's staring.

"Why, shor' nuf," Ray flirted in a fake southern accent.

I could have choked on Ray's treackly attempt at flirting, but Lucy's outward lack of guile struck me as both clever and disarming. She turned the heads of every man in the room.

When people started to leave, spots with the archaeologists opened up. Lucy, Linda, and I grabbed more coffee and sauntered over. I threw my leg over the bench to sit down next to Mike. He and the others were comparing notes on how differently each camp was set up. The Ikpikpuk folks, for example, shared tents, and would share them for the whole summer. Extra tents were just that, extras put aside for an emergency.

"You've probably heard that we have a crappy Zodiac raft to put our gear and food in as we float the Colville," said Leslie. "One of the boatmen always sleeps under a tarp in the Zodiac so we can have our own tent like you guys do. The three boatmen take turns."

"I got one of the big tents," said Ross "because I'm a big guy."

"That you are, Ross," said Debbie. "We have our own tents at Lookout Ridge. Lynne and Dave are shacked up, so that frees up some space."

Corey raised an eyebrow, shook his head in agreement, and took a puff of his hand-rolled cigarette. He stared intently at Lucy, then looked at the ashtray.

"We have our own tents in Howard Pass, too. Malcolm took one of the big supply tents for himself because he's the big cheese," I said.

"And he keeps all the artifacts we collect in there. He also brought a bunch of archaeology books with him," Lucy added. "His tent is our museum and library."

"And then there's me," Linda said. "I don't get to go anywhere except my not-too-comfortable cot in the project supply tent. I never leave Umiat."

Al, pouring another cup of coffee, overheard the last part of the conversation.

"Don't you worry, Linda. I'll take you out in the Jet Ranger on a slow day. We'll go see us a few sights."

"When? When can we go?" she asked.

"I'll have a part of a day off next week some time. You can help me sling Blazo over to our fuel stash on the Colville. Sound good?"

"Can't wait!" Linda said, starting to throw her arms around the handsome pilot, but shyly restrained herself at the last minute. I supposed she thought all of Umiat would gossip about her hugging the dashing pilot in the crowded mess hall.

After the men left the room, Debbie leaned in and said, "I've got a juicy piece of news. Al wooed and bedded Lynne on her rotation, then dumped her and snagged Carol on *her* rotation. Lynne was bummed out until she moved in with Dave."

"What a dog," Leslie said. "How stupid. They're on the same crew."

That day, we dubbed Al Helio Skyscrewer. I sat there, imagining him making passionate love to me while he kept his reflective aviator glasses on.

"What a shit," I said. Who would want him anyway? But, he *is* sexy."

"Georgeie!" Lucy said in stern surprise.

I realized that up here gossip served an important function, educating me on who was cool and who wasn't; who could be trusted and who couldn't be; who was fun, and who was a dud. Plus, I'd always liked gossip.

Walking back to our tent camp, the hum of the generator soothed me. I enjoyed the comforts of Umiat but found myself looking forward to Howard Pass despite bears and other terrors. My homesickness had temporarily placed itself on a back burner somewhere as I continued my musing about Al in the helicopter.

CAMP 2, ANIUK RIVER

As we approached our camp in the 206, something seemed different, and not in a good way. The snowy slopes of Isikut and Ikhlhuk mountains still showed brilliantly beneath low wispy clouds and Rough Mountain Creek glinted in the intermittent sun, but something was off.

"What's going on? Where's my tent, for Christ's sake?" I shouted from the back seat. I searched for my crewmates on the ground and saw no one.

"Maybe they struck camp. Why are we leaving? What's wrong?" Lucy asked.

Then I saw tents, sleeping bags and pads, personal gear, pots, pans, and food placed in neatly arranged piles. I only hoped the Howard Pass crew was inside the one large tent left standing.

"Nothing's wrong. Today must be moving day," Al answered nonchalantly. "When you get out, leave your gear on board," he added. "That way, you won't have to reload it. Keep your daypacks with you, though. You may not be the first ones to fly over to the new camp, wherever that is."

He set down the chopper a short distance from camp so the neat piles wouldn't blow away. Then, the Howard Pass crew burst out of the cook tent like the Keystone Cops.

"Oh, thank God," Lucy said.

"You weren't really worried, were you?" Al asked.

"Well, yes I was!" she said loudly over the sound of the rotors.

"Me, too!" I said.

Al laughed and shook his head.

He kept the rotors turning slowly. I unbuckled my safety harness, unfolded myself out of my seat, and jumped onto the ground with my daypack.

As soon as Lucy and I were clear of the rotors, Ron and Toni carefully loaded the helicopter with supplies. Malcolm got in, taking the front seat next to Al, while Toni climbed into the back next to boxes of our freeze-dried food and a sack of onions. Malcolm's right hand kept hold of one of the two shotguns, while with his left hand, he unfolded the quad map and looked at it intently. The chopper lifted off, taking the first load of people and supplies to our new home on the Aniuk River.

Those of us remaining on the ground quickly formed a circle to trade news from base camp.

"How was Umiat, George?" Ron asked, taking his hat off and running his hand through his hair.

"Wonderful. I read my book, ate a lot, and took two showers."

"You didn't go hiking?" Helen asked.

"Nah," I said. "I was happy to be in a room with four walls and a roof."

"Hey, that's okay. It *is* supposed to be R&R," Tom said.

"Corey, John, Mike, and I hiked over to the Red Spot on the bluff just north of Umiat," Lucy said. "You can see the airstrip in the distance, and the Hilton shines in the sun, kind of like Disneyland."

"Dick the Cook's food's great there, isn't it?" said Tom.

"Oh, yeah. Especially Dick the Cook's blueberry cheesecake," Kelly said.

"Better than DC or even New York City," I added, feeling I should contribute something to the conversation.

I thought my urban, East Coast, inexperienced tenderfoot self was showing again.

Why would I want to hike when I have the creature comforts of the Umiat Hilton to enjoy? Wasn't flying from Washington DC to Umiat and on to Howard Pass enough of an adventure for now?

Feeling the need to prove my mettle in the great outdoors, I volunteered to go over on the next flight rather than waiting for the end of our move. When the Jet Ranger returned, we loaded it with more gear, and I claimed the coveted front seat next to Al before Helen had even put her foot on the skid. Forgetting frequent bouts of self-doubt, I became occupied by lustful thoughts about the rakish pilot. So what if he was a cad?

He is *handsome. I can almost see those rippling muscles through his leather jacket.*

We traveled low to the ground for a few short minutes.

"This is exciting! I can see individual tussocks zipping by beneath my feet!" I said.

Al said nothing but turned to give me a predatory grin. He may have winked at me, but I couldn't see behind his aviator sunglasses. He sucked a Tootsie Roll pop in a way I had never seen before, caressing it with his tongue. I recognized my horniness as a good thing—I had room in my brain for sensations other than apprehension.

* * *

103

The new campsite was only about two and a half miles away from our first camp. The setting was as beautiful and primitive as the first spot had been, but the valley here was wider and the Aniuk River was definitely a river, not a creek. It roared powerfully on its journey north to the Colville. The mountains could have been one mile away or three. I couldn't tell.

I jumped down from the chopper like a pro, unloaded some of the gear, and walked over to Malcolm.

"Say, Malcolm, why are we camping next to the river instead of up on a terrace or something?" I asked.

"Look around you. There isn't any high ground. It's okay; it's not too muddy, and we won't be here for long. We'll be fine unless it pours buckets," he answered, smiling mysteriously, like the Mona Lisa.

I tried to hear humor in his voice but could detect none.

"But we could have camped a couple miles over there," I gestured, pointing to a narrow, steep-sided valley towards the direction I thought was east.

"We'll camp over there later in the summer. There'll be shitloads of archaeology there, mark my words. We'll get some sites from this camp on a few long days and get the rest from the other camp at the end of the summer."

"Aha. Of course."

I didn't really see why we couldn't go there directly, and I couldn't tell east from west, but Malcolm undoubtedly knew what he was talking about. With complete confidence, I accepted what he said, sphinx like smile and all.

Camp began to take shape. Some of the personal tents and the cook tent were already up. Helen and I set up the rest as the chopper flew in with Kelly and Ron. Malcolm asked them to make a water run and fill our four Jerry Jugs.

"Christ, those are heavy," Ron said, when he returned a short while later. "Each one weighs forty pounds full, you know," he said with an air of authority. He puffed heavily and stumbled over to the cook tent.

"Better than carrying one and walking lopsided, I guess," said Kelly.

Guys, I cannot *wait* for my turn," I said, rolling my eyes.

In less than ten minutes, the whirr of the returning chopper grew loud. Tom and Lucy arrived and sprang into action. Lucy chose a place to stake out the food tarp and Tom took his personal red and white tent from a pile of equipment and set it up a reasonable distance away from the rest of us.

So they can screw in peace.

After camp was set up and Malcolm declared camp "ship-shape," he and Toni climbed into the Jet Ranger, happy looks on their faces.

"It's Malcolm's turn? Really? He's going to Umiat?" I asked.

Perhaps sensing my surprise, Ron said, "Malcolm's put me in charge while he's in Umiat. You were in the air and didn't hear. Don't worry, it won't hurt a bit. I don't bite."

Please, God, let Ron not be a dick. Who cares about his photographic memory anyway? I grumbled to myself.

Al and company disappeared in the blink of an eye, leaving me without my security blanket. I guessed I'd just have to buck up. Maybe Ron would be okay after all.

"Let's sit in front of the cook tent and talk about our game plan over lunch," he said.

"We live to serve," said Tom. He and Helen made deep bows.

Lucy and I traded glances, and she chuckled. We rolled our eyes at precisely the same moment.

"It'll be fine," she whispered to me. I nodded my head.

Ron would be okay, I supposed. I fingered my bear whistle and relied on my new mantra, Trust Your Equipment. In this instance, Ron was the equipment.

Kelly and Helen brought lunch fixings for the six of us from under the tarp. Our main course was pilot bread and the remainder of a block of Tillamook. The cheese packed a lot of energy into a single slice. On warmer days, like this one, greasy and flavorful beads of fat sweated from the orange brick, making it even more delectable.

We sat in a tight circle, like a wagon train in the old west protecting its people from Indians. Munching away and admiring the two Coleman stoves Al had just flown out to us, I watched intently as Tom assembled one of them, filled the metal reservoir with Blazo, pumped the reservoir to create pressure, hooked it up to the burners, and carefully lit the stove with his lighter. He set a pot of water on to boil.

The stove assembled, I turned my attention from Tom's magic and thumbed through my field notebook looking for the next blank page to write a brief entry.

June 21. Solstice. Finally left Rough Mountain Creek for the Aniuk River this morning. Really pretty camp. Malcolm tells us we'll have exciting finds later in the summer. So, will the Aniuk be dull in comparison? Weather today is warm for a change. Light breeze. No bugs. Nice day. Hope it doesn't rain. Ron's in charge until Malcolm gets back.

I wanted to add something about the thrill of my original flight in the helicopter but decided not to. Someone would read my notes at a future date and see how naive and afraid I'd been. Previous days' entries already showed my greenhorn status. Why add to the picture?

Satisfied with my short but hopefully important written contribution, I bit into my third pilot cracker, loaded with peanut butter and cheese. Kelly, sitting next to me, leaned to her right to reach for the jam, putting her weight on her butt cheek.

"Ouch," she said, "What the hell was that?"

She got up, dusted the duff from her hindquarters, and looked down at the ground where her right cheek had been and saw a large gray chert flake with a sharp edge. We had done it again—picked a place that had been popular in the past.

"If that had been obsidian, it would have cut right through your jeans," Helen said.

"Jesus, I guess so," Kelly replied, clearly impressed with both the flake and the toughness of her pants.

"Well, ladies and germs, this is a great place to start work today," Ron said. "Finish your lunch and let's look around camp. Empty your tents of heavy stuff and lift each one up. There could be artifacts underneath every last one of them."

I went over to my tent and reached in to get stuff out, then lifted it up.

"Got some goodies here," I said, looking down at several chert flakes.

"Us too," said Tom.

* * *

We didn't need six people to explore the site at our new camp, so Ron, Tom, and Lucy surveyed south along the river. Helen, Kelly, and I stayed in camp to record the first site. Kelly shot in the base line with the Brunton compass, she and Helen plotted the artifacts with a thirty-meter tape, and I drew the map.

"We are a great team, the All-Girl Survey Crew," Helen said confidently, looking at the baseline and about twenty pieces of red flagging tape showing the distribution of artifacts.

"Funny how almost all of the artifacts were directly underneath our tents," Kelly said.

"Someone sure liked it here," I said. "You know, I think I'll try my hand with the Nikon to add to my skills, but Kelly, you can keep the damned Brunton."

"Go for it, Georgeie. You know what to do," Kelly said.

I grabbed the camera and struggled with the shutter speed and F-stop, hoping to get them both right. I twisted the focusing ring. At last, the artifacts came into focus and the light meter indicated with a yellow dot that the shot wouldn't be over or under-exposed. The flake scatters and overall site pictures were difficult to focus, but the photos of the general setting were easier—all I had to do was set the focus on infinity and take the shot.

"Why the hell are there so many moving parts? This is so hard to focus," I said.

"You want a crystal-clear focus on that bear when he charges, don't you?" Helen said.

"Shit, I didn't think of that," I said, stopping to inspect the surrounding terrain for signs of wildlife.

"But you wouldn't stop to photograph a charging bear anyway, would you?" Kelly laughed.

"Hey, where's the shotgun, anyway?" I asked, worry in my voice.

"Got it right here," Helen said, grabbing it to show me.

"Okay, I feel better," I said, forcing a smile.

* * *

We had yet to see a bear close up, but we had seen bear scat every day. We'd take guesses about how old the shit was—two hours? Two days? The rule of thumb was if the shit was shiny, black, and soft to the trowel's touch, you should begin looking over your shoulder. Encountering steaming scat meant scram or kiss your ass goodbye. Soon, I could determine if the tracks were old or new. None of us encountered steaming turds, however.

I had paid strict attention during bear training in Fairbanks the week before we flew to Umiat. The descriptions of all the kinds of bear encounters scared the shit out of me.

"You can survive an encounter with a grizzly if you think fast," our instructor, a slight, balding man with thicker-than-Coke-bottle glasses, began. "Most of the time, the bear wants nothing to do with you. But if you see one nearby, stand together, wave your arms, and make a lot of noise. Bears can't see well, and they can sneak up on you by mistake. When you stand together, the bear thinks you're one large, loud, threatening animal. Plus, they think we smell bad, and that's good."

There had been a few titters in the room at the mention of us smelling bad.

"Never travel alone. You can't look like a big creature if you're by yourself. I know you want privacy when you're taking a crap, but stay close, okay?"

More titters.

"If standing together and yelling doesn't work, then fire the shotgun in the air. Most bears will run away at the sound. Not all, though.

"If he begins to charge, you can't know if he's bluffing or not. Hold your ground, but if he doesn't show any signs of stopping and you don't have a shotgun handy, roll up in a ball, your hands behind your neck, and play dead. Don't run—the bear will chase you and the bear will win. Lie there on the ground, motionless. Wet your pants if you have to, but don't run!"

Still more titters. I did *not* think it was funny. And there was more:

"If you *do* have a shotgun, and the bear is right there, you're going to have to shoot him, or at least disable him. Aim for the shoulder and break the front leg, but remember, you're going to have to finish him off. If you're a very good shot, a sharpshooter, there's a remote chance you can shoot him in the eye and he'll die instantly."

By the end of the lecture, no one was tittering anymore, and I was sick to my stomach. Most of us had not fired a shotgun until target practice the day before. I couldn't be counted on to disable and then kill a bear, no matter how much adrenaline might be coursing through my body. Looking around the room, I saw only a handful of people who looked self-confident enough for me to trust them with a gun. Fortunately, several of them were on the Howard Pass crew.

Jerry, the diminutive instructor, asked for questions but was met with stunned silence. Malcolm thanked him and announced that each crew would have two shotguns loaded with alternating rounds of double-ought buckshot and slugs. He held up an example of each and passed them around. They felt heavy in my hand.

There was nothing good I could see about me coming into contact with a firearm of any kind, especially as a lefty for whom the safety would automatically be on the wrong side of the stock.

Malcolm had insisted we caravan downtown to Big Ray's the following day to buy cowbells or whistles for noisemakers along with other last-minute purchases. Kelly found a mirror with a small bell attached to it in the small bird section of the pet aisle. A parakeet would look at itself, peck at the mirror, and ring the bell incessantly to avoid boredom, or so the label said. The clever gadget could be used not only as a bear bell, but also to signal passing planes with its mirror.

* * *

I forced myself from my bear reverie back to recording the site, but not until I touched the bear whistle hanging around my neck to make sure it was still there.

In the distance, Ron, Tom, and Lucy headed single file down the toe of a nearby slope while I finished writing the last of the camera shots in the photo log.

Another possible first to add to my skills occurred to me: "Hey, how about me cooking dinner tonight?" I said hopefully.

"That's mighty brave of you, George, just no more freeze-dried food. That crunchy shit is getting old," Kelly said.

"Agree. I'm cold and dripping snot and I don't feel like struggling with freeze-dried this evening," Helen said.

"I'll see what I can come up with," I answered, barely concealing my excitement at tackling the Coleman stove. Camp cooking may not have been a big deal to anyone else on the crew, but to me it was breaking new ground.

* * *

After changing out of my boots and into my sneaks, I found pots and pans and an unopened food carton under the tarp. Among the treats inside were boxes of macaroni and cheese and several canned hams.

Malcolm, knowing the importance of variety in food to crew morale, had brought selections from his spice collection, so I had a choice—chili or curry flavored mac and cheese. I chose curry, a favorite one-pot meal on my hot plate at home; I'd even make peanut sauce with the peanut butter, cinnamon, sugar, and garlic salt on hand. My plan energized me.

The first step, however, was the hardest and the scariest— lighting the stove.

I can do this and not blow myself up. Go slow...

I reflected on my phobia of sudden, loud noises that had begun before I could even remember. My parents and I lived on the top floor of an old brick apartment building. My mother was holding me in her arms during a severe thunderstorm, so she told me a few years later. A bolt of lightning struck the steeple next door and a deafening crack followed. She almost jumped out of her skin, holding me tightly. I began to scream. I bet I screamed bloody murder. Maybe I'd picked up on her fright. I don't know.

I cautiously detached the propane cylinder from the stove, shook it, and heard the sloshing sound indicating it didn't need to be refilled. I pumped the cylinder with the plunger until I could feel pressure, then lifted up the grill, cleaned the two burners, and inserted the cylinder back into the stove. After taking a big breath, turning the switch to the on position, and carefully touching a lit kitchen match to one of the burners, the stove ignited without incident. My relief was instantaneous. I put two pots of water on to boil and lit the Primus to put extra water on for hot drinks.

By the time the other team returned to camp and crawled into their tents to get rid of their daypacks and boots, I had the usual array of hot drink containers lined up near the front of the tent. I poured hot water into a cup for each person as they entered.

"Hey, thanks, George" Tom said. "Think I'll have me some cocoa."

"You cooking tonight?" asked Ron. "Should I just hold my nose and swallow?"

"Do not mock me, sir, or you'll get no supper!" I taunted him.

"Okay, okay!" came the reply.

With a flourish, I dumped three boxes of macaroni into the boiling water. In a few minutes, after Lucy dumped the excess water outside, I added a cut-up ham, the spices, and cubes of cheese to the two pots.

"I have made a gourmet curry-based mac and cheese dish with canned ham chunks and lots of Tillamook cheese, all the way from Oregon," I announced. "My creation can be topped with this gourmet peanut sauce, the recipe courtesy of a former boyfriend who probably regrets dumping me, or should."

"This stuff smells great, Georgeie!" Kelly said enthusiastically. She clapped me on the back and led the others in a "hip hip hooray!"

I had an even bigger chance to prove my mettle during dinner.

"Uh-oh," I said, trying to turn the Primus off.

Flames suddenly engulfed the little stove.

"Shit. Look out," Lucy said. "Someone better take it outside before it explodes."

I grabbed the stove by the bottom of the canister and ran outside with it.

"Holy shit, George. What are you doing?" Tom yelled.

"I don't fucking know," I answered, watching the stove intently.

Kelly, right behind me, grabbed a Jerry jug and doused the flames.

"George, you saved us, but you're nuts!" Helen said, clutching her throat.

"Yeah, I guess so." I said, totally surprised at myself.

We permanently shitcanned the Primus that night.

* * *

After dinner, I returned to my tent, still a bit shaky from my brush with danger. I sighed, took off my jeans, lay on top of my sleeping bag, and picked up *The Source,* but found it impossible to keep my eyes open. I crawled inside my sleeping bag with my wool socks on and felt happy with myself. Outside my tent, I heard Tom say, "You're my hero, George!"

* * *

The next day, Ron, Kelly, and I had only careened a half-mile through a tussock field to access a steep rocky slope called a talus when we found an interesting site. We dubbed the site Kelly's Quarry because Kelly first noticed the multitude of flakes on the ground. Ron, in his role as seasoned Arctic archaeologist, took a deep breath, looked up at the brilliant blue sky for inspiration, and began an impromptu lecture on quarry sites.

"The bottom of a talus slope is not the easiest place to recognize a site. Rocks and boulders continually roll down talus slope so you really can't tell if some of those flakes are manmade or byproducts of rocks smashing into other rocks, so you have to look for other clues."

I caught Kelly's eye as she looked up from her dusty boots and over in my direction. We sighed.

"But here's a bunch of other kinds of rock that stand out from the base material of the slope, that grainy dark basalt—it's all over the place," Ron continued. "And look, there's shit piles of all kinds of chert—deep jade green, black, and light brown; red is jasper, and the gray is chalcedony. So, the site's the real deal. And, for those of you fond of trivia, the word chalcedony comes from the Biblical place name, Ur of the Chaldees."

"That's a fun fact, Ron," Kelly said, a trifle impatiently. "Now can we get on with business? I'm chomping at the bit here, and I know what basalt and chalcedony look like."

"Even *I* know what the stuff looks like, Ron," I said petulantly.

"All right, all right. I get the message. Let's fan out and find us some goodies."

Kelly took a step, then stopped: "Christ Almighty! Look at this!" she shouted.

She stooped to pick up a large, thin, triangular jasper projectile point so close to her boot she could have stepped on it. The point was almost two inches long, finely worked on both sides, and diamond shaped in cross section.

"Wow! That's beautiful. May be Northern Archaic. I bet it's 5,000 years old," Ron said, taking the point from Kelly, turning it over in his hand, then passing it to me. "This is so important! It'll help characterize the archaeology around here. When we find something wonderful like this and document it, we'll maybe keep the oil and gas companies from plundering the area."

I was still looking at the point in stunned disbelief—the edges were so sharp, the point looked like it had been chipped the day before. The brownish-red artifact was recorded, photographed in situ, and collected by its discoverer. A selection of flakes was also collected to show the range of material. Kelly and I set the datum and took distance and bearing of the artifacts with the dreaded Brunton compass, while Ron drew the site map and took photographs. We were so entranced by Kelly's Quarry we spent the entire day finding many other goodies and recording the site.

"Ya know," I said, "this is the first artifact we've found that actually looks like something I saw in a textbook, but it's much better in color than black and white."

"Yep it is. Hey, it's after seven. Let's pack up our shit, get back to camp, and show off our point. The other guys will be green with envy." Ron gloated happily.

* * *

Over dinner, the rest of the Alaska crowd agreed with Ron that the point probably dated from the Northern Archaic, between 4,000 to 6,000 years ago.

"God, it's gorgeous," Tom gushed. "You sure you didn't make it and plant it here, Kelly?"

"Haha," she answered. "I wish I were that coordinated and talented."

As exciting as the point was, even more exciting was the large honey-colored grizz Lucy spotted about ten p.m. while brushing her teeth by the river.

"Hey! Hey! Bear! Grab the shotgun!" she yelled.

My pulse quickened as I hurried out of my sleeping bag, putting my jeans and sneaks back on. We ran to the river's edge, but I was ready to hide behind my tent in a futile attempt to escape notice, should the bear venture closer. I knew better and stood together with the others like one giant animal as we'd been taught.

Ron grabbed the binoculars to get a better look.

"He's about a half a mile away, I think. Looks like he's digging for ground squirrels or shrews, I guess."

"He's a big 'un, all right," Tom said seriously.

I took a turn with the binocs and stared at the huge animal. I felt the hairs on the back of my neck bristle. "Holy fuck. Look at the size of his claws!" I gasped.

"Longer than your fingers, and he can run real fast," Tom said, as he took the binoculars from me. His voice remained composed, no doubt from having encountered many bears in the past. I missed Malcolm during our scare but noted how calm Tom made me feel.

"Holy Christ," Kelly said.

"What's he doing?" asked Lucy nervously.

"Looking for dinner," Helen answered.

"He's tossing ground squirrels in the air like they're toys," Ron said in fascination, looking through the binocs.

Mesmerized by the way his fur caught the sunlight and changed color from blond to brown and back to blond as he moved, my eyes were riveted on the huge creature. Observing the bear intently for a long time, I imagined you could probably identify a particular bear, even from a distance, by his roundness, the way he moved, the size of the hump behind his head, and the color.

After what seemed like more than an hour, the grizz ambled away and up a nearby terrace.

"That's what I like to see, the south side of a bear going north," Ron said with relief.

"The bear went over the mountain to see what it could see," Lucy sang softly.

We watched until he disappeared from sight and watched where he had been for a while longer. Tom and Helen stared into the distance even longer, sitting on the patch of Visqueen at their tent door, arms draped around each other, the shotgun within easy reach.

* * *

The next morning, after a surprisingly good sleep despite my bear jitters, I stuck my head out of my tent. The wind howled and sleet pelted my face.

God Almighty, how can the weather up here change so fast?

Quickly dressing and lighting a cigarette, I ran to the cook tent. Lucy handed me a cup of coffee.

"Oh, boy, oatmeal. Let me transform it into oatmeal royale," I said, putting gobs of brown sugar, butter, peanut butter, and raisins into my Girl Scout tin cup over a wad of oatmeal, then mixing all together with an Army surplus spoon.

"That's some meal, George. It'll last you until tomorrow," Ron said.

"Well, sit on it, Ron," I answered. "This kind of morning calls for a lot of fat and carbohydrates."

"I do believe the little lady is right," Tom said. "I wouldn't come between her and a meal, Ron."

"I'll think of something clever to say after I've had a cup of coffee," I said.

"Well, maybe you'll like this, George. I think it's too cold and windy to work this morning," Ron said.

"Sleet is not my favorite climate to survey in," Tom said.

"I like you again, Ron. I've already had my bout of hypothermia and I only have this shitty thin raingear to wear."

"We have an extra poncho you can have for the summer," Helen said.

"You guys. I feel like the orphan everyone is giving their old clothes to."

"For Christ's sake, you know we're all in this together," Kelly said, "but my red turtleneck is not a hand-me-down. I want it back at the end of the summer."

"Tell you what," Ron interjected, "let's spend the morning working on our notes and adding to them, if you need to. When you're done, you can pick up your favorite book or walk around a little if you keep close to camp. We'll reevaluate the weather at noon."

"When Malcolm comes back tomorrow, we can show him our wonderful point! He won't mind that we missed a day. And, we'll have a bear story for him," Tom said proudly.

"I'd like to draw the point in my notes," I said. "Okay?"

"Sure, have at it," said Ron.

"Thanks," I said, grabbing the bag with the coin envelope in it, I beat a retreat to my tent.

I lay the point aside for the moment, picked up *The Source*, and was completely absorbed in a matter of seconds. I was reading the chapter about the Crusades and the story of Volkmar who had been sickened by the slaughter of the Jews in Palestine. It dawned on me that the book was actually a history of the Jews.

I contemplated Michener's chronicle of rich and tragic Jewish history as a link to my family. I thought about them back home in New York, a world that seemed far away physically, but close emotionally. The man my mother married five years after my father died was a Jew whose parents emigrated from Poland around 1900 due to the pogroms. They left behind friends and relatives, all of whom were killed in the Holocaust. Concentrating on my more recent Jewish family helped me to not focus on the father I'd lost decades before.

The constant sound of the wind lulled me to sleep. I had forgotten all about drawing the point or working on my notes.

* * *

I woke a few hours later to the sound of Ron telling me to roust my ass out of my toasty sleeping bag. I dragged myself out of my cocoon, unzipped the tent door flap, and looked outside. The wind was down, the sky robin's-egg blue. The weather had done a one-eighty yet again. I breathed in air that smelled of recent rain.

Although we split up into our groups of three again to cover some promising terraces to the north and south, neither team found anything. Disappointment showed in my face, and, I thought, in the faces of the others.

Because we'd already run out of places to survey, we knew we'd move camp to our next destination, Fauna Creek, the following day. Malcolm had left instructions to pack ourselves up if we finished exploring the area.

"Malcolm will be so proud of us," Kelly said over dinner, "and he'll shit when he sees the point."

"We are *so* smart." Lucy added.

Tom produced a doobie after pawing through his gear. We passed it around patting each other on the back for being of above-average intelligence.

"Uh oh. I never drew that point. Let me sketch it this evening," I said. "That's how smart *I* am!"

Later, I pulled the coin envelope out of my down vest pocket, sharpened my pencil with my Buck knife and quickly executed a good, if not perfect, drawing. I took an extra minute to admire the artifact before I put the point back in the envelope.

It sure is right purtty.

* * *

The next morning, we heard the always-welcome hum of the chopper in the morning. Malcolm and Toni dashed out of the 206 like the Keystone Cops, followed by the well-muscled Helio Skyscrewer.

Malcolm had a brief chat with Ron, then said to us: "Alright, looks like we're moving to Fauna Creek. Good thinking, you guys, to remember packing up camp. Shows initiative and the reluctance to be bored for more than half an hour. I've got the general location picked out on the quad map so I'll go ahead and take Georgeie with me. But first, let's see that point!"

Ron handed the coin envelope to Malcolm. "Oh, my God, this is incredible—a Northern Archaic point. A piece of the puzzle! Good job, boys and girls."

After Malcolm had finished gushing over our prize specimen, Lucy told him about my heroism the night before.

"You did that? You're so brave!"

"I had no idea what I was doing, Malcolm," I said.

He hugged me and dubbed me Most Improved Camper of the summer thus far.

"As a reward, you'll be first over with me to Fauna Creek, and when we set up the cook tent, I will personally make you a cup of hot Tang."

"And we could shoot the Primus before we fly into Umiat with Al," Tom added.

Malcolm considered this for a few seconds then said, "Nah, I want Rick to see its charred remains. So, take the carcass and put it in the Howard Pass tent. Shitty stove."

Malcolm and I stuffed the helicopter as full as possible and climbed on board. Relegated to the back seat so Malcolm could pinpoint the best place to set up camp, I stared over his shoulder at the topo map. I'd been chosen to fly over to the new camp first and felt proud. As I looked at the vast swathe of tundra spreading beneath us, I felt more or less at home.

CAMP 3, FAUNA CREEK

Fauna Creek became my favorite camp the moment we landed, nestled as it was in an Alpine valley resembling the Swiss countryside. I knew the relaxing burble of the stream would lull me to sleep each night we were there. Subject to a balmy cross-breeze, the growing population of mosquitoes would rarely show themselves, and I knew the sun would always shine on us. I fantasized about finding a mammoth tusk or two eroding out of the creek. Why else would it have been named Fauna Creek?

Because Fauna Creek was smaller than the Aniuk, we found it easier to cross, not having to take off our boots and go barefoot or put on our sneakers to wade across. We'd also have enough space to spread out a bit because of the large, flat terrace the camp occupied; all of us would have privacy. The cook tent and the blue tarp would be a fair walk away. There would be no bear entanglements over food here!

That afternoon, Toni, Lucy, and I found three flake scatters on low, bare terraces flanking the stream. The flakes were not that interesting, but, because I was beginning to trust my eyes, all sites, no matter how small, still felt exciting. I found the first site that day, green chert unmistakably glistening among the lichens and wildflowers. Our finds made it a successful day for the All-Girl Survey Crew. My discovery of rare green chert made me feel special.

Better than our discoveries were those of Ron, Kelly, and Malcolm. Their treasures consisted of microblades and our first wedge-shaped microcore. Over coffee at the end of the day, the microblades and five-centimeter-high core were passed around and an animated discussion ensued.

"This core is made of really great fine-grained super-duper gray chert. It's totally smooth to the touch. See the nine longitudinal, parallel scars where microblades were struck off? That's called the face or front," Malcolm said, admiring the piece.

"Oh, yeah, it's a good one," Ron said, taking the artifact and staring at it intently.

"Core and blade sites are tricky," Malcolm continued. "Most in this area are surface sites so you can't date them. And the interpretation of microblades and this kind of core keeps changing. Some people think they're old, and other guys think they could date to any time from the end of the last glacial age to a couple hundred years ago. They were probably used over the millennia— very successful technology Very useful."

"What's the core for?" Toni asked. "We don't have anything like this in Texas.

"It's where you get microblades—they're the tools struck off from it. In Russian a core is called a nu-clay-OOZ, or nucleus. Get it?"

"Uh-huh," Toni said. I shook my head yes, as did Lucy.

"It's a dead ringer for ones found in Siberia and Mongolia," Ron interjected like a tenured professor, rocking back and forth on the balls of his feet.

"I've seen pictures of them in Chester Chard's book on Siberian prehistory. This is the second artifact I recognize from a textbook, but it's sure is better in real life. I've wanted to go to Mongolia ever since I wrote my MA thesis on the prehistory of the Gobi last year," I said, taking the core from Ron and rolling it over in my hand and forgetting about the cup of Folgers I wanted.

"I think Georgeie's met her match," Toni said.

"Earth to George!" Ron said, snapping his fingers in front of my face.

"Well, fuck me dead," I said, playing along. "I'm in love."

"Okay, okay, let's pry the core out of Georgeie's hands and get some dinner going," Malcolm said. He smiled and put the core back in its coin envelope, tucked the envelope safely into a paper bag along with the microblades, and stuffed the bag into a pocket of his green down vest.

"I sense the spark of a seasoned archaeologist in you, Georgeie," he said, "but you can't take it home with you."

"That's the coolest thing I've ever seen or touched," I answered.

"Welcome to the Big Boys' Archaeology Club, George," said Ron in a somewhat paternalistic tone.

Kelly began rattling pots around, getting ready to cook up a large quantity of freeze-dried beef and rice with hard-as-rocks freeze-dried corn. I grabbed a smoke and began to head back to my tent to get my notebook and put my sneaks on.

After dinner, I brushed my teeth by the creek and stared into the distance at the mountains

June 25. Moved camp and surveyed immediately to the east. I like this camp. Pretty. Good weather. Behind in notes. Must finish writing up quarry site from the other day. The Northern Archaic point looks like it was made yesterday and the wedge-shaped core is phenomenal. I recognize them from some textbooks so I have a good idea how old they could be. This is fun. Ron and Kelly go to Umiat tomorrow. Will be our turn next.

The next couple of days passed easily enough with more discoveries, although nothing like the point or core. I actually dreamt about the core one night. In my dream, I was telling Uncle Mikey all about it, sounding like a self-confident grad student and seasoned archaeologist, not the neophyte I was.

The weather was good and we covered a lot of ground. Fauna Creek continued to be my favorite camp, with enough topography to make it interesting, but not too much that hauling water was more than the pain than what it could be on a steep slope.

* * *

I always missed Kelly when she was gone, she of the bountiful wardrobe and absent father. I could fit into her sweaters, but not her jeans. My ass had always been large. I was thrilled with her supply with makeup and jewelry in Umiat. She'd given Lucy and I permission to raid her stash to be as attractive to our male counterparts as possible.

After dinner, Lucy said, "Hey, it's our turn to go into Umiat tomorrow. Did you forget?"

"Not a chance. Seems we were just there, but who am I to quibble?"

I'd like to stay here and find more fun stuff, but, boy, do I want a shower, good food, and the possibility of romance.

I slept in Kelly's red turtleneck so I'd look good when I arrived in Umiat and I awoke the next morning ready to greet the day.

Breakfast was Spam, powdered eggs, and instant coffee That was okay, I'd have real everything in Umiat, and I'd be clean, too. Just as I was thinking about the 206 and scheming about base camp, I heard its rotors heading in our direction.

Ron and Kelly jumped down from the helicopter on a glorious day of sunshine and blue sky, still full from an Umiat Hilton breakfast. Choices for breakfast at the Hilton rotated daily, but always included fresh milk and eggs instead of powdered milk and dehydrated eggs, real sausage instead of canned Vienna sausage, perked coffee instead of freeze dried, and canned orange juice instead of Tang. I'd usually go for my favorite combo, bacon and pancakes.

Kelly was so full of coffee, she ran behind the cook tent to pee. She reappeared, zipping up her jeans.

The new arrivals immediately saw that the other tents had been struck and piled in a neat row next to our food and sleeping bags, a sure sign we would move to a new camp. "We're moving again? Where?" he asked Malcolm.

"We're going back to the Aniuk, but further east than before, towards Inyorurak Pass, and nearer what I'm guessing will be the mother lode of sites," he answered.

"Yeah. Let's blow this pop stand. It's a drag. We're done here," I said, sucking on a cigarette.

Inyorurak Pass, with its many terraces and side drainages, promised to be rich in sites because it was a major caribou migration route. It functioned as a kind of funnel. We'd already seen a few head of caribou, the vanguard of the Noatak River herd that would migrate through in a few days, engulfing our camp on their way west.

"Food on the hoof," Helen said.

"All right, gang. The day's a-wasting. Let's get this show on the road," Malcolm said. "I'm taking Helen with me on the first load."

In a whirr of wind and dust, the chopper, with Sam at the helm and heavy with equipment and food, the chopper lifted off and quickly disappeared to the north. After thirty minutes it returned. I knew Malcolm must have found a good spot fairly close by and that he and Kelly would already be setting up camp and getting the traditional pot of coffee ready for the rest of us.

After Sam ferried two more loads to the banks of the Aniuk, he came back for Lucy me to whisk us off to Umiat. The Jet Ranger also carried our mail to parents, friends, and lovers in the Lower 48.

UMIAT

I rode up front with Sam in the Jet Ranger on the way back to base camp, savoring the luxuries that awaited me in Umiat. Umiat was the breath of fresh air, the sigh I needed amidst the exhilaration and adrenalin of the field.

I looked over at Sam. His stubbled jaw worked overtime as he chewed tobacco. He didn't seem to be in a talkative mood, so I looked out at the tundra and the sky through the windows and roof. I imagined the chopper was a glass bubble carrying me along on a tremendous adventure into the unknown while I flew through the immense landscape. I knew I was living a fantasy, and the fantasy was real. I chuckled to myself.

When we touched down, my thoughts turned immediately to a glorious shower. Lucy and I grabbed our toiletries, change of clothes, and dirty laundry, and made a dash for the Hilton. I felt filthy and unattractive, the dirt caked on my neck making me feel particularly disgusting. I would only put Kelly's turtleneck back on after I was clean.

In the field, dirt covered me most of the time. I routinely wiped my nose on my sleeve or crushed a mosquito on my cheek without first wiping my dirt-encrusted hands. My fingernails were ugly and jagged because the blade on my Buck knife was too large and dull for cleaning or manicuring them. Umiat passed for civilization, and I wanted to feel as pretty, feminine, and sophisticated as possible. I would wash up, primp, and, wearing Kelly's bright red turtleneck, hope for some excitement.

Lucy and I encountered Linda while we walked towards the Umiat Hilton.

"Guess what?" she said.

"What?" I asked.

"The guys at GSI are throwing a party tonight in honor of those two birthday boys, Ray Smith and Dick the Cook. Dick the Cook turns thirty on July tenth and Ray just turned twenty-three. The party will be in GSI's pre-fab house next to the Quonsets."

"Aha! The booze shipment must have arrived, and I bet some dope was smuggled up in several of the boxes, too," I said, a smile on my face.

Finding the Hilton bathroom empty, we rushed up onto the wooden platform by the two showers, drew the curtain shut, stripped, and were soon in a heaven of hot pulsating water.

"My dad's coming up the end of August," Lucy said while I lathered up. "He's going to meet me in Anchorage. We'll take the train to Denali for a few days before heading back to Georgia. We've always been close and it will be good to have some time together, just the two of us."

I'd heard her mention the visit before but had put it out of my mind. I could tell she was the apple of her father's eye and he was proud of her accomplishments. I imagined the pride her dad felt, knowing she was working on the frontier as an archaeologist. If he'd known about our recent bear encounter, he might have felt differently. I bet she never told him.

I was not as lucky as Lucy. My stepfather was probably too old to come to Alaska. He certainly couldn't go on a hike with me—

my mother would forbid it; afraid he'd have another heart attack. She'd instilled in me such a strong fear of intimacy after my father died that worry and doubt governed my life. I longed for a bond like Lucy had with her father, but I feared it, too. People leave. People die. Especially men. Better not to get too close to begin with.

* * *

When we got to the mess hall, Dick the Cook had the fan on and the windows open. I admired the carefully patched screens that would keep our meal free of mosquitoes.

"Hey, girls," he said, turning towards us. He'd been cleaning the grill in anticipation of the lunch crowd.

"Hey, Dick. What are we having for lunch?" Lucy asked.

"Well, let's see, I think I'll cook us up some hamburgers and cheeseburgers," he said, then continued whistling.

"Oh, yum," I said.

He had already finished mixing a big salad and set it out on the serving table along with an assortment of thick, gooey salad dressings in somewhat sticky bottles. His unappetizing salads consisted of old vegetables and wilted greens with brown and slimy spots. Try as he might, Dick the Cook could not cut out every spot on every head of lettuce without it becoming as holey as Swiss cheese.

I focused my interest on his slices of chocolate cake and blueberry pie instead. Even the lime Jell-O captivated me. It shook and shimmied as Dick the Cook carried it from the refrigerator to the counter in a faux cut glass dish. Lucy and I grabbed a pop from the cooler, slices of chocolate cake, and took our places at the table closest to the kitchen.

Soon, the boisterous lunch crowd began pouring into the mess hall, pairs of work boots shaking the peeling linoleum and the plywood floor underneath it. Two officials from Fairbanks had just flown in to inspect the instruments in the air control tower. They brought with them copies of that day's *Fairbanks News Miner* whose top headline announced another increase in gas prices. President Carter was taking the heat for the situation. The news, remote and surreal, was taking place in an alternate universe, one to which I was now only vaguely connected. I felt like a disembodied spirit reading the front page of the paper.

Didn't I live in DC? Isn't it hot there now? I asked myself.

Three mechanics, also new in town, lined up at the counter, grabbed burgers and fries, swooped down on the tired and unappealing salad as if it were ambrosia, and sat down at our table. Their plaid work shirts smeared with grease and their dirt caked Carhartts seemed almost dressy to me now.

Mechanic One had a pack of Kools in his breast pocket. I stared at it—my supply of cigarettes was getting low. He explained they were here for a few days to help the Smiths with some difficult repairs and then fly north to Kaktovik to look at their radar facility. Difficult repairs? Jay and Ray had told us they could fix anything.

"Hey, guys," I said. The Mechanics tipped their baseball caps in reply.

My appetite had grown exponentially since I'd been up north. We usually hiked five to eight miles a day and ate God knew how many calories to keep our energy from flagging throughout the workday. As we sat back down, Mechanic Two glanced at our plates and said something about little ladies with big appetites.

"Well, we hike all day long out in Howard Pass looking for archaeological sites," Lucy explained.

"No shit! Archaeologists? I wanted to be an archaeologist! I took an archaeology course in school one semester," Mechanic Three said. I looked at him closely while he talked. He had the thickest head of blond hair I'd ever seen, and stubble so attractive and masculine it would have brought me to my knees had I been standing up.

I smiled my most engaging smile, "Yeah," I began, "we've found some cool stuff—even some arrowheads."

"How old?"

"Could be 5,000 years old or so," I answered, sounding self-assured.

"Well, that's so cool," Mechanic One said, reaching around and grabbing dessert from the end of the counter.

"Wow. Huh. Imagine that," Mechanic Two muttered as he wiped blueberry pie filling from his mustache with his sleeve. "I'll be damned. Archaeologists. You don't run across your kind a lot."

"We're some of the first archaeologists up here," Lucy said.

"Well, I guess so. And ladies at that!" Mechanic Three said.

The three mechanics made short work of dessert and got ready to leave.

"We gotta go, ladies. Lots of grease work on the pickup trucks to do," Mechanic Two said.

"May I bum a smoke? I'm running low," I asked Mechanic One with the pack of Kools.

"Yeah, sure, here ya go. Take a couple," he replied. "But remember, you owe me and I'll collect later!"

He winked and I smiled brazenly. We said our so-longs and I dove into the one piece of Boston cream pie I found hiding behind the chocolate cake. Lucy filled her pockets with oatmeal cookies.

"I'm going to look for Corey and see if he wants to take a walk with me and eat some cookies. I kind of like him, I think," she said.

"Have fun," I replied. "I'm staying right here with my book."

I poured more coffee, lit another cigarette, and quickly lost myself in Michener. While I would not find any artifacts belonging to Crusaders, as the people in the book were doing in the current chapter, I would find glimpses into the wild and cold past of the Arctic. I imagined an Eskimo 1,000 years ago, trying to build a fire on the tundra, cupping his hands around a small flame. Then, he lost the arrowhead he was working on, and I would find it in 1977. The scenario was kind of exciting.

Dick the Cook scrubbed the pots and washed the dishes, humming as he worked, while I daydreamed. Suddenly, Ray bounded in wearing his worn overalls, headphones dangling around his neck.

"Say, Dick, you got any more cookies?" he asked. "Nope, I don't, Ray. Won't have any until lunch tomorrow. But I have this piece of coconut cake I've been hiding in the back just for you."

"Oh, man! Can you make another one?" Ray asked, his face and all the freckles on it lighting up. "For you, kid, sure," came the reply.

After Ray inhaled the last morsel of cake, he struck up a conversation with Dick the Cook about the upcoming hunting season. Ray wanted a caribou with at least a thirty-inch rack. He planned to take one of the small planes and land it at any of the uncharted airstrips or gravel bars dotting the Slope and hunt from there.

"Wanna come?" he asked.

"Maybe," said Dick the Cook, "but I want to take some time off and go down to the Lower 48 and see my girl and the kids, you know."

"Ah, hell, they can wait for winter, can't they?" asked Ray.

"No, not really—I miss em. You'll have someone to miss, too, when you grow the hell up one of these years," he laughed.

Ray snorted a mock rebuke, then finished his snack and headed out the door. "Gotta go. Plane coming in from Bettles soon," he called over his shoulder.

"So long," yelled Dick the Cook, "and wash your hands before you come back."

* * *

No matter what the GSI guys had planned, Dick the Cook would probably show up for the party for less time than most of us, drink one beer, eat a slice of birthday cake, and return to the Umiat Hilton to prepare the kitchen for the following day's breakfast. He'd be in bed by midnight and up at four to fire up the grill, replenish the coffee urn, and begin making French toast and pancakes. Ray, on the other hand, would shut the place down.

After a succulent dinner of lamb chops, Lucy and I returned to the Howard Pass tent to dig into Kelly's makeup stash and tried on her lipsticks, each of us finding a shade flattering to our sunburned skins. I asked Lucy to check out my attire.

"Hey, you look great," she said. "How about me?"

"Ravishing. Maybe we'll get lucky tonight," I said, giving her the thumbs-up.

"I'll be after Corey tonight. Maybe I'll get lucky with *him,* Lucy replied.

We left the Howard Pass tent and walked over to GSI to join the gathering horde. I felt confident in Kelly's close-fitting red turtleneck.

Music blared. Jim Morrison seductively sang "Light My Fire" while five or six guys sat on the floor passing a bong. The guys wore colorful flannel shirts and tan Carhartts or faded jeans, most of them held up with suspenders and all dotted with oil and paint. When they saw Lucy and me, they stopped their talking and stared.

"Hello, ladies. I'm Skip," a bearded redhead said. "Want some booze?"

"Sure," we said simultaneously as Skip passed the bong with one hand and reached behind his back with the other hand to bring out around a bottle of scotch.

"Ice, ladies?" he asked.

Ice up here? Holy shit! We sure don't have ice in the Pass.

"Oh, yeah," I answered. "Where'd you get the ice?"

"We have a freezer in the back room," Skip answered nonchalantly, stroking his beard. "Help yourselves."

He got up unsteadily, put a hand on the back of a chair for balance, and walked us over to a table that held a dozen different bottles of liquor, a stack of Styrofoam cups, and a cracked plastic bowl filled with ice. Skip poured me some of his scotch, and Lucy, always the aesthete, saw a half-gallon bottle of white wine and poured some over her ice.

Skip reclaimed his seat on the floor and hid the bottle, but not before I noticed his left thumb was black.

I bet that *hurt,* I thought.

One of the guys pointed out the great snacks they had—potato chips, pretzels, and Cheez Doodles. Mike brought a can of project-owned mixed nuts to add to the festivities. Leslie brought some project-owned pilot bread and a box of Ritz crackers, part of her private stash from a care package.

The GSI prefabricated house had been barged up to Barrow in sections the year before and flown down to Umiat along with the furniture, a stove, and beds in a giant Herc C-130 cargo airplane. Yet the few chairs and the two yellow Naugahyde couches occupying the living room looked dreary and old. A large stove in the middle of the room heated the entire building. Several ropes and cords, dotted with clothespins and file clasps, radiated out from the stovepipe as clotheslines and were tied to wooden support beams. Damp looking wool socks hung from some of the clothespins. Fake wood paneling adorned the walls. A tiny, almost miniature red and black buffalo plaid Woolrich shirt hung from a hanger on a nail stuck into the stovepipe.

"What in the hell is that?" Ross asked.

"Well, one of the guys put it in the washing machine and then threw it in the dryer. It's wool, can't you tell? Pretty stupid, if you ask me," a roustabout from the airfield explained.

I lit a Camel bummed from Skip and pretended to talk to Lucy while checking out the guys. Lucy similarly engaged me in vacuous small talk.

"Not much to write home about," she said under her breath, "and where is Corey?"

I opened my mouth to answer when a big guy with curly brown hair came over and introduced himself as Chris. He wore blue jeans, a faded brown T-shirt, and a green down vest. Clean-shaven, he was the only man I'd seen without a beard in the three and a half weeks I'd been in Alaska except for the soldiers at Fort Wainwright.

"Hi, ladies," he said. "I live in this pre-fab paradise, thanks to GSI. What are you gals doing up here?"

"We're archaeologists with the big project," Lucy said

"Wow. You're the first girls we've seen up here in quite a while. At least I'm sure you're the first professional ones, you know, ologists of some kind. You're the first wave. You're pioneers."

I was surprised at Chris's response, and highly honored. I supposed we *were* the vanguard of professional women on the North Slope.

Meanwhile, the bong made its rounds and when it got to me, Chris said, "This isn't your cheap shit marijuana, it's our best hash—really strong and smooth." I sucked up the hash as best I could while Chris kept the bong lit with his lighter. I passed the bong to Lucy, who inhaled deeply.

The room began to spin almost immediately. I sat down on the couch, then tried to get up to replenish my supply of Cheez Doodles. It took forever to get to the table. I grabbed the entire bowl and brought it back to the couch. Donovan now sang "Mellow Yellow." I sang along, and soon many other folks were also singing out of tune, and loudly, too.

Just then, the front door opened, sending a blinding beam of daylight into the room.

"Shut the door!" someone yelled. "You're blinding me!"

Sam and John from Lookout Ridge were outlined in the bright midnight sun. John carried a guitar, while Sam toted his fiddle and a banjo.

"Y'all want a hootenanny?" John asked.

"Yeah!" came the collective response. Someone took the needle off the Donovan record with a screech and turned off the record player. Sam leaned the violin case against the booze table, opened the case, and slowly, reverently, brought out his fiddle. While he and John tuned their instruments to each other's, one of the roustabouts brought them both cups of bourbon and ice. Sam took a sip and lit a Camel straight. Once he had smoked the cigarette about halfway down,' he rested it on the table edge to signal he was ready to play.

John said, "Let's do "Your Cheatin' Heart" first."

"Okay, let's do 'er," Sam said.

They played a few bars and where you would have expected us to start singing, there was silence. Sam stopped playing and looked around, a disappointed expression on his face.

"Y'all know I don't sing. I guess John don't either, so someone has to sing." He shook his head and cradled his fiddle in his arm, ready to play. Several of us began to sing "Your cheatin' heart, won't let me be, I'm here alone, while you go free."

We sang loudly and freely, at the top of our lungs. It wasn't the best singing, but it was happy singing. Here we were in the tundra, in a prefab house at midnight in broad daylight, ripped, singing Hank Williams. Corey had finally slipped into the house but Lucy hadn't noticed yet.

Lucy and I looked at each other and laughed. Everything seemed so funny and surreal.

"Is this for real?" she asked.

"I don't think so. It's definitely a dream, but look who just got here," I said.

"See ya later alligator," Lucy said as she wound her way through the crowd to Corey. They began a lively conversation and I hoped they'd get together.

After an hour, Sam said in his usual soft way, "We only got time for one more tune. I fly out early tomorrow, and that means some of y'all do."

He took a swig of his bourbon and ice, put the cup down, and plucked a familiar chord on the fiddle. I instantly recognized the "Orange Blossom Special." John kept pace with Sam on the banjo and, hardly realizing what I was doing, I grabbed the guitar and began to keep time with the fiddle. Soon, everyone was clapping and stomping their feet. Leslie and Mike grabbed each other and started an impromptu square dance. We ended the song hooting and hollering, threatening to bring the house down around us.

So what if we behaved raucously—the music wouldn't reach Fairbanks, Deadhorse, or even Barrow. No one beyond GSI and the Hilton could hear us.

"Okay, ladies and gents, let's cut the cake! A grand finale for a spectacular evening," someone said when the Orange Blossom Special finished its run.

"You do it, Ray," Dick the Cook said. "I made it. You cut it."

"Sir, I am honored," Ray answered.

Dick the Cook's sheet cake looked scrumptious. The entire confection was covered with chocolate frosting. A reasonable likeness of the two birthday boys piped green icing decorated the top. Red rosettes with green leaves adorned the edges.

"There aren't any forks," Mike said.

"Use your hands, then," someone said, "and we don't have plates, so use a paper towel."

"You know there's a hint of marijuana in the cake, so eat two slices. Then you'll fall asleep before you get the munchies again," Ross said, smiling broadly.

I grabbed a large piece with my hands and inspected it for flecks of marijuana before cramming the delightful cake into my mouth.

Pioneer life is great!

* * *

By the time I got back to the Howard Pass tent, I was hoarse. I was still quite

stoned and, by then, tired. I fell asleep immediately and some hours later was rudely awakened by Linda knocking on the door.

"Breakfast, you guys!" she yelled.

I flung myself out of bed, grabbed my clothes, and stumbled down the road to breakfast. Hung over and *still* stoned, I inhaled breakfast, grabbed some coffee and doughnuts for Lucy, wherever she might be, and beat it back to the tent.

"That was wild last night," she said, entering the tent. "I am so out of it."

"Of course you are—you must have had more than a little fun last night. A little horizontal cha-cha maybe? I wanna hear all about it, but we gotta go. Sam's already loading the chopper. He was way ahead of me when I left the Hilton. I wonder if anyone but me noticed you and certain man were missing at breakfast."

"Oh, stop. I have a wicked hangover." Lucy yawned, took a bite out of a chocolate doughnut, and started getting her shit together. We walked down to the helicopter pad where Linda was loading a resupply of food. She handed me the letters that had come in for the crew. There was one for Ron and one for Toni. Nothing else.

"Oh, well," I said wistfully, "Next time there'll be more brownies from Mom."

I hopped in the front seat next to Sam and waved goodbye to Linda. The rotors picked up speed and we lifted off.

Sam, the man of few words and shy demeanor, did not appear interested in adding any hash marks to his bedpost. He preferred silence or talking about our impromptu bluegrass band.

"That was good music last night, Georgia," he said. "Put your seat belt on."

I obliged, then asked, "What do you do in winter, Sam?"

"I go back to Tennessee for a couple of weeks, then hop a plane to Costa Rica, and don't come back until April."

I asked him a couple questions about life in the tropics, but he focused his attention on a distant rainstorm heading our way instead. Eventually, I gave up and looked out the window at the green hills and valleys of tundra. Soon, I was gently rocked to sleep by the familiar vibration of the helicopter. Lucy snored in the back seat.

CAMP 4, BACK TO ANIUK RIVER

When we got back to Howard Pass, we moved camp to the Aniuk River again, but to a different stretch. The new camp bore no resemblance to our other three. A multitude of birds, jaegers and terns mostly, occupied a sea of tall grass surrounding a flat open area. The grasses swayed like a field of wheat, reminding me of pictures I'd seen of the African veldt, but cold and surrounded by snow-covered mountains. I missed Fauna Creek immediately and hoped we wouldn't stay in this location a long time.

A community of ground squirrels lived in extensive and complicated networks of burrows hidden in the grass. Their high-pitched squeals earned them the name *sik-sik* in Inupiaq. Inquisitive by nature, but especially at mealtime, they had to be shooed away repeatedly from the cook tent. Even so, in a couple of days, they could eat holes in the bottom of our boxes of rice and oatmeal.

One morning, I caught two of them by surprise while they were enjoying a meal of pilot bread under the blue tarp. They shrieked and sped off into the nearest burrow, scaring the hell out of me.

* * *

After waving goodbye to Tom and Helen, we loaded up our daypacks for work. Less than fifty yards away, I found a wonderfully shiny black obsidian object. We were batting a hundred in finding sites in our camps.

"Oh!" I cried, picking up the artifact. "Look at this! Holy shit!"

The others ran over. Malcolm took the object from me. His eyes widened and his mouth fell open. He held it up to the sun between his thumb and forefinger. The edges were translucent. "Obsidian, a perfectly symmetrical, conical core! It's wonderful. Good job, Georgeie. Good eye."

"What can you tell us about it, you guys?" Lucy asked, addressing the Alaska crowd and looking rapturously at the small cylindrical artifact.

"Well, from its shape, it looks like cores found in the Aleutians," Malcolm said, "and in Siberia and Mongolia, too. Hard to say how old it is, but the ones in the Aleutians are thought to be 8 to 10,000 years old. This kind of core is rare up here, and because it's obsidian, *really* rare."

"See where the microblades were struck off? See how beautifully regular in width and length the blade scars are?" Malcolm said, holding the core close to where I could see several parallel lines.

"Wow. Shit fire," Kelly said.

"Whoever made and used this artifact probably carried it on several hunting trips and dropped it here by mistake—I'll bet you anything," Malcolm said, fondling the piece.

"And the core would have been missed because you could still strike some smaller blades off the face. Must have been valuable," Toni added.

Six pairs of eyes looked lovingly at the core, and six pairs of hands took turns holding the artifact. Clearly, the Alaska crowd was astounded with our new find, and that meant Lucy, Kelly, Toni, and I were also astounded.

"Georgeie, write this mother up and let's all of us break for lunch and consider our good fortune. We'll look for more artifacts after lunch and record the site," Malcolm said.

"This is the best find of the summer so far, isn't it?" Kelly said as she put a piece of flagging on the ground where the core had been.

"I'm going to draw it tonight," I said.

"Go for it," Malcolm said.

Again I explored the artifact's smooth surface before carefully putting it in a carefully labeled coin envelope.

That night, I wrote in my field notes:

July 1. Moved camp to Aniuk and surveyed around new camp. Found conical core—obsidian! Really cool. Like ones in the Aleutians. Cores like this originally from Siberia/Mongolia. I hope Fitzsimmons will appreciate my story about it.

Nice weather today. Light breeze. No bugs to speak of yet.

* * *

On the following day, Lucy, Kelly, and I, a version of the Howard Pass All-Girl Survey Crew, walked three miles north of camp in clear, slightly chilly air. We found three flake scatters on a terrace overlooking a lake with a view up to Inyorurak Pass, only the second time I'd seen it clear. I calculated from the topo map that we could see about five miles before a forbidding box canyon turned north. Behind the mountains, the rain looked heavy at first, then lifted as a rainbow formed.

Ready to survey the terrace thoroughly, we found ourselves surrounded by brilliant red, blue, and lavender wildflowers, prompting Lucy to sing "The Sound of Music." The tundra had turned a deep green from the dead brown of a week earlier. Summer had finally made its brief appearance in the Brooks Range. Lucy cupped a larkspur in her hand, looking contented and peaceful. We took off our packs and sat on the ground.

One month ago I had not known either of these women. They were quickly becoming my confidantes and best friends.

Kelly seemed to feel like talking.

"I met Phil just after Gary and I broke up around Christmas," she disclosed as we gathered our supplies. "Phil's not *the one*, I know that. I really don't know if I'll ever find someone to settle down with."

Lucy sighed. "I haven't been in a long-term serious relationship yet, but I really loved this guy last year at school. He didn't love me and he dumped me right quick."

"Like I told Lucy in Umiat, I'm dating a guy back east and I know there's no future in it," I said, "but he's fun, and a friend, and we worked together for a while. I've had a few relationships I'd hoped would be serious, but they didn't work out, so I'm not thinking about getting married right now."

The three of us agreed that while we were in our twenties, we'd enjoy life and experience as much as possible. After all, wasn't that what we were doing now, coming all this way to an almost completely unexplored wilderness?

Kelly got out a Marlboro and offered one to me. I accepted the cigarette and lit it with my Bic.

"I really want to get back at Al," she said.

"Why, what'd he do?" Lucy asked.

"Well, during my first weekend in Umiat, Al paired up with Lynne from Lookout Ridge."

"I know who you mean." Lucy said, "The pretty woman from California with curly black hair and blue eyes. Nice person."

"We heard more about it in Umiat last time so we have an update," I said, eager to add to the dirt. "Al's started sleeping with Carol, even though the two girls are on the same crew. They come in on different rotations though. Al figured Lynne wouldn't find out, but guess what? Someone spilled the beans. Lynne was devastated."

"What a slut Carol is," Kelly said.

"Lynne's okay now because she's sleeping with Dave, so don't worry about her, but I agree with y'all, it's totally shitty," Lucy said.

"Georgeie, you're going to be the instrument of our revenge," Kelly said solemnly.

"What? Me? Our revenge? Huh?"

"Yeah. Go sleep with Al. Let's face it, you have the balls to do it."

I considered Kelly's flattery for a split second and said, "Okay, I'll do it. I like Lynne. Okay. I'll do it for her. Not sure how that helps her, but why not?" A smile of anticipation crossed my face.

"Yeah, what does Lynne get out of this?" Lucy asked.

"I'll tell her afterwards that you did it for her, for revenge, and she'll put the whole affair with Helio Skyscrewer behind her. She'll forget about it faster," Kelly said.

"She's sleeping with Dave now, so I think she's getting past it," Lucy added.

"I'll fix his wagon anyway," I said, blowing a perfect smoke ring as the memory of Al's mirrored sunglasses and black leather jacket filled my mind. I could never resist a dare.

Kelly must have already figured out that I would be up for the challenge. Maybe she thought Lucy wouldn't take the bait, being a little more reserved and slightly younger. I got a boost from Kelly's confidence in my prowess. I was even proud.

After solving the Al problem, we ate an unhurried lunch and recorded the site, then headed back to camp, crossing two icy streams and a tussock field. Winding our way down the slope and back towards camp, Lucy's cowbell, her personal version of a bear bell, clanged loudly as she maneuvered through the tussocks

Giddy with the possibility of a northern tryst, I plotted my moves as we walked.

I'll wait for a party in his Quonset, put on my clean khakis, something feminine of Kelly's, comb my hair, and wear lipstick. Booze and hash will help. I'll be irresistible. Not sure quite how, but I'll make it happen.

As we entered camp, Ron greeted us with something about the cows coming home from the field.

"See if *you* get laid this summer," Kelly muttered.

The three of us laughed loudly. Ron looked puzzled by our giggles and cocked his head to one side like a dog trying to understand better his master's commands.

* * *

Early on July fourth, I dreamt about a snowstorm in New York. Turning over in my sleeping bag and burrowing in, sleep would not come because my nose was too cold. Cautiously, I unzipped a small portion of my tent flap to see snow swirling all around camp. Laughter drifted over from the cook tent. Putting on my jeans, I quickly dressed and practically fell into the cook tent, whimpering, "Coffee, please."

Ron and Kelly seemed crestfallen and said nothing. It was their turn to go to Umiat, but with all the snow, it didn't seem likely the chopper would make it. The rest of us made an attempt at lightheartedness.

"You don't really want to go to base camp and eat real food, do you?" I teased.

"You don't really want a shower, do you?" Lucy added.

"You'll be in Umiat before you know it. Don't worry," Malcolm said, touching Kelly's shoulder and pouring more coffee. She smiled wanly and sighed.

"Well, I guess I'll go read for a while," he said.

"I sure hope the chopper makes it in," Lucy said. "I bet it can fly through this."

The weather gods must have heard our discontent. Only two hours late, the Jet Ranger arrived as the snow tapered off.

I'd been catching up on field notes and lazily napping inside my tent when the chopper came in, ready to take Ron and Kelly to Umiat. I peeled myself out of my sleeping bag to walk over, help unload the chopper, and shoot the shit.

Sam had that day's run out to Howard Pass. I'd had a futile crush on him as soon as I'd seen him. He was years older than me, how many I didn't know and I wasn't going to ask. His shyness somehow added to his allure. When he *did* speak, his soft Tennessee drawl seemed like smooth bourbon. "Georgia, will you pass me a toothpick?" was a phrase that made me swoon back in Umiat. He'd invariably follow his shy request by scratching his salt and pepper beard and running a hand through his thinning hair.

I loved it when Sam played the fiddle, the saw, or the banjo in Umiat and I longed for more music. I'd laughed and sung until I got hoarse the first night. He overcame his shyness, I thought, by playing the banjo just as I overcame mine by singing. Sam rarely drank and never touched dope. He seemed virtuous to me and above reproach. Keeping to himself, he didn't flirt with any woman on the project that I could see. He seemed more unavailable than even Ian.

Tom and Helen brought mail with them. In seconds, Kelly and Ron flung themselves into the 206 and waved at us in happy hysterics. I imagined the seats previously occupied by Tom and Helen were still warm.

Not to be rushed, Sam readied the helicopter while Malcolm started to hand out the mail. He spit tobacco juice on the ground— the first step in his take-off ritual—then carefully checked the bungee cords holding Ron's and Kelly's duffels on the skids. He climbed into the pilot's seat and slowly went through his safety check. While this happened routinely every time the chopper took off, I imagine the two travelers thought the routine a bit too thorough that morning. Finally, Sam lifted off and was soon gone.

Malcolm handed me a big parcel with my name on it in my mother's handwriting. I ripped into it in a frenzy and dumped the contents on the ground. The box was full of warm clothing, including a sweater, two of my stepfather's turtlenecks, and a new red down parka.

"Oh, my God," I cried. "Look at all this stuff!" I said as a small, partially crushed, tinfoil package fell out of the small mountain of clothing.

"What's this?" Lucy asked with anticipation.

Not too carefully, I tore open the tinfoil to find a batch of Mom's brownies. I jumped up and down in joy. I clutched the parka and the slightly moldy brownies to my chest in a mixture of glee and gratefulness to the gods for the warm clothing and the homemade treat.

"Jesus! I'm saved. I'll never be cold again!"

I danced around; a woman possessed. Toni, Lucy, Malcolm, Tom, and Helen jumped up and down in excitement with me as I put on my new parka and laughed.

"Oh my God!" tears of relief formed at the corners of my eyes on this cold Independence Day. "And brownies. She makes the best brownies. I can smell them through the tin foil."

"I think this occasion calls for a joint, Mom's brownies, and some coffee, okay Malcolm?" Tom asked.

"Yeah, sure," Malcolm said as he reached for a brownie.

The joint wasn't as "knock your socks off" as the hashish I'd had at the party in Umiat, but it was a nice, mellow high and a great accompaniment to the brownies. We were still with it enough that if a big brown grizz approached camp, we'd have reacted quickly. We spent, I don't know how long rolling around laughing in the snow with one of the shotguns in easy reach, just in case. My exuberance and the effects of the joint dampened the home-sickness brought on by the best brownies in the world.

"I wish *my* mom would send *me* brownies," Toni said wistfully as she enjoyed my mom's treat.

* * *

By lunchtime, the snow had increased again and visibility worsened. Malcolm called a weather day. Since we had recently spent an afternoon in our tents due to high winds, he decided the day should not be a total loss and called for a study session in his tent, accompanied by the remaining brownies. We talked about North Slope archaeology with Malcolm's small library of textbooks to consult. J. L. Giddings' *Ancient Men of the Arctic* and *The Archaeology of Cape Denbigh* were handled and read from reverently, not unlike a holy book. If Malcolm had possessed the voice of Darth Vader, Giddings' pronouncements would have been even more awe-inspiring.

As I dug through the small library, the current issue of *Anthropological Papers of the University of Alaska,* dedicated to articles by and for my soon-to-be mentor, caught my eye

"Hey, this volume is devoted to Fitzsimmons," I said, hoping to impress and to steady my nerves at the same time. He was so famous, and I was so... not.

"You watch yourself back there at UConn," Malcolm said. "Uncle Mikey can be a tough customer."

"So, you've said," I replied.

"He sues anyone who disagrees with him," Malcolm said.

Tom shook his head in agreement. Helen examined her hands, and Lucy's brow furrowed. What a strange moment for me to notice that the three of them had adorable dimples.

"What? You're kidding," I said.

"Be careful. He's temperamental, a real prima donna. I saw him once when he and I happened to visit Wazoo at the same time. He's a real charmer. Could sell you the Brooklyn Bridge. Was wearing a nice suit with French cuffs and puffing on a big cigar," Malcolm said.

Now *my* brow furrowed.

"He's not even in the anthro department," he continued. "He left in a huff, abandoning the other profs and several of his own students. They don't like him. Lots of bad blood. He set up his own department, in fact. I wonder if the anthro department kicked him out."

"Don't worry," Ron interjected, "He puts his trousers on one leg at a time like the rest of us do."

Oh, God. What have I gotten myself into?

The crew started to refer to him as Uncle Mikey. They gave Fitzsimmons the name to ease my anxiety about studying with such a famous man, and to poke fun at his immense ego. I listened to my new friends cautioning me about life at UConn. I felt doubtful about my future with Uncle Mikey now, but decided not to worry about him until I left at the end of the summer.

* * *

The following day brought more bad weather. It snowed in the early morning and later warmed up just enough that it rained. About midday the Jet Ranger flew through the weather in a surprise visit, carrying Rick and two guests. After they got out of the chopper, Rick said he was visiting all four camps to see how things were going and to introduce us to two archaeologists from the Lower 48.

"Howdy, I'm Dwight," the taller one said, walking over to us and removing his cowboy hat. He bowed slightly to the crew. His gaze took in the women. He flashed a blinding white smile surrounded by a handsome and thick red beard. I immediately wanted to run my fingers through it.

"And I'm Jim," said the other one, doffing his baseball cap to reveal a head of curly blond hair.

Kelly had told me days earlier she'd met Jim on a project in the Southwest the year before, and knowing he'd be flying out of Umiat, decided to seek a more fulfilling relationship with him. Perhaps she'd already scored a direct hit when she was in Umiat.

Jim and Dwight had traveled to the Slope to test remote sensing equipment that could locate sites without having to take a trowel or entrenching tool to the earth. The equipment had to be tested from the helicopter.

Hunky Al had also flown in at the helm of the chopper. He shut down the 206 and joined us. I smiled at him coquettishly, or so I thought.

Dwight, we'd heard through the Umiat grapevine, had already fallen for Lynne. Apparently, he'd been writing her poetry to take her mind off Al. Did he know she was already shacked up with Dave out at Lookout Ridge? I didn't know.

I still planned to sleep with Al, of course. He had to be punished.

Dwight, Jim, Malcolm, and big boss Rick chatted for ten minutes or so and walked around the campsite. Malcolm brought out our best artifacts for a show and tell. Al looked on, but his gaze frequently drifted to me, then to Lucy, then to Toni, then back to me.

I have made a sacred vow, I thought, *and I will give the man in the leather jacket a night to remember.*

After a few minutes, Al herded the visitors back to the chopper. "Weather's not good, folks," he said.

We watched Dwight and Jim pile into the back seat of the Jet Ranger with fearless leader, Rick, in front.

After takeoff, Toni said, "That Dwight's a tall drink of water," Had she licked her lips, or was it my imagination?

"And that Jim and his curls—my, my," Lucy sighed.

"He's Kelly's, you know," I whispered to her in my absent pal's defense.

"Oh, I know, but a gal from Georgia stuck up here in the snow can dream, can't she?"

* * *

That evening in my tent, it occurred to me we were becoming predatory about sex. Was this what happened to you when you lived out in the bush? It sort of seemed like the natural thing to do. You got tense; you got scared; you had a bear encounter—you needed a release!

Couplings had occurred and there was hope of more to come—Kelly and Jim probably, Al and I maybe, Lucy and Corey almost certainly, and then there was Ian, the handsome head of the Ikpikpuk crew who liked to wink at me.

My mind wandered. *What I wouldn't do to park Ian's boots under my bed. And then there's Al. Maybe that's what I need to do— get laid. I wonder who my first conquest will be.*

I stifled a primitive grunt, then put down *The Source* and closed my eyes.

* * *

Rain pelted us most of the next day, but by evening the sky cleared to an azure blue, the winds died down, and the temperature climbed into the fifties. Unfortunately, the change to fair weather brought hordes of mosquitoes.

I considered the descriptions of mosquitoes I'd heard as tall tales, or exaggerations at least, but was soon proven wrong. The Alaskan mosquito was huge. The body so big, you could almost see individual hairs on its legs, and the proboscis looked like a wide-gauge needle, especially when poised to pierce your hand. The unpleasant whine emitted by the pests was the least of my worries.

Thankfully, we had large quantities of smelly Army surplus mosquito repellant with us for the project. I squirted the noxious white liquid on only when I had to, at the last possible moment, and perfected the art of coating my clothes instead of my skin, beginning with my hat brim, proceeding to the shirt collar, and ending at the cuffs. Usually, my jeans repulsed all but the largest mosquitoes, and rarely did they fly up my pant legs.

I avoided putting the stuff on my skin so I wouldn't smell like a chemical dump and because it destroyed various substances. The glue in my hat brim fell apart. The yellow paint on my pencil turned to goo. Even the printed label on the plastic squeeze bottle melted after a few days. No way would I touch that poison to my skin.

All of us eventually swallowed a bug or two or ate one of the little bastards after it kamikazed into our oatmeal or Cream of Wheat while emitting a high-pitched whine. One flew into Ron's ear that day. It took him an hour and several Q-Tips to kill it and stop the whining that filled his head. On several occasions, I had to blow my nose excessively after one or two of the fuckwads flew up my nostril.

Kelly and I had discovered the bugs didn't like cigarette smoke. Consequently, we lit up whenever the wind died down. Smoke became our main line of defense. When one of us saw or heard a swarm heading our way, either Kelly or I would yell "Incoming!" grab our head nets and light a smoke. Radar O'Reilly would have been proud of us—we seemed to hear the whine before everyone else did.

That night, I finished *The Source,* fascinating from beginning to end. In the final chapter, Michener revealed a secret to the reader, but *not* to the characters in the book. Had the archaeologists excavated their trench three feet to the east, the interpretation of the site would have changed, and history would have been written differently. The last drawing in the book showed a cross-section of the main trench, with a black pillar at the lowest level of the site, adjacent to the pit, unexcavated and undiscovered.

"Wow, Holy God," I muttered in my sleeping bag on reading the last paragraph.

It's luck. You never know.

* * *

The next day, we put in many long sweaty hours surveying as many terraces and lakeshores as possible within five miles of camp. Both teams hiked down to the stretch of Rough Mountain Creek nearest the Aniuk, then walked along either side of an unnamed stream. For all our sweat, we found nothing. Even worse, the light breeze blowing across the bluffs wasn't strong enough to inhibit the bugs from swarming, landing and biting.

"Hey, y'all," said Toni, "I'm going to cook us a nice hot curry when we get back to camp. That's something to look forward to."

"Hip hip, hooray!" Lucy shouted.

"I'm so miserable I would almost welcome freeze-dried corn," I said.

"Bet you're not *that* desperate," Lucy said.

"Guess not," I said. "Toni's curry will be just dandy, and maybe mosquitoes don't like sweat oozing with hot sauce."

Dinner would be the high point of our bug-infested day.

* * *

"I don't understand it," Malcolm said later. "There should be sites all around here."

"I know," said Tom, "but that's just how it is, I guess. Looking at the map, I'm thinking it might be because there are only a few vantage points, and more of the ground is boggy."

"Hey, guys, don't forget the conical core. That was something," I said, visualizing the magic obsidian cylinder in my mind and reveling in the fact that I'd found it.

"Well, that's true, for sure, but when we get over to Inyorurak Pass, we'll find shitloads of even more incredible stuff. The couple of known sites over there are doozies."

After dinner, I retreated to my tent to peel off the most recent layer of moleskin stuck to my sore feet and enjoy a quiet evening by myself.

Oh, so that's where the word tenderfoot comes from.

Mosquitoes buzzed around the tents in the evening heat. I missed the cold and the breeze. Sure, I had almost died of hypothermia a couple of weeks before, but my brain had a short memory for suffering. The heat and the little flying bastards were now my misery.

* * *

Our final day along the Aniuk was July seventh, my twenty-sixth birthday. The event didn't register when I woke up, because it was so out of context.

A soft voice with a southern drawl called to me from just outside my tent. I opened my eyes, yawned, and raised myself up on my elbows.

"What? Am I late for breakfast again?"

"No, lady fair. I'm bringing you coffee for your birthday."

"Thanks, Lucy," I said. "I actually forgot."

I opened my tent flap. Lucy handed me a cup of Suisse Mocha instant coffee. I took the coffee and smelled its sweet aroma. "Ah," I said gratefully.

"You're going to have to leave the comfort of your tent for your breakfast. We know how much you like bacon, and you wouldn't want a molecule of bacon grease to attract the bears anywhere near you tent, would you?"

"Okay, I'm coming."

I stared outside at the cloudless blue sky and felt the sun beating down through the tent. Closing my eyes, I smelled a light breeze pungent with moss and wildflowers. The Aniuk rambled on happily nearby. My birthday would be perfect except for the bugs.

I made a dash for the cook tent, trailing a few whining mosquitoes.

"Happy birthday!" yelled the crew.

"Bacon's almost ready," Helen said. "Here, I've prepared a luscious piece of pilot bread for you with lots of peanut butter." She handed me the delicacy and filled my cup with black coffee.

"Uh, huh?" I said, reaching for the coffee and pilot bread.

"We have gifts, too!" said Lucy.

"Aw, jeez, thanks," I said, surprised by the attention." Gifts? How?"

"It was easy. Everyone contributed something and Kelly collected them and gave them to Malcolm before she went to Umiat," Helen said.

"Why the fuss?" I asked

"Yours is the only birthday we'll have while we're out here, so it's a big deal to all of us," Tom said.

Malcolm handed me five small packages wrapped in comics from a month-old faded and tattered *Seattle Post-Intelligencer*. The packages had been carefully wrapped because there was no Scotch tape to secure the edges, and duct tape was too valuable.

With great curiosity, I opened my tiny gifts.

"Oh, my God," I said in astonishment.

In front of me were a pack of Winstons, two packets of cocoa, a box of raisins, a baggy full of cotton balls, and a small vial of Bonnie Bell lotion to wipe the dirt off my face at the end of the day. I was moved close to tears as Toni and Helen, closest to me, leaned in for a hug. I hugged back.

I will always remember this day. Always.

No one seemed embarrassed by my emotions, as my family would have been back home. Things up here, good and bad, had more of a sense of immediacy and intimacy than at home. We depended on each other for life, limb, and morale, and I had begun to fit in.

"This is the best," I said, wiping my nose on my sleeve. "Thanks."

* * *

Birthday or not, it was still a workday. After breakfast, Malcolm, Toni, and I surveyed north along the Aniuk, covering low and high terraces, again finding nothing. I didn't care. My new friends had celebrated my birthday with me north of the Arctic Circle. The sheer novelty of it was hard to take in. I reflected on the day as we walked:

Here I am in the company of huge mosquitoes, arrowheads, bears, moose, tussocks, helicopters, drugs, and bearded men. No one back home would understand the joy of opening a box of raisins wrapped in comics. No one.

I shook my head in disbelief, then reflected on my twenty-fifth birthday the year before in DC. My college friends had taken me to a Chinese restaurant for Peking duck. One of my roommates had substituted smutty fortune cookies for the real thing, much to our amusement and that of the kitchen staff. Twenty-five had been a great birthday—a real howl! But this? I couldn't think of words to express this experience.

* * *

After too many hours trudging through tussock fields to find a terrace with no sites on it, we headed in, ending my birthday with a banquet. Tom and Helen caught and gutted grayling, built a fire, and roasted the fish crispy brown. Lucy made an attempt at corn chowder with freeze-dried corn and powdered milk. It had the consistency of paste and tasted like it. I thanked her for her efforts. My birthday cake consisted of a stack of Krusteaz pancakes with a sauce of wild berries, jam, water, and sugar—a wonderful treat.

"I'm so full," Tom moaned, rolling around on the ground.

"I'm so full, I can't even belch," Lucy added in her lady-like manner.

I lay down, patted my full stomach, and stared at the bright blue sky and laughed. I felt tighter than a tick, as the saying goes.

Just then, the whine of an airplane engine pierced the air. We watched in disbelief as a floatplane began its final descent to a nearby lake.

"Who in hell is that? Let's go see," Helen said, putting down the half-washed dishes.

As fast as humanly possible, we splashed across the Aniuk, stumbled through a tussock field, and reached the lake in time to see the plane taxiing to shore. The pilot cut the motor and jumped out of the floatplane, holding the plane's mooring rope.

"Who the hell are you? You scared the shit out of me," the handsome bearded pilot said.

His passengers climbed onto the wing, then stepped into the shallow water. They looked slightly frightened by our scruffy appearance. I stared at the couple's brand-new- looking safari jackets and clean waders. *That was me when I first came up,* I thought. In the twenty or so days I'd been in the field, I'd acquired a "lived-in" look.

Our fearless leader took control of the situation immediately. "Hi, I'm Malcolm. We're a team of archaeologists surveying for the government. Who are you guys?" he said softly and slowly as if addressing a delegation from another planet.

What's next, Klaatu, Barada, Nikto? I wondered.

The man turned to the pilot and asked, "Do people just show up like this often?"

"Not a lot," the pilot said. "Usually, the control tower in Kotzebue or Umiat will tell me if someone's out in a wilderness area so I can fly over and check on them; at least dip my wings." Then, to Malcolm he said, "I'm Mike, Mike from Bering Air. Pleased to meet you."

They shook hands. The couple did not offer their hands, but swatted mosquitoes from around faces instead. Toni handed them some bug dope and said, "Be careful. It's strong."

"Thanks," the woman said. She looked at the almost-obliterated writing on the container and cocked an eyebrow, then rubbed the repellant on her face and hands. I cringed, hoping her skin would survive the noxious formula.

"We're floating the Aniuk to the Noatak in a Zodiac. We'll be picked up at Noatak Village in two weeks," the man said.

"That's quite ambitious," Malcolm said, sounding tentative.

After exchanging a few pleasantries, the couple decided to set up their raft and organize their gear.

"Well, I better be off," Mike said. "It's a long flight back to Kotzebue, but I'll make sure these folks are set up before I leave. Say, are you finding stuff?"

"Yeah, nothing really spectacular, but enough to know there were people up here a long time ago," Malcolm answered vaguely, presumably to keep site locations safe from potential pothunters.

"So, things are good?"

"Yeah, and besides, it's her birthday," Tom said, pointing to me.

"Happy birthday, gal," the pilot said.

I took off my baseball cap and bowed.

We waved the pilot off, said our goodbyes to the passengers, and began the trek home.

"I sure hope they have a shotgun," Tom said, looking over his shoulder at the ascending plane, now the size of a small bird and sounding like a nearby mosquito.

* * *

When I turned in that night, tired from all the excitement and reflecting on my special birthday, I wrote in my notes:

July 7. My 26th birthday started with Suisse Mocha coffee in bed, then sourdough pancakes and bacon. And, get this, there were presents wrapped in funny papers! Cigarettes, lotion, raisins, cocoa, and cotton balls. Wow! Also had to work. Hot, almost humid day. Floatplane landed after my birthday dinner. Turistas are going to float down to Noatak. I sure hope they make it. Found nothing today. Umiat tomorrow.

UMIAT

Most people I had known up to this point in my life would have considered Umiat a dump, but, to me, it had become the center of civilization and height of sophistication. Unlike many of my fellow campers, I still liked to spend my days off in its comforts—reading, socializing, tasting morsels of Dick the Cook's first-rate food, and taking as many hot showers a day as possible.

The men on my rotation weren't that appealing, but I worshipped Umiat's permanent fixtures, Dick the Cook and pilot Sam, and looked forward to spending as much time with them as possible. Both men seemed off-limits, almost like camp counselors, there to keep us happy and safe. Al was also a permanent fixture in Umiat. Helio Skyscrewer had his own Quonset, no doubt filled with bongs, candles, and sex toys, and I wanted to have my way with him, but valued the friendship of Sam and Dick the Cook much more. Plus, hanging around the mess hall meant I'd be the first to eat Dick the Cook's chocolate chip cookies. And if I asked nicely, maybe Sam would play the saw for me.

Sometimes, I spent entire afternoons in the mess hall talking to some of the other archaeologists on the project. I especially liked John, the soft-spoken divinity student with the long black beard and blue eyes I had been getting to know during my time in Umiat. He didn't seem super religious and, in fact, I thought him relatively normal in a quiet, thoughtful way. Once I found out he was a divinity student, I began to call him Preacher John, and he seemed to like the name.

"I won't come back to Alaska," he said at lunch one day. "This is sort of my training for my real job. Lots of divinity students study archaeology and history. Some of us go to Israel to experience the Holy Land, but I decided to see the Last Frontier instead."

I mulled this over. "I took a course in circumpolar anthropology at GW when I was a junior and got hooked on the Arctic. I sure underestimated how raw and wild Alaska is. It's new, like it's still being created," I said.

"Tell you what, Georgeie, let's walk out to the Red Spot and continue this conversation," Preacher John said, stretching and cleaning his wire rims with his red bandanna.

"Oh, I don't know," I replied somewhat defensively. "I really enjoy sitting here in the mess hall reading Michener and talking to Dick the Cook."

"Oh, c'mon, just this once, so you can say you did it," Preacher John prodded.

"Okay, all right, I guess."

The Red Spot, located above the base of Umiat Mountain, was a landmark for approaching aircraft, and a popular destination because it was only three miles northeast of the Hilton, on level, mostly dry ground. An easy walk on this sunny and mosquito-free day, I really couldn't say no.

We walked out, headed right, and crossed the end of the airstrip. The windsock showed a slight breeze from the south. On our short journey, we compared notes about school, friends, families, and movies. We both liked *Rocky* and *Saturday Night*

Fever, not only for the fight and dance scenes and the music, but also for the movies' portrayal of American families. I had a good friend, an Italian American, whom I'd known since 1964. I'd met her family many times and eaten dinner at her house but couldn't remember them sitting around the dinner table smacking each other like the Maneros or the Balboas. I never heard anyone in her family swear like the movie families did.

We reached Umiat Mountain, actually a large terrace, and climbed the fifty feet to the Red Spot. It reminded me of the mysterious Red Spot on Jupiter but turned out to be an oval area of bright red dirt exposed during Umiat airstrip construction in the forties.

We sat on the ground, looking south towards town. I sat close to Preacher John, giving him every opportunity to put his arm around me, but he didn't seem the least bit interested. Perhaps, I thought, he was starting divinity school early.

The whine of an airplane engine broke the stillness. I put my hand up to shield my eyes and examined the sky.

"There it is," I said, pointing to the ever louder and bigger dot approaching from the south.

A chorus of truck engines came to life in anticipation of meeting the plane. We watched as three trucks raced down the airstrip towards the Cessna when it set down. The men popped out of their trucks, opened the storage compartments, and pulled some cardboard boxes out of them. Most important were two big mailbags—mail day was always exciting.

"Hey," Preacher John said, immediately standing up and dusting red dirt off his pants, "Let's go see if we got mail."

I followed him down the trail, then heard a scuffling sound and a giggle to my right. Corey and Lucy appeared from around the north side of Umiat Mountain. They were holding hands and laughing.

"Hey! Mail plane!" Corey shouted.

A collective whoop rose up as the four of us rushed back to camp.

* * *

Lucy got a letter from her dad and I got a letter from Mom.

Did you receive the care package with the parka? my mother asked in the letter. *Were the brownies okay?*

I had already written to her saying everything was great and that everyone had enjoyed the brownies, but I guessed our letters had crossed in the mail. What I hadn't mentioned in my note was the brownies' slight moldiness. Back home, they would have been pitched out then and there. Here, the mold had been somewhat carefully scraped off and the brownies consumed in five minutes.

There were letters from home for Ron and Kelly, too, and a letter for Toni from someone with extremely masculine hand-writing, her boyfriend, I assumed. Toni had not been inclined to say much about him so far, so he became the object of considerable curiosity by the other women of Howard Pass.

* * *

Lucy and Corey were developing real feelings for each other. That much was obvious to everyone in Umiat. Corey began to walk with us from the tent camp to the Hilton for every meal. Better put, he began to hang around with us no matter where we were to stay close to Lucy as much as humanly possible

Lucy confided in me that she found his bohemian lifestyle fascinating but perplexing. A poor anthro grad student at UAF, he lived in a cabin without running water on a dirt road called Dead End Alley. His bright blue eyes lit up his tanned, unwashed face especially when rolling a cigarette or looking at Lucy. His vow not to take a shower or wash his clothes for the entire summer hadn't put her off after all; it was part of his mystique. I thought, although I didn't know, that by the end of the summer, when their romance might fully blossom, Corey might acquiesce and clean himself up. Perhaps they would save water by taking a shower together.

One evening in the mess hall, Corey showed us some of his artifact drawings. The trick, he said, was keen observation plus the use of a ruler in centimeters.

"Say, Corey, I've drawn a few artifacts out in Howard Pass, but they're not as good as yours. How bout some pointers?" I said.

"Sure," Corey said in quiet self-confidence. "See these small dots? That's called stippling. The closer together the dots, the darker the shading on the projectile point or flake. You can vary the stippling subtly for a complexly shaped piece."

"So cool," I said.

"Practice with a really sharp pencil in the field. You can even smudge the stippling to add more shading," he added, turning his attention suddenly from me to Lucy. She caught his gaze and I thought her eyes actually smiled.

Lesson over! They'll find some privacy somewhere now and screw.

In the empty Howard Pass tent I went to work, practicing stippling a hypothetical projectile point with a mechanical pencil on a piece of graph paper. Although an extremely pleasurable activity, my hand eventually grew tired, and having used up most of the pencil, I picked up *The Source* and soon fell asleep.

CAMP 5, KIINGYAK LAKE

When we flew in from Umiat on an uncharacteristically hot morning, and Malcolm and Toni left us for the pleasures of base camp, we moved to a new campsite. Malcolm had told Lucy and me to keep our daypacks handy and hop back in the 206 after offloading the food resupply. I had only the briefest chance to look at our new home, Kiingyak Lake, sparkling in the sun.

"The helicopter will take you, Ron, and Kelly about five miles to the east," Malcolm said. "There's a broad terrace over there overlooking the Aniuk," he said, pointing to a spot on the topo map and then gesturing in its direction. The terrace stood out prominently on the map.

"Yeah," Kelly said, "should have some shit on it."

The terrace did look intriguing, its contour lines on the map narrowing then spreading out to represent its tabletop shape. As interesting as this feature seemed to be, my headache from smoking some dope the night before prevented my complete concentration.

Malcolm continued, "Should take you most of the day. So, go on. Git! Kelly's already packed your lunch. You can check out our new camp later."

"Yes, sir," I replied, saluting our fearless leader. "See you in two days."

I clambered back into the chopper, a little shaky. The strong heat from the sun beating through the Plexiglas broiled me alive in my jeans, long johns, wool socks, and flannel shirt. I knew I would throw up, then spontaneously combust.

Thankfully, we flew for only a few minutes before setting down on top of the terrace. I jumped out and onto the ground, somewhat dazed and overheated. The whirring of the rotors circulated the wind like a fan and cooled my skin until Sam lifted off again. The tundra looked green, moist, and inviting, with small patches of snow still dotting the mountains, but the air felt like an oven, even on this scenic terrace covered in **lichens** and wildflowers.

We got ready to seize the day and put on our daypacks. Kelly took the shotgun. The three of us walked over the huge terrace under the bright sun for about two hours, saying little to each other, despite Kelly's attempts to start a conversation. Surprisingly, we came up empty-handed.

"Well, fuck. I can't believe there's nothing up here," I said glumly.

"You'd think this would be a great place to hang out with a nice breeze, no bugs, and a great view. People from all over should have come up here all the time to chip stone tools for us to find," Ron said, sounding disappointed.

"I don't really care. I'm too fucking hot—hot and miserable," I moaned.

"Okay, let's forget about it and eat lunch," Kelly said, carefully putting down the shotgun, sitting down, and unloading food from her daypack.

We had perfected the mealtime habit of sitting in a tight circle while looking past each other to scan the horizon for curious and hungry animals. There would be no surprise bear attack at lunch on this or any other day.

We hungrily grabbed at our supply of tinned meat, cheese, jelly, and peanut butter. Ron wiped the sweat off the back of his neck with his dirty white handkerchief, then spread a large quantity of peanut butter on a piece of pilot bread.

In the habit of putting peanut butter on pilot bread with my Buck knife and then licking it off, I reached into my daypack to get the knife, but couldn't find it. My knife was too dull to do anything but spread jam, peanut butter, devilled ham, or canned roast beef—nothing harder than Tillamook cheese. The knife was probably lost inside my sleeping bag roll back at camp.

"Say, Ron, may I use your knife? Mine must be in camp," I said.

"Sure," he said, handing me his Swiss Army knife.

I smeared peanut butter on my pilot bread and, without thinking, licked the blade. I sliced my lower lip. It stung like hell.

"Shit," I yelled. I wiped the blade on my jeans, leaving peanut butter and blood on the denim, and handed the knife back to Ron while feeling my lip with my fingers.

"Are you okay?" Kelly asked, grabbing my rapidly swelling lip with *her* fingers, and pulling it away from my teeth to observe the damage.

"Ow! Watch it," I gurgled.

My lip bled profusely. Attempting to make light of the situation, I smiled, revealing blood-soaked teeth. My mouth tasted salty. Beginning to laugh, I pulled my bandanna out of my back pocket and held it against my lip.

"Tilt your head back, George," Ron said.

"Oh, shit. How bad is it?" I asked looking up into the sky.

"You'll live," said Kelly. "You're a brave little soldier, Georgeie. You didn't cry at all!"

"I was too surprised," I laughed.

My lip stopped bleeding in a few minutes, but still hurt. It would probably sting for a few days. I'd put some antibiotic cream on it back in camp. Not wanting to lose any newly gained sourdough points, I didn't voice my worry that the scent of blood could attract a bear, but I imagined the thought occurred to all of us.

* * *

After lunch, we began our return trip to camp. To avoid a big bend in the river, we cut across a tussock field. Hot, sweaty, tired, and cranky, we slogged through cold water between the tussocks while the air above us swarmed with mosquitoes. Any freshness that remained from my showers in Umiat was gone. I knew I smelled like a combination of sweat, damp wool, bug dope, and wet dog.

We trudged into the Kiingyak Lake camp around seven in the evening. The small lake's circular shape revealed its history—a huge mass of ice had sunk into the permafrost and melted at some point at the end of the last glaciation, leaving a roundish shoreline. The water beckoned to me. The round shape reminded me of a swimming pool—a dark one.

When Tom saw us coming and knew we were all safe, he flung off his clothes, threw himself into the lake, and immediately started screaming, "Oh my God! Holy Christ!"

I was not in the habit of taking my clothes off in front of guys I wasn't sleeping with. Actually, I couldn't even recall taking my clothes off in front of other women except during gym class. I considered the extent of my misery, however, and knew I was so hot I'd have to take the plunge.

I'm so stinking hot, I don't care. And I'm wounded, too. To hell with it.

"Okay, here I come," I said, ripping off my clothes. The instant I was naked, mosquitoes descended on my tender flesh in a thick swarm. I jumped in as fast as humanly possible and shrieked at the shock of the glacial water before my skin became dead to all sensation. Had my heart stopped beating?

"Shit!" I screamed, inhaling and exhaling furiously.

As the others shed their clothes, the little fuckwads swarmed behind each one until that person flung him or herself into the lake. Everyone's reaction was basically the same as mine and in the same sequence—jump in, scream, check heartbeat, swear, repeat steps two through four. Lucy smacked the water with her arms as if in a panic. Helen's face may have turned blue for a moment—I couldn't be sure, but she'd definitely lost her healthy pink complexion. Ron resembled a myopic seal, bobbing up and down in the water without his glasses.

Bugs or no, I couldn't wait to get out. On the shore, Tom already had his clothes on and was hopping into his shoes. My skin remained numb for a few seconds as I jumped onto the bank and raced to get my clothes back on before the flying bastards found me.

I did not plan to look at anyone's nakedness because I didn't want anyone looking at mine, but I couldn't help but catch a glimpse of Tom and Ron. I'd heard men's genitals shrivel when they're cold, and now I knew shrinkage to be a true phenomenon.

* * *

That night, dinner was a drag. We ate in the cook tent instead of outside, but several of our mosquito companions found their way inside anyway. When we had finally squashed all but the most tenacious invaders, we dug into a meal of freeze-dried chili and corn. Ron rolled up his shirtsleeve to inspect the number of mosquito bites he had acquired. I counted thirty-seven on my right arm. Kelly took first prize with fifty-five on her arms.

She felt compelled to bring up the Swiss Army knife story.

"Yeah, she's right," I said. "See how swollen my lip is?" I regaled the crew with my tale about the Swiss Army knife.

Ron leaned in for a closer look.

"If you touch my lip, you're a dead man," I said snarling.

Ron snapped his head back immediately. "Okay, okay. I was only going to look at it again," he said.

"Don't tempt fate, Ron," Helen giggled.

A round of applause rose up from my friends. I proudly stuck out my swollen lower lip for all to admire.

"Now you guys go wash the dishes," Helen commanded.

Our conversation continued after they left.

"That was mighty brave of you, George, your not screaming, I mean," Kelly said. "You're so brave, I'm gonna call you Killer Bitch!"

"Aw, shucks, guys, twern't nothin. I accept my new name. We're all bitches out here," I replied.

"Kelly, you're Feisty Bitch because that's just what you are," Lucy laughed.

Kelly followed up with, "And Helen, you can be Little Big Bitch because you're kind of tiny but have big muscles. I guess that makes you, Lucy, Southern Bitch."

"How exciting," Lucy interjected. "My own Bitch name."

"And Toni will be Amazon Bitch because her legs are so damned long. I'll break the news to her when she gets back," I said, laughing through my puffy lip.

The Bitches of Howard Pass stayed in the tent, our hands cupped around cups of hot chocolate or Tang, laughing far into the evening. From then on, I became Killer Bitch. I thought about it every time I licked Buck my knife. It made me smile.

* * *

The next day, a light wind from the north kept the bugs away and the temperature, a comfortable fifty or so degrees, seemed balmy. In the morning, Ron, Lucy, and I walked around nearby Nigtun Lake where we found an uninteresting and recent assemblage of artifacts consisting of five Winchester rifle shells, two five-gallon Aviation Gas containers, and a stone cairn. We recorded the artifacts and their positions dutifully despite the site's obvious modern assemblage because, as the saying goes, archaeological finds only get older and more interesting with age. At least the presence of artifacts proved that someone had used this place recently perhaps, or maybe a few decades ago, but none of us could say where the hunters came from or where they called home.

In the afternoon, we forded the familiar Aniuk and Etivluk Rivers, and an unnamed creek on our way out to a low terrace west of camp. At each crossing, we took off our boots and our many layers of socks, rolled up our jeans, waded across barefoot, and stopped on the far side to reassemble ourselves. The rushing Etivluk felt warmer than I had expected. After the previous day's plunge into Kiingyak Lake, anything would.

Our wilderness routine usually allowed for a brief break after crossing a stream to refill canteens, get back into our socks and boots, and shoot the breeze, so we sat on a flat spot of tundra next to the Etivluk, dried our feet with our socks, and broke out the chocolate supply. I grabbed a package of peanut M&Ms from my daypack and passed it around.

Ron started the conversation by saying he wasn't sure what he was going to write for his dissertation at Brown.

"I want to write up one of the Eskimo sites I worked on during the pipeline a couple of years back, but the pipeline collections are in Fairbanks, and I'm not."

Ron shifted his weight from one haunch to the other, picked at his beard, and continued, "My advisor has all the Onion Portage artifacts from over on the Kobuk River in Providence, so I'll probably do that instead. It's a cool site and parts of it are probably really old. The cores are really different looking, too, like discs. Would be interesting," he said, looking thoughtfully into space, then retied his bootlaces. I thought he looked a little restless as if the upcoming academic year might give rise to some uncertainties.

"I've still gotta finish my MA at the University of Georgia and decide what I want to do after that," Lucy said. "Get a PhD? Maybe. But right now, it's 'Finish that thesis.' And when I'm done with that, I'll decide what to do with my life, be an archaeologist, or maybe a politician or a dogcatcher. I just don't know."

"Fitzsimmons at UConn is an Aleutian expert," I threw in, "so I'll probably write something up on his Umnak Island collection.

Maybe I'll even get to go out there and dig. But I'm *really* hoping he'll get me to Siberia to excavate with his buddies in the USSR." Absentmindedly, I picked a pale blue wildflower and held it beneath my nose. It had no smell.

"Now, George," Ron admonished, "you've been warned! Fitzsimmons is a charmer and a taskmaster and not above a little skullduggery, excuse the pun. And he may send you to Siberia for good! 'Georgeie who?'"

"It's too late now. I've been accepted and I even have some funding, but I'm scared of him because he's so famous. What if I have nothing intelligent to say to him?"

"You'll be fine. I know you will," Lucy said encouragingly. She patted my hand.

Her confidence in me helped, but I still felt intimidated by the inevitability of working for Uncle Mikey.

"If I survive the summer and learn some field archaeology, that'll help," I said. "At least I'll have stories to tell, maybe not as many as Uncle Mikey, but they'll be vivid. "There aren't any bears in the Aleutians, but *you'll* have some bear stories to tell, and he won't," Ron said.

"Well, I guess I will."

We passed the rest of the day with no major discoveries, only a couple of nondescript flake scatters. Our journey back to camp retraced our crossing of the three streams, complete with breaks for raisins and peanut butter cups, and shooting the shit about our futures.

July 10. At Kiingyak Lake. Hot. Day made miserable by fucking mosquitoes. Hate them. Our terrace had a few flake scatters, but nothing spectacular. Friggin' bugs.

179

* * *

The following day, the weather was warm, delightfully breezy, and sunny. I woke up, yawned and, within three minutes jumped into my clothes and joined the others in the cook tent.

"What a great day to move to Flora Creek for our next adventure," Ron said cheerily and too wide-awake for my lethargy.

"Well, aren't you all happy sounding, Ron?" I said.

"I guess it's your company," he answered with a smirk.

"Hey, grab some fried cream of wheat and syrup so we can pack up the food before Malcolm gets back," Helen said.

"Alrighty," I answered, wondering at my good mood. Perhaps I had begun to really get into it up here, bugs and all. Three cups of coffee helped.

We ate a quick breakfast, washed our dishes, packed up the food and most of our equipment, knowing the Jet Ranger would come soon, bringing Malcolm and Toni back for our move.

The usual hour for the chopper, sometime between eight and ten, came and went. Ten turned to noon and noon turned to three in the afternoon. When I'd head into the cook tent for a cup of coffee and run into someone else, we'd voice our concerns.

"What do you think happened to the chopper?" I asked Tom about four.

"Damned if I know," he said. "They could have a faulty part or the weather over there might be shitty, I don't know. And there's no way we can find out."

I wandered into Lucy on the way back to my tent.

"This is upsetting, the chopper being so late, I mean," she said.

"I hate the uncertainty," I replied. "I've always hated uncertainty; I mean you just don't know anything. It's scary."

Lucy shrugged her shoulders and continued in the direction of the cook tent, cup in hand.

Ron had advised us to keep our tents up, just for this kind of situation. There was really no reason to strike them until we heard the whirr of the helicopter. I retreated to the solitude of my tent to continue my love affair with Michener. Notes could wait. I napped.

* * *

The welcome whine of the Jet Ranger finally brought us out of our tents around four thirty in the afternoon. Al cut the engine and soon a jubilant Malcolm and an aloof but happy Toni were back with us.

"Christ, I'm glad to be back!" Malcolm said, jumping down on the ground. "There was engine trouble yesterday and a part had to be flown up from Fairbanks. There was no way to tell you. There are no telephones in the field, are there? I'm *so sorry.*"

"I kept thinking about you guys," Toni said. "I knew y'all would be worried. Waiting was horrible."

"It was horrible here, and shit, we were getting worried, but we're fine now," Kelly smiled, hugging Toni and then Malcolm.

"Me next," I said and was rewarded with strong, enveloping embraces.

After hugs were shared all around, Malcolm said, "Okay, let's go. Time's a wasting. Chop chop! Let's not make Al miss dinner."

We made a mad dash to strike our tents, then were quickly relayed to the new camp. Al took off almost immediately to make up for lost time and taking Tom and Helen back to Umiat with him.

CAMP 6, FLORA CREEK

Because it was more or less the end of the workday by then, we pitched our tents and stowed gear and food beneath the now tattered blue tarp and called it good.

"Let's think about dinner," Malcolm said. "I've had enough excitement and frustration to last me a week. For once, I'd like a joint, and I have one right here."

He took the joint out of the breast pocket of his Woolrich shirt.

With a few hits, my grasp on reality pleasantly loosened. Flora Creek splashed along happily to its rendezvous with the Etivluk. I expected to hear the tweet of a songbird in the peaceful green tundra, blue sky, and white wispy clouds, but all I could hope for was the squawk of a surprised ptarmigan, the Alaska chicken, if I stepped on its nest.

"Let's dance the hora in celebration of the return of the chopper from the sky, bringing our gods back to us," Malcolm said. "Get in a circle and hold hands. Now go to the right and dance like Zorba the Greek."

Those who hadn't learned it in high school gym class quickly got the hang of the fast-paced circle dance. I whirled around in the excitement and relief of being reunited with Malcolm, as well as the possibility of new discoveries. Soon, all of us were dancing as fast as we could and yelling hava nagila to any startled creatures lurking behind the low brush.

Not paying strict attention to where his feet were, Malcolm tripped on a rock. I thought he'd landed on his ass and expected him to get up immediately. Instead, he grabbed his ankle, his face contorted in pain.

All singing and dancing instantly stopped. Here was a situation we didn't need—the helicopter had just taken off, not to return for two days. We had no way of contacting anyone, not even a sideband radio to signal campers or hunters who might be only one or two valleys over. We had no way to signal a passing plane except with Kelly's bird mirror.

"Oh, shit! I can't move it. What the fuck have I done?" Malcolm yelled.

His face had gone white.

Crowding around Malcolm, everyone looked spooked—I'm sure *I* did.

"What do we do? What if it's broken?" Lucy said, a hint of panic in her voice.

"Let me check it out," Toni said with the authority of someone who knew what she was doing. "I had EMT training back in Texas."

"Thank God," Kelly said, her voice tight.

Slowly, Toni took off Malcolm's right boot and sock. Tears ran down his face and he groaned pitifully.

"Oh, my God," I said under my breath. The ankle seemed to swell before my eyes.

"Okay, Malcolm, we're going to carry you to the stream and put your foot in the cold water. That should help a little," Toni said calmly as four of us carried him horizontally to the water's edge like pallbearers. The icy water did little to soothe the ankle, which continued to swell.

"I'm not going to try to rotate it yet," Toni said. "Let's wait until you're more comfortable. Then, maybe we can determine if it's broken or just badly sprained."

"Oh, God. I know it's broken," Malcolm said, looking down at his ankle in what I took to be shock and fright. Lucy held his head in her lap and stroked his hair. We sat in a semi-circle around him, chatting and listening to the soothing sound of the creek.

After a few minutes' rest, Toni said, "Okay, Malcolm, let's get you back to your tent. You're going to lie down and we're going to look after you," She spoke in a calm voice I couldn't have mustered just then.

"I'll unroll his sleeping bag and make sure everything is okay in his tent," Lucy added.

"I'll help," I said.

Lucy and I ducked into Malcolm's tent to arrange his gear, which had been thrown inside after our move. Ron and Toni slowly got Malcolm upright. He draped his arms around their shoulders and hopped over to his tent on his left foot, grimacing with each step. I followed close behind them, my eyes never leaving his foot.

Please, God, don't let him stumble and fall again.

Thankfully, Malcolm had insisted our first aid kit contain painkillers. After grabbing the kit from under the tarp and reading the labels on the vials, Toni gave him two different tablets, unsure which one would be the better one. I handed her a Valium from my personal stash and contributed my bottle of aspirin to the effort. Kelly brought a cup of water from the creek and urged Malcolm to swallow the painkillers.

"Okay, lie down now," Lucy said gently. She propped his calf up on his daypack, his ankle dangling over the edge. He grimaced. I made a pillow from his stuff sack filled with some clothes.

"Lie back, Malcolm" I said in as steady a voice as I could muster. "There. Let us take care of you."

"Okay," he said quietly. "But be careful, please."

Lucy and Kelly helped ease Malcolm down on top of his sleeping bag. Toni examined the injury closely and lightly pressed on various spots.

"I don't think it's broken, but I don't know that for sure," she said.

She moved the ankle slightly, causing Malcolm to cry out.

"Ow! Jesus! God!" Malcolm winced, then muttered "Fuck, fuck, fuck" as he tried to get comfortable.

"Sorry, Malcolm," Toni said, "I'm trying to see how badly it's sprained. I think you've wrenched all the muscles in your ankle and some in your foot. You must have hit that rock really hard and twisted everything on the way down."

"Oh, Christ, I should have known better."

"Hush, Malcolm, you'll be all right. You have five nurses at your service," Lucy said. "Toni's your doctor and an angel, too, so you'll be fine."

"Let me wrap your ankle in an ACE bandage," Toni said in her professional manner. I remembered the first aid training we'd been given in Fairbanks and I was grateful for it, but even happier Toni had more training than the rest of us. I felt incredibly thankful for her sure hands and cool head. She seemed detached in a doctorly kind of way; but she always seemed detached to me.

I didn't think I could tend to such an injury. Not even close.

While Malcolm slept, Ron and Kelly caught grayling and pan-fried them for dinner while I made macaroni and cheese, and Lucy and Toni fetched water. After we had eaten, we crowded into

Malcolm's tent, bringing him his meal, complete with a cup of warm Tang. If only there had been a supply of whiskey, it would have been used to steady our nerves and improve the taste of the Tang. We lingered afterwards to keep him company and watch Toni inspect his ankle. Malcolm seemed a little calmer listening to us engage in small talk.

That was me just a few weeks ago when I was so cold. People gathered around me, watching me thaw out and shiver. You need people out here all the fucking time.

Toni unwrapped the ACE bandage from Malcolm's foot, still dangling over the edge of his daypack. We leaned in and held our collective breaths. At the sight of the purple, yellow, and now green bruises and the skin swollen tight across his foot, there was a collective exhale.

"You'll live, but I'm afraid it's not any better," she said.

"It hurts like hell, God dammit," Malcolm said with some effort.

Still blown up like a balloon.

"You'll be in Umiat in less than forty-eight hours, and then it's on to Fairbanks," Kelly said reassuringly. "You'll see your girl-friend. Won't that be nice?"

"Not really. I'm not up for anything more than sleeping."

"Well, let her take care of you," I said.

"Uh-huh," came the drowsy reply.

I took the dirty dishes outside, making sure no crumbs remained behind to attract any animal, large or small. While washing the dishes in the stream, I scanned the landscape for anything moving. I drank in the clear evening, but it did not relieve my feelings of helplessness.

Back in the tent, we began to swap stories, hoping to distract Malcolm from our predicament of having one person unable to run or walk. Tom had several favorite "injured-in-the-wild" tales, but when he started to relate the story of a friend's misjudging the width of a ravine and breaking a snowmobile twenty-five miles from the nearest cabin, Malcolm cried "Enough! I need another pain pill and then I'd like to go to sleep."

He let us tuck him into his sleeping bag leaving just his nose poking out at one end and his foot sticking out of the other.

"I'll sleep with the shotgun tonight," Ron said when we got outside, "He's not up to bear watch tonight. He can't put weight on his leg and he's taken a bunch of drugs, too."

"It's my turn to take the other shotgun," I said assertively, despite my reluctance to handle the weapon. After finding the shotgun in the cook tent where it had been stashed, I walked towards my tent, saying goodnight to my friends. I checked twice to make sure the safety was on.

Once inside my sleeping bag, I recounted our mishap in the vaguest terms possible, making no reference to dope.

July 12. Helicopter got here very late. All worried. Was a bad part. Moved to Flora Creek. Malcolm fell and sprained his ankle. He'll have to go back out on the next chopper. Hope it's not broken. If ankle is broken, how will that affect our field season? Will we be pulled out? God, I hope not.

* * *

The next morning as I headed out, I saw Malcolm kneeling at the front of his tent, staring disconsolately into space while taking a pee. I discretely turned my head, then, hearing him zip up, ran over to help him stand.

"It lives!" I yelled over to the crew who were going about their morning chores and making breakfast.

"I'm in a shitload of pain, George," he said, a frightened look on his face. "The pain pills are taking the edge off, but I'm in a world of hurt."

"You poor bastard," I said. "Why don't I bring your breakfast to you?"

"Nah, not a good idea. I can smell bacon, and that's something that shouldn't be anywhere near my tent."

"You gotta point," I said, putting my arm around his waist while he draped his arm around my shoulder. "Someone want to give me a hand?" I shouted.

Ron walked over and got on Malcolm's left side, and we pointed ourselves toward the cook tent. Presumably hearing our five-legged shuffle, Toni ducked out from the cook tent and studied our progress. Together we made our way over to her. We helped Malcolm turn around, get down on his butt, and scoot inside while keeping his foot elevated. Kelly gave directions from inside:

"That's right. Ease it back. A little to the right. That's good," she directed as if she were guiding a large truck backing up into a small driveway.

"Malcolm, how's the ankle?" asked Lucy nervously once Malcolm was resting comfortably near the front of the tent.

"Not so great," he answered. "I can't get a sock over it, it's so swollen."

Instead, he wore a garish homemade lime-green and royal blue crocheted bootie over the ACE bandage.

"Your bootie is making a more colorful entrance than your foot," I joked.

"I made it, you know," he said, sounding a little annoyed at my comment.

"Make me a pair, would you please?" Lucy said, eyeing the DayGlo bootie, while stirring a pot of oatmeal with one hand and turning over strips of bacon with a fork in the other hand.

"Uh-huh," Malcolm grumbled. He looked too pooped to say more.

Helen handed him a cup of coffee.

"Let's take a look at that ankle." Toni said seriously.

He carefully extended his leg to rest on Ron's thigh. Toni unrolled the bandage while Malcolm tensed. I thought I saw all the hair on his lower leg stand up stiffly in anticipation, but perhaps I imagined this in my own nervousness.

The ankle was as swollen as it had been the night before, if not more so, and had turned several additional shades of purple and yellow.

"It looks like the northern lights out by Chena Pump Road," Ron said in amazement. "It's a beaut, Malcolm."

"You can't put any weight on it, you know," Toni said.

"Yes, I know," Malcolm replied with irritation. "I feel like a turd, like a fool. Here I am in charge of a crew on the fucking North Slope and I do this! Shit, it's throbbing. I was so frustrated, waiting around Umiat all day. And then I get out here with you guys and all I want to do is to blow off a little steam—look what happened!" He smacked himself on the forehead with the palm of his hand.

"You're going to have to file an accident report unless you're extremely lucky and the ankle heals itself by the time the chopper flies in tomorrow," said Ron.

"Oh, God, I know," Malcolm groaned.

"I'd minimize the substance abuse aspect and maximize the relief aspect—you know—we were so relieved to get you back but so unfamiliar with the new campsite that you fell," I suggested.

"I'm an ass and I'm going to have to face the music in Umiat and Fairbanks. My ankle's not going to mend itself in twenty-four hours. And, guys, I'm sorry if I'm irritable, but I'm in pain and scared shitless. I mean, how badly have I hurt myself?"

"If it were me," Kelly said, "I'd be a far greater pain in the ass than you are now."

"Thanks, I think," Malcolm said. "You guys are the best."

We considered staying in camp to look after Malcolm that day, but he insisted we go out, and no one could justify a weather day on such a warm, cloudless, and even bugless morning.

We worked out an acceptable game plan. Four of us—Lucy, Ron, Kelly, and I—would survey the low terraces across from camp on the far side of Flora Creek and Toni would stay with Malcolm.

Reluctantly, we packed up after breakfast and left them with a walkie-talkie and a shotgun. We decided to leave the walkie-talkies on all day to feel more connected to camp instead of just checking in every couple of hours.

* * *

Directly across the creek, we found a large flake scatter of gray and green chert and proceeded to record and photograph the area. Luckily, we could keep an eye on camp in case an errant bear, wolf, or wolverine wandered too close for comfort.

"My heart isn't into finding sites today," Lucy sighed as we ate lunch.

"Me neither," I said. "I just want to make sure Malcolm and Toni are all right. Let's finish up and head in early. No one wants to be out here today anyway," I said.

"Yeah, let's go," Ron said as he stuffed his gear back into his daypack.

When we got back to camp, about two in the afternoon, I looked in on Malcolm through his mosquito netting and could see a copy of Michener's *Caravans* rising and falling on his stomach. Satisfied he was sleeping peacefully, I walked over to the cook tent. The usual pot of hot water rested on the Coleman stove. Toni sat quietly, engrossed in *Shogun* by James Clavell.

"How's he doing?" I asked, gesturing with my head in Malcolm's direction.

"There's no change in the ankle. He's definitely going to have to go out on the next chopper," she said.

"He's going to have to go to Fairbanks, isn't he?" Lucy asked as she and Kelly entered the tent, Lucy following close behind.

"Oh, yeah. There might be a medic in Umiat, but nothing else. The ankle needs an X-ray, and then they'll have to see how bad it is," Toni said in her doctorly voice.

"They have all that stuff in Fairbanks," Ron said.

"He's going to be gone for a while, isn't he?" Lucy asked, idly staring at her cup of cocoa.

"Uh-huh. You can't tell how long an injury like this needs to heal," Toni replied.

We were all despondent.

"He'll put me in charge while he's gone, I guess" Ron said. "No offense, but Tom and Helen and I have the Alaskan experience, and the rest of you are still cheechakos. When I'm out, Tom or Helen will be in charge."

"We'll be okay. If you get out of hand, I'll give you shit," I said while fishing a Winston out of the breast pocket of my navy flannel shirt. I noticed the elbows were starting to fray.

By this point in the summer, I had a good foundation in survival skills, wilderness living, and archaeological survey, thanks to our fearless leader, although I still felt like the weakest link. It would be hard and morale would be low, but we'd do Malcolm proud and get on with our work. I was grateful for Ron, who'd been on the Slope before, but if he got too uppity, we'd kill him and hide the body, Tom and Helen would take over. No one need ever know.

* * *

When the Jet Ranger came in the next morning, Toni ran to meet it. I couldn't make out the entire conversation from inside Malcolm's tent, but I could hear a loud expletive, the engine shutting down, and someone running in our direction.

Al ducked inside, an alarmed expression on his face. Malcolm lay on a sleeping pad, surrounded by his loyal crew, his foot propped up on a stuff sack.

"Oh, my God, what happened? How bad is it?"

"It's bad," Malcolm said weakly. "I'll tell you on the way to Umiat. I'll have to go to Fairbanks for an X-ray, too. I need to leave as soon as possible."

"His ankle's probably badly sprained, but it could be broken. I really don't know," Toni said, "but it's not getting any better out here."

"I'll radio Umiat as soon as we're in the air. The medic will call Fairbanks," Al replied.

"Oh, my God, Malcolm. Are you alright?" Helen asked as she and Tom pushed inside.

"Malcolm, what the hell happened?" Tom asked, a frightened look on his face.

"Guys, you'll hear all the gruesome details from the others, but I really need to get going *now*. I'm in a lot of pain," he said, his voice quivering. "Ron's in charge while I'm gone. When he's gone, Tom will be in charge," Malcolm said, trying to shift his leg to a more comfortable position.

Raising himself up on one elbow, he handed Ron the Howard Pass quad map and some notes he'd made on Rite-in-the-Rain paper the previous evening. Ron took the map with solemnity and glanced over Malcolm's notes, his blue eyes narrowed in concentration. He stroked his beard absentmindedly.

"I've marked on the map where I think you should survey the next few days," Malcolm said trying to concentrate. "I'm going to be gone for a while, so move camp to Akuliak Lake, then to the Etivluk, then farther north on Flora Creek. We'll end up in Inyorurak Pass for the end of the summer where there's cool shit, especially the Kinyiksukvuk Lake area."

"Okay, Malcolm," Ron said, his forehead creased in worry. "I'll do my best."

I noticed he chewed his beard when anxious, rather like Malcolm, who was now inching himself toward the door of the tent on his butt with his foot in the air, still encased in the ACE bandage and the gaudy bootie he'd knitted in happier days.

"Wait a minute. Not so fast," Lucy said, getting up to hold the tent flap back. Tom and I scooted outside, ready to help Malcolm up. He winced as he searched for a comfortable position for us to hoist him to his feet. He raised both arms up, almost in an attitude of supplication. As I grabbed one arm, and Tom grabbed the other, I could feel his helplessness.

"Alley-oop!" said Tom enthusiastically, and we began our wobbly dance toward the helicopter.

Helen carried his daypack and gear. Kelly brought along his copy of *Caravans*.

The group inched along slowly like a funeral procession, the three of us in front. Malcolm limped on this good leg, the journey taking all of his energy and concentration. Perspiration dotted his forehead.

"Just a little further, Malcolm," I said, attempting to sound upbeat.

"Uh-huh," came the pained response.

"Let's get you back to civilization," Al said as we reached the passenger door of the helicopter. I could feel Malcolm's weight sag against my shoulder when we came to a stop.

"We'll put you up front where you'll have more legroom. I'll fly as gently as I can. No acrobatics today!" Al said confidently.

He jumped into the pilot's seat and immediately fired up the engine.

Once we loaded Malcolm into the passenger seat, propped his foot up on several sleeping bags, and belted him in, Toni climbed up into the back seat. Al wasted no time flying towards Umiat. Toni would stay in Umiat until Malcolm could catch a ride to Fairbanks.

We watched them ascend into the cloudy sky until they were out of sight. Even then, we continued to watch where they'd been until the whirring of the rotors faded away and Malcolm was really gone.

* * *

Doubt and melancholy filled the camp. No one said much of anything after the chopper left. I packed up my gear. Lucy, Kelly, and I, that day's All-Girl Survey Crew, would follow the Aniuk until it met Flora Creek, then deadhead back to camp, while Ron, Tom, and Helen proceeded upslope looking for promising flat terraces.

As I geared up for the day, my mind wasn't on work. I wasn't even aware of the drizzle that had begun to fall. Kelly, most likely noticing me staring into space, offered me a Winston. After a puff, I was ready to leave. The All-Girl Survey Crew moved out with a goodbye wave to the other group.

Anxious questions punctuated the silence during the hike to our first destination, a level, well-drained area adjacent to and just above the Aniuk a mile away:

"Do you think he'll be back?"

"Will we get in trouble?"

"Is his ankle broken?"

"Will they pull us out of the field?"

"Will I have to go home *now*?"

"How can we do this without Malcolm?"

We had no way of knowing without the answers to two more immediate questions: What would the medic in Umiat say, and what would the X-ray in Fairbanks reveal?

* * *

Our workday proceeded sluggishly and we found nothing. Could we have missed something important because of the pall hanging over us? Possibly, but on the way back to camp, we *did* stumble on a peculiar place, a place that matched our leaderless and rudderless unease.

Kelly had encountered the clearing by accident when she sought cover to relieve herself near a thicket of alders.

"Guys, look at this," she yelled over to us, "I don't know what this is, but it's very strange."

Lucy and I elbowed our way through the brush and were soon looking at the Dead Spot, as it came to be called. Hidden completely by a thick ring of stunted and dead willows and alders was a cleared space, roughly circular in shape, and large enough for a campsite. Almost devoid of vegetation, only a thin layer of gray moss and *lichens* covered the ground. The grayness imparted a deathly pallor. Once inside the ring of alders and willows, you could not see beyond the clearing because it was so flat.

A half-buried caribou rack, sacrum, unidentifiable long bone, and two or three vertebrae occupied the center of the clearing.

"I can't tell if these bones were put here, or if bears tore the caribou apart. And why is the vegetation all dead?" Lucy asked rhetorically.

"It feels like it's someone's private place; somewhere we shouldn't be," I said.

"Yeah, and I can feel a thousand pairs of eyes staring at us from the brush," Kelly replied nervously.

We puzzled over the Dead Spot for several minutes. Perhaps the features were nothing, or a weird coincidence, but the place seemed too disturbing to be natural. We wrote up a description and mapped the place as we would any archaeological site and recorded it as fast as possible. I sensed we were invaders and felt relief when we hoisted our packs on our shoulders for the hike home.

As we crossed the creek to leave the Dead Spot, a large brown grizz stared at us from the nearby alders. We froze, then looked away to lessen the possibility of a charge. I heard him sniff our scent. That was too close for comfort, but none of us panicked. We held our positions. An eternity later, I heard noisy rustling as the bear turned around and ambled up the side of the nearest peak, hind end glinting in the sun.

"I bet he was watching us the whole time we were here," I said softly.

"He was probably a lot closer when we were recording the site," Kelly said. "Maybe he lives in these alders."

"I wonder how many of his friends and relatives were watching with him," Lucy added. "A big grizz living in the Dead Spot. How crazy is that?"

"I don't think he liked our smell, thank God," I said, relief in my voice,

We picked up our pace and hightailed it back to camp in case the bear decided to give us a second look.

* * *

Over dinner, we told Tom, Helen, and Ron about the place.

"Probably nothing," said Ron.

"But there was that collection of bones in the middle," Kelly said. "And that's not nothing."

"It was like we shouldn't have been there. Really creepy," Lucy said.

"Probably just the aftermath of a fire. That would keep it gray and dead looking for a while," Helen said.

"But you never know, do you?" Tom intoned in a *Twilight Zone* voice.

"Well, you never *do*," Helen snorted.

* * *

The next day, with a sunny sky and breeze enough to keep the mosquitoes at bay, the same iteration of the All-Girl Survey Crew crossed Flora Creek and walked past the still unsettling Dead Spot again. You could not see the clearing from the creek.

We turned our attention to a new day that promised exciting finds.

"Six weeks ago, I was suffering in a heat wave in DC and couldn't jog around the fucking block," I said. "Now, I'm walking God knows how many miles a day, pack on my back, with you guys," I said.

"Well, I guess you needed a change of pace, didn't you?" Kelly laughed.

"And who thought it would be this wonderful?" Lucy added.

As promising as the day and the terrain looked, we came up empty-handed. About five in the afternoon we headed in, our chatter turning to the perennially favorite topic of men.

"I'm can't wait to see Corey," Lucy said. "I think about him all the time. What will our first encounter be like?"

"It's time to jump his bones, don't you think?" I asked.

"It's past time," she laughed.

"I still want Jim, you know, the remote sensing guy," Kelly said. "Of course, I was just dumped by another numbnuts archaeologist, so why would I go out with another one?" she asked no one in particular. "We didn't make it in Umiat, but I'll ring his chimes in Colorado someday soon," she added.

"You've heard me talk about my boyfriend from work," I said, "and you know it's not serious. The sex is pretty good, but he's not for me anymore. I'm not sure I can relate to him. Hope I still fit in with my old friends, though."

"Know what you mean," said Lucy. "That Georgia clay doesn't look that appealing right now."

"Who knows what will happen to any of us," Kelly added.

We hiked back to camp in silence.

I sensed I was changing in ways I'd never contemplated. How could I not when confronted with a reality so different from the one I'd known? I was adapting—more self-confident, more competent, more daring. The others were experiencing more subtle changes and adapting to new people and situations, but I had to change the most because I'd come from way behind. I had the farthest to go and I was on my way.

* * *

Two days later when Toni returned from Umiat, all I could think about was Malcolm's condition. Fuck the showers and Dick the Cook's food. I wanted to know how he was. We ran to meet the chopper. Toni tossed her daypack and sleeping bag on the ground and jumped out.

"What's the news?" Helen demanded.

"Malcolm's off to Fairbanks," Toni answered. "He went south this morning, so we don't yet know how badly hurt he is. The foot's still swollen and just as tender to the touch as it was two days ago. I brought his meals to the Howard Pass tent because he wasn't up to walking down to the Hilton, but a couple of times, Jay or Ray gave him a ride. Ray had an old pair of crutches lying around, so Malcolm's using them now. He's relieved to be out of the field and on his way to recovering from whatever is wrong with his ankle."

"Okay," Tom said slowly. "That implies he's upright from time to time and not constantly taking pain pills."

"Well, the pain's still pretty bad, but he's dealing with it," Toni sighed, "and he asks for help when he needs it. Even getting out of the Howard Pass tent can be quite an ordeal. That front step is really high. He has to kind of inch himself down, clutching the door frame with both hands."

"Poor Malcolm," I said glumly.

"This calls for a joint," Tom said. "Let's have a toke before we go off in the big bird."

"I wouldn't do that if I were you," Ron said in a commanding voice.

"Oh, c'mon, Ron. Who died and made you king?" Tom asked.

"Malcolm," he replied.

"Oh, bite me, Ron," I said. "No one will ever dance the *hora* out here again, okay?" I was already frustrated with our interim fearless leader.

What'll be next, safety briefings in the morning?

"Okay, okay. You know my concern is just for our wellbeing."

"Uh-huh," I said, rolling my eyes.

With that witty retort and a hit from Tom's joint, he and Helen were in the air, headed to Umiat.

We moved efficiently and without mishap on another sunny and warm Brooks Range morning. When the chopper left, I realized I had lost my fear the Jet Ranger would not return in two days—a good sign.

CAMP 7, AKULIAK LAKE

When we moved to Akuliak Lake, I had the chance to examine a large and spectacular outcropping of black metamorphic rock awaited us at our new camp. It reminded me of the episode in *Star Trek* where a creature called the Horta made of rock and living in rock, marauded intruders. I remembered a line of Dr. McCoy's: "I'm a doctor, not a brick layer, Jim!"

Perhaps a Horta lived here, too.

As I dove into my tent in the soft, fresh-smelling tundra, I noticed a few oddly shaped hollows integrated into the outcropping. Surely, a herd of Hortas must inhabit them. And if one were wounded, who better than archaeologists with our trowels to patch it up just like Dr. McCoy had finally done?"

"Aha! This humongous outcropping is a site!" I yelled over to Ron, who had been appointed Tom Terrific for his two-day leadership term. He was standing a short distance away from me observing when the light bulb appeared over my head.

"See what a fun this place is?" Ron said.

"It's just like that *Star Trek* episode—" I began.

"Spare me! Not a trekkie!" came the not-so-serious reply.

I stuck my tongue out at him and finished putting up my tent. He stuck his tongue back and we called it even.

July 18. There is a village (?) site made of black metamorphic rock near our new camp at Akuliak Lake. We're camped next to the outcropping—it's loaded with hollows—house pits and smaller cache pits. There are some hunting blinds, too, and at least one tent ring. Doesn't seem right without Malcolm. A little chilly, and clear. No bugs.

* * *

It took the five of us (Malcolm being in Fairbanks; Tom and Helen enjoying the pleasures of Umiat) the entire next day to begin recording the basic measurements of the Akuliak Village Site, as we called it. Certainly, it was the largest and most complex site we'd encountered. None of us had seen anything like it before. I set about sketching the major features on large sheets of graph paper, carefully measuring dimensions of rocks and the distances between them, working on the basic site plan all day. I tweaked it far into the night before I was happy with it. The site was more than 100 meters across and about five meters top to bottom as I drew it. The site reminded me of photos I'd seen of pueblos in Arizona and New Mexico. How many people had lived here?

That night over dinner, we speculated about the site's functions.

"Well, it's probably not a habitation site," Ron said at one point, "because it has so few artifacts. It doesn't seem like anyone lived here, just like they passed through, or used it as a base camp."

"Yeah, gotta be a camp," I said, feeling pretty sure of myself.

"Here's what I think," Toni said. "Some people found the rocks and thought they could use them to their advantage, so they rearranged some into tent rings, hunting blinds, or wind breaks. The smaller circles of stones are the tent rings, right?"

Ron nodded. "They would have held down portable skin tents. That one very large circle may have been a *karigi.*"

"A what?" Lucy asked.

"A place where the men spent their free time telling stories or making and repairing hunting equipment. I found a couple of flakes inside it. For sure it's for a larger group than a family."

"And the hunting blinds or wind shields are made of rocks piled up high enough so a hunter could scrunch down, hide from prey or avoid the wind, but still able to see outside from in between the rocks," Kelly said, "or that's what I think anyway."

"I think we've all solved it," I said, lighting a cigarette and inhaling contentedly. "Malcolm will be so proud; he'll bring us more chocolate."

"I wonder how he is," Ron said. "His ankle looked like a piece of fruit gone bad when he left for us."

"Wish I knew," sighed Toni. "He's my patient, after all."

Once again, a dark cloud settled over the group. We stood silently in our now-familiar tight-knit circle near the cook tent as water boiled for a dinner of freeze-dried beef Stroganoff.

Aside from missing Malcolm and wondering when or if he'd come back, I was homesick that day. It was the middle of July; I had left DC on the third of June. I would get on a plane out the twenty-third of August, arriving in DC late that night and stay a couple of days with friends on Capitol Hill. Then, I'd fly home to my mother and stepfather in New York. I would have five days with them before going to Uconn to begin my studies with Uncle Mikey while they drove to Florida to begin retired life. Leaving Alaska, then leaving my friends in DC, and saying goodbye to my parents would happen almost simultaneously, leaving me forlorn, wounded, and alone again. What a bummer.

* * *

At breakfast the next morning, Ron stared at the topo map, stroked his beard, and announced, "Lucy, Georgeie, and I'll walk down to the foot of the outcropping, near the lakeshore, and record that small site we've seen while hauling water. Toni and Kelly will stay here and tidy up the last of the Akuliak Village site and fix us a great dinner."

"I'll carry the shotgun, Ron," Lucy said.

"Thanks, friend," I smiled. "You know I can hardly use it—the safety is on the wrong side." I smiled wanly, still trying to shake off my gloomy mood from the night before.

"We'll keep the walkie-talkie on and the other shotgun loaded up here," Kelly added.

"Okay, gang, let's get this show on the road."

"Aye aye, Ron, your worshipfulness," Lucy said, with a crisp, faux salute.

* * *

The site on the lakeshore held an interesting mix of recent Native and non-Native artifacts: rope, a modern tent floor, a few empty Blazo cans, a broken Coleman stove, a stone biface, and a tent ring.

"Why are so many things we find so ambiguous?" Lucy mused.

"Who knows why," Ron said, "There's no way of knowing whether Indians or Eskimos used the site or not—maybe both. Malcolm's into the overlapping cultures thing."

"What about the biface?" Lucy asked.

"I'll look it up in Malcolm's library tonight. Maybe late prehistoric Eskimo, but that's just a guess," Ron said

"It's so cool to think about who was here, you know?" I said.

* * *

After lunch, I called Kelly and Toni on the radio to tell them we were headed northeast along an unnamed drainage toward Inyorurak Pass, the beautiful and tantalizing gash in the mountains I'd seen from the helicopter.

"We're almost finished writing up Akuliak Village. All is calm, and we'll be fixing y'all a great dinner," Toni said.

Before packing it in, I practiced taking more photos with the Nikon. I still hadn't gotten the hang of it completely and found official photography, even in this beautiful setting, rather tedious, preferring my simple-to-use Brownie camera instead. "I don't like the frigging Nikon. It's too complicated," I said peevishly.

"Well, why don't you try map reading instead?" Ron suggested.

"As long as I don't have to use the Brunton."

"Try the Silva. It's so much easier."

"Okay. I love maps. Always have. I can read the topo okay, but I'd like to learn some more."

"Georgeie, start by orienting yourself and the map to a particular point."

I grabbed the map and tried to find Ikhlhuk Mountain to the southwest.

"That's not gonna do it, George. Focus on Isikut Mountain instead. It's in front of Ikhlhuk," Ron suggested.

"Okie dokey."

I turned myself due south.

"All right, I think I see it, except there's a blank space at the top. Is that a small glacier?" I asked, puzzled.

Ron explained: "No, that's actually a blank space. The peak hasn't been surveyed yet, so we don't know the exact shape of the mountain."

"Really?" Lucy and I exclaimed together.

"'Fraid so. You'll have to orient yourself by the highest point you can see on the north face of Isikut."

"Okay."

After an hour's practice, I could match the contour lines of mountains, drainages, and terraces with what was actually on the ground. The topo maps weren't that great to begin with. The only scale for the North Slope was 1:250,000, meaning one inch on a map covered about four miles, a huge area. Plus, the maps used English measurements, and we were measuring sites in meters. More and more, I noticed the upper reaches of mountains weren't drawn in because there was no survey data. The Dark Ages had ended not too long before. I resolved to study the map in my tent later that evening.

* * *

The walk back was easy because well-worn caribou trails encircled the lower mountain slopes, avoiding the wet, tussocky ground on the valley floor. The slight breeze and warm temperature made it a T-shirt, bug-free day.

Halfway back to camp, we came across a dead caribou lying on the trail.

"Awwww, poor baby," Lucy said.

"It's a young one, probably two years old. Hasn't been dead long—no smell and still intact," Ron observed. The big brown eye stared lifelessly at the sky through beautiful, thick lashes.

I said nothing. I remembered my conversation with Kelly the night before and the feelings it had brought out. Death was upsetting, even the death of an animal. What had killed it? Had it been in pain? Had it been scared?

My mind drifted back to my father: *Did you know you were going to die that night in 1956? Did you think about mom and me? Would you be proud of me now?*

Out of fear and respect, I avoided looking at the caribou directly as I passed it and remained melancholy the rest of the way back to camp.

* * *

As we got nearer to camp, my spirits began to lift. The pungent smell of chili wafted through the air. I ducked into the cook tent to find Kelly happily stirring a diced canned ham into the pot, an odd pairing with chili, but new to us, and therefore an adventure of sorts. Toni had just finished cutting up our last fresh onion. She added it to the pot where it sizzled in canned butter, olive oil, and chili powder. The aroma made my nostrils flare in anticipation.

Ron came in, a box of pilot bread under his arm and a can of roast beef spread in one hand. These he'd retrieved from beneath the weathered blue tarp. "Nothing like a little roast beast on pilot bread as an hors d'oeuvre," he said cheerily. I rolled my eyes.

The meat spread's main appeal was the flecks of grease that glinted when you slathered it on your knife and then onto a pilot cracker. Of course, the flecks may have been little pieces of bone, too. Whatever the flecks were, they were not the worst thing about Ron's love for the tasty goo; the worst thing was Ron's calling it roast beast every frigging time.

During dinner, Kelly decided we should plan something spectacular for Malcolm's homecoming, whenever that might be.

"There must be fresh-caught grayling!" Lucy declared.

"Of course," Kelly said, starting a list in her notebook. "And we need a cake. Georgeie's Krusteaz pancake-mix cake was not that great, so I hear, and we need something more elegant anyway."

"How about using Malcolm's sourdough starter?" I said.

"Great idea," Toni said, "positively fucking brilliant. A sourdough cake! Yum."

"We'll have to use the pancake mix as flour," Ron reminded us. "We don't have regular flour."

"That's okay. Maybe I can concoct chocolate frosting out of cocoa, butter, and sugar," Kelly said.

"How about we write him a welcome-home song to the theme of *The Mary Tyler Moore Show* or *Gilligan's Island*?" I added, trying to give the party a literary flair.

Any tune that would let us work in words and key phrases like "horny," "Umiat," "Howard Pass," "mosquitoes" "chocolate," "let's get high," "tundra," "fuckwads," and other popular sayings from our summer would suffice. After fifteen minutes of serious discussion, we agreed on the perfect song—"Gilligan's Island." Perfect—we were the Castaways.

Our planning efforts distracted me from the caribou, returning east at the end of the summer, and the subsequent move of my parents to Florida. Instead, I thought about my boyfriend in DC and how we weren't right for each other anymore. I'd changed too much out here, and he probably hadn't changed at all. Why should he? His humdrum life was going on as usual. Maybe I'd breeze through town without seeing him. That would be okay, although a night of sex would be welcome.

I brushed my teeth, got cleaned up for the night, and crawled into my sleeping bag to make sense of the topo map. In the bottom left-hand corner, I read the following:

"Topography by photogrammetric methods from aerial photographs taken 1955. Field annotated 1956. Map not field checked."

This is the final frontier. These are the missions of the Howard Pass Eight—to explore strange new worlds, seek out new life and new civilizations, to boldly go where no white man has gone before.

CAMP 8, ETIVLUK RIVER

When Tom and Helen returned from Umiat, bequeathing seats in the chopper to Ron and Kelly, we moved camp to the expansive Etivluk River, near Fay Creek. We had already decided to take off the rest of the day because the chopper showed up late and the new camp wasn't set up until after four in the afternoon. For some unfathomable reason, none of us seemed the least worried when the helicopter arrived late, perhaps because we/d already weathered that kind of scare the day Malcolm hurt himself.

Shit like this happens all the time. We're fine. Chopper's gonna come, I'd thought while eating peanut butter on pilot crackers earlier in the day.

Although we were always on our toes to some degree, I felt I could relax here and not worry too much about critters since the Etivluk crossed a broad valley with a view in all directions There were no alders or willows to hide behind and the toe of the nearest mountain slope was a mile away. But the weather sucked that day—unseasonably hot, muggy, and smoky. The air burned my eyes.

"What's with the haze?" I asked Sam during his short visit.

"That's smoke. There's a tundra fire burning about fifty miles to the west of here. You're downwind of it. Smells shitty, don't it?"

"Sure does," I said.

"You folks be careful. Don't think the smoke can't get too much worse in the two days I'll be gone, but if I hear anything bad in Umiat, I'll be out here to get ya."

We thanked Sam for his delivery of fresh onions and oranges, the new bar of Tillamook extra sharp cheddar, and for looking out after us. We watched as he disappeared into the low-lying smoke.

"New camp. Let's celebrate with some hash," Helen said.

"Yes, let's, but no dancing!" Toni yelled.

I took a drag on the hash pipe. My eyes ceased to burn almost immediately.

I spent the lazy afternoon washing my hair and dirty clothes in the river. Once in a while, when the breeze kicked up, I'd get a whiff of the disagreeable smoke and notice my eyes stinging again. I decided to enjoy a few moments of solitary reading in my tent before dinner.

I had been so captivated with the Michener I'd read so far and felt so deprived of another good book, I snatched Kelly's copy of *Centennial,* Michener's book about Colorado as soon as I could. "I've been to most of the places mentioned in the book and I can tell you who the characters in the book are supposed to be," Kelly had said.

She had started to tell me about her favorite parts when I'd cut her off: "Hey, I want to read it myself!"

July 18. Moved to Etivluk R, 4 miles SE of Fay Creek, late in day.

Nice camp directly on river. No survey today. Warm and buggy.

Washed self and undies in river. Lazy day. Sam says there's a tundra fire to the west. Not sure how that will affect us.

* * *

The next morning, it was still warm and buggy, but there was no smoke or haze to speak of because the wind was blowing from the opposite direction. The five of us headed out for our day's work together, discussing and choosing a promising route from the topo map.

"I'm sure glad Malcolm is missing the heat," I said.

"I'm sure not glad to be missing Malcolm as much as I do," Lucy added.

"It's so hard without him," I added petulantly. "He's our lucky charm, you know. Keeps us from danger."

"Some talisman. He almost did himself in," Toni said.

"He's watching over us, you know," Kelly said, "and he knows when we're naughty or nice."

"Like God," Lucy said.

"Well, let's hope he's back soon," Toni said with a sigh. "Hope he's not in too much pain."

The conversation shifted to another important topic—food. In a few short weeks, food had become the most popular topic among us, second only to sex.

"I wish I had a moon pie and a Dr. Pepper," Lucy sighed.

I wrinkled my nose in disgust.

"I want a steak," Tom said emphatically. He wrinkled his brow and showed his teeth, like a meat-eating monster of some kind.

"I want a Diet Coke," I added.

"Chocolate ice cream," Helen sighed.

"Tequila with a worm in the bottle," Toni said, snapping her fingers to signify an "ole."

"Tequila? I want champagne. More sham-PAHG-nee, monsur!" Lucy said, raising a hand in the air as if in a toast.

"Hear, hear," I said, also raising an imaginary glass in an imaginary toast.

"I would do anything for a chair with a back," Tom said. "I'd like to be sitting out here at the end of a workday in a comfy chair, feet propped up on a Blazo can, looking at the tundra, sipping a mint julep—"

"I suppose you'd like a butler, too," I interrupted.

"Would be nice. Maybe I could put my feet up on you instead of the Blazo can."

"You're disgusting," I said. "You'll never make it into The Explorers' Club."

"Those guys knew how to explore. They always had someone to carry their stuff, and they brought *everything* with them" he replied.

"Yes, bwana, I suppose you're right. Besides my Diet Coke, I'd like a lipstick and my *Glamour* magazine," I said, sounding to myself a tad too girly for the wilderness.

We trotted along for a while, no doubt with visions of delicacies and creature comforts dancing in our heads. Then, about a mile and a half south of the river, we stumbled across two long rows of stone cairns ending in a V. I'd never seen anything like it.

"What's this?" I asked.

"It's a caribou fence," Helen said. "Hunters would stand behind each cairn and scare the shit out of caribou, forcing them into the wide end of the V. Once they stampeded into the narrow end, there was no escape. You'd spear them or shoot them with arrows. Pretty simple."

"Rows of *inuksuks* were great for hunting caribou," Tom said. "The word means kind of like a human being in Inupiaq; but, you know, they're cairns who are supposed to look like people and scare the caribou into a lake or something. People stand behind them yelling and scaring the critters. Get it?"

"Yup," I said, imagining the slaughter.

The fence occupied a particularly pretty spot, a high meadow on the slope of Kavaksurak Mountain. We took off our daypacks to explore the area and walked around the cairns. The aroma of lichens, moss, short grass, wildflowers, and fragrant Labrador tea was exhilarating. I breathed in deeply.

The longer arm of the V looked to be about 1200 feet long and consisted of forty-two lichen-covered cairns. The shorter arm of the V was about half as big.

"Ya know," Helen said, looking at the structure, "it's almost time for the caribou migrations to begin."

"We've already seen a few from the Noatak herd, and in August, the main Porcupine River herd will come through," Tom added.

"Then we might see several thousand at once Malcolm told me," Toni said.

"Really? Thousands? I can't imagine what that would look like. Sounds like science fiction," I said.

* * *

The next day the chopper arrived with Ron and Kelly. Lucy and I were packed and ready to go.

"Any word about Malcolm?" I asked Kelly.

"Still in Fairbanks. The ankle is badly wrenched but not broken," Tom said glumly.

"When will we get him back?" Lucy asked.

"Don't know. They say maybe August sometime," Helen said, her eyes looking down at the ground.

It was not the answer I wanted to hear. While we hadn't been pulled out of the field, the lack of Malcolm's friendship, leadership, and sense of humor created a void in the Howard Pass Eight. I comforted myself with the knowledge that I was going to town.

UMIAT

N ow that the summer was more than half over and most of us had gotten our bearings and while keeping a sense of humor, soon-to-be Preacher John joked the first night around the dinner table that it would be great fun to have a fashion show.

"A fashion show?" asked Leslie. "Why in God's name would we have a fashion show here. What in hell would we wear anyway?"

"Well, it's the middle of the summer and we've all become callow sophisticates by now. We could use something completely different to liven things up," Lucy said.

"And *now* for something *completely* different! A fashion show in Umiat!" I said, imitating John Cleese's British accent as best I could.

"Could be interesting," Debbie said, "Look at all the different kinds of raingear we have up here, all the unique clothes and accessories. We could have a contest for who's wearing the dirtiest, most raggedy flannel shirt, or whose baseball cap has the best catchphrase on it."

"I've always liked Ray's cap myself," I added. "Says Peterbilt. Great double entendre" A glimpse at the brand name on Ray's cap usually made me horny, although not for Ray, just horny in general.

"I like the idea," Debbie said, smiling and running a hand through her blonde hair.

After a spirited bullshit session, a plan emerged.

"We'll host it in our tent tomorrow night," Mike said.

"Thank you, Ikpikpuk crew! Mighty nice of y'all," Lucy said.

"Let's have live music, of course. That's you, Sam, and Preacher John," Debbie declared.

"Whoever has any marijuana or hash left, they can donate it to the cause," Ross said, an anticipatory buzzed-out grin appearing on his face.

"And GSI has booze," Mike said, "so we gotta invite them."

"And Georgeie, Sam, and Preacher John, because you're the band and also judges, you can't participate in the fashion show," Leslie said.

I feigned tears, "Boo hoo."

The idea of me playing the guitar in front of everyone who happened to be in Umiat the following night made me slightly nervous, but it'd be cool—there'd be booze, weed, and the GSI guys. It would be okay. I forgot my nervousness as we continued planning.

"Al should be a judge, too," Preacher John said. "He's always here when he's not flying. I bet he gets bored."

Helio Skyscrewer? I don't think so.

"Now, it's up to each crew to come up with outfits from all the clothes and other crap we have around Umiat, so let's get going. Huddle in your respective tents to plan the best and most diabolical get-ups to beat out the other guys for first prize," said Preacher John, a saintly but crooked smile crossing his face.

"Whoever sees Sam first, tell him he doesn't have to prance around in a dress or anything so he'll come and play," one of the Lookout Ridge campers said.

* * *

My creative juices were flowing. I determined to throw my energies into making a costume for Lucy that would guarantee Howard Pass first prize. Before she and Corey disappeared into one of the many abandoned Quonset huts for the afternoon, I told her I needed her baseball cap.

"I'm going to make you famous tomorrow night."

"You're not going to embarrass me, are you?" she asked in her drawl.

"Oh, no, I wouldn't dream of it!"

She eyed me with suspicion, then handed me her cap.

"Well, you want to win, don't you?" I asked.

"Okay, just do it," she said, walking out of our tent and in the direction of the Lookout Ridge tent to find Corey.

I knew what I needed. I went to the supply box in our tent and found some Elmer's glue and a cardboard box of PIC mosquito coils. I took one of the green, flat, spiral-shaped PICs from the box and stuck it through a metal holder, then glued it and its holder to Lucy's cap, like a beanie with a rotor on top.

I knew we'd win when I lit the PIC and she walked into the Ikpikpuk tent to parade herself down the makeshift runway made of cast-off rubber car mats.

What else could I add?

While we all had raingear, Lucy was the only one of us who brought chaps instead of rain pants. The red chaps would be alluring with nothing underneath them and would clinch first prize for sure. I grabbed them out of Lucy's daypack, held them up, and realized she'd never go bare-assed. Then I remembered the pair of lacy black panties I'd brought with me just in case.

In the supply box was a laundry bag of communal spare clothes the crew contributed to in case some of our clothes got trashed in the field. I dug my panties out of the bag and threw them on Lucy's costume pile. I added Kelly's wonderful red turtleneck I had borrowed, and a black bra from her stash. None of us had worn bras in the field, but Kelly had brought one and left it at base camp.

"Okay, this is it," I thought, rubbing my hands together in glee as if I were plotting something of great importance, like a coup in a foreign country. I had the beanie with rotary PIC, chaps, panties, red turtleneck, black bra on the outside. What about her feet? Tossed in the back of the tent was yet another Kelly indulgence, her Dr. Scholl's sandals.

"We win!" I cried, jumping up and down, as if I were on a trampoline. The tent floor shook in my exhilaration.

* * *

The fashion show loomed large in the following day's planning. Of course, I had already completed my wonderful costume for Lucy.

When she saw the entire ensemble, Lucy said, "You expect me to prance around in this getup like a tart? People will laugh at me!"

"Oh, no they won't. They'll think you're hot. It'll be fun. Try it on!"

"Okay, let's see."

Lucy wiggled out of her clothes and tentatively stepped into my creation, one piece at a time. She looked at me for reassurance. Grabbing her baseball cap with the PIC, she put it on her head. "How do I look?" she asked.

"You know the PIC will win us our prize once I light it," I said.

"George, I do believe you're right. I like it! Even the black panties and bra. I'll strut my stuff and we'll win. I hope Corey won't think I'm nuts or a slut."

"You? Never! Don't forget to put the black bra over the turtleneck," I gloated.

We snickered at my creation for at least ten minutes.

* * *

When the hour came, we piled into the Ikpikpuk tent with the exception of the four contestants. Ikpikpuk had cleaned its tent to make it presentable. A cot was placed on either side of the flattened rubber runway. The band would stand at the back of the tent on flattened cardboard boxes. Preacher John, having found the project's emergency supply box, gave each attendee a candle to hold.

I took my place in the back, wielding someone's guitar.

"How can I hold this damn candle and light a joint at the same time?" Ross said.

Aside from this one frivolous complaint, the mood was effervescent. Whistles and catcalls began almost immediately. The band, including me, tuned up. We followed Sam's fiddle lead on "Tennessee Waltz."

Linda, who was serving as one of the judges, shouted for silence, then announced, "Representing Howard Pass, we have Miss Lucy!"

The plywood door opened. Lucy stepped regally onto the runway and walked down the center of the tent. The air hung thick with marijuana and smoke from the PIC.

"Wow, she's hot!" someone yelled.

"Oh, baby!" came another catcall.

"Give me your Pic!" came from the far corner.

"Hey, blondie, I wanna get in your chaps," yelled a drunk GSI cat-train driver.

Corey glanced at the guy, glaring. I guess he approved of Lucy's getup, but not the comment.

Lucy responded to the hoots and hollers by shimmying her breasts and leaning back, limbo-style. I had never witnessed her so wild and unbound. My guess is that she'd had quite a session with Corey earlier in the day.

Lookout Ridge was called next. Debbie's flagging tape streamers, glued onto a hard hat provided by GSI, fluttered behind her as she walked down the runway in a full set of yellow rubber raingear. She was naked beneath the bib overalls. On the back of her rain jacket Preacher John had written "Dig we must." She also carried a purse improvised from empty freeze-dried beef stroganoff bags.

She got catcalls too, many referencing her butt and her almost visible breasts.

"Bring those melons over here, Butter Butt!"

"Shake it, don't break it!"

Colville River, the third entry, featured Leslie wearing a colander from the Umiat Hilton decorated with a few valuable condoms still in their wrappers. Her bright orange survey vest bulged with various items stuffed into the dozens of tiny pockets—a plumb bob, ruler, pencils, a Silva compass, and other essentials that I couldn't quite see from the back of the tent. She strutted down the runway, bumping and grinding.

"Bring me a few of those condoms, girl!"

"You're gonna need em!"

Ikpikpuk, the host crew, went last. Mike's LL Bean boots were completely covered by silver duct tape. He also sported tampon fish-lures hanging from his baseball cap.

"Boo, get off the stage!"

"We want the women!"

The contestants left the Ikpikpuk tent so the judges could deliberate. After the briefest whispered discussion, Dick the Cook called the contestants back in.

"Howard Pass wins based on the lighted PIC, the red chaps, and the black lingerie!" he announced.

Thunderous applause and yells rose into the twilight. Lucy hugged one person after another, the PIC still curling smoke from her head. Lookout Ridge came in second, primarily due to the melons. Colville River took third, and Ikpikpuk came in last because their contestant was not a woman. They sulked at first because they lost but were awarded Miss Congeniality for hosting the show and making us all comfy, high, and happy. The band dedicated "Rock Around the Clock" to them.

We carried on until around two in the morning, or more truthfully put, all partiers were kicked out of Ikpikpuk's tent then to get a few hours' sleep before our flights back out to the field after breakfast.

News of the fashion show traveled fast. By my next rotation, everyone on the project knew about it and the event became the subject of gossip and retelling, details changing slightly each time the tale was told. Lurid descriptions of the experience soon escaped Umiat in the form of letters home to many parts of Alaska and the Lower 48 as well.

BACK TO CAMP 8

The trip back to the Etivluk was perfect in every way. The clouds were cotton balls against a bright azure sky. The temperature hovered in the sixties, but the sun streaming through the Plexiglas made it seem warmer. I napped without a care.

Before leaving for Umiat with Toni, Sam ferried Tom, Helen and me five miles north, near Disappointment Creek. I snapped three photos of the previous day's caribou fence with my Brownie camera from about 1,000 feet up. As Sam started to set us down next to the creek, we felt something pull sharply at the chopper from below.

"What the fuck was that?" Tom yelled.

Sam tilted the helicopter to the left and then the right to get a view of the skids.

"Oh, shit. There it is. It's a wolverine! Look at the size of that thing!" Helen yelled, pointing down to the left skid.

We had surprised the stocky animal in a small patch of grass and alders. I had never seen one before except in a picture during one of our training sessions in Fairbanks, but the reactions of my comrades signaled that a wolverine was vicious.

"Jesus fucking Christ!" Tom yelled over the sound of the rotors.

"Wow, I've never seen one this close," Helen shouted. I heard the strain in her voice.

"I can't see it! Move your goddamned head, Tom," I yelled into the melee.

Aggressive and nasty, the animal clamped on to the skid with its claws and teeth as Sam calmly attempted to land. Only by rocking the chopper back and forth did Sam get the creature to let go momentarily. As the chopper pitched to the left and the whine of the rotors changed, I saw the wolverine and gasped. Its badger-like brown striped face and thick, gorgeous brown and tan fur glistened in the sun as it twisted its body to keep itself attached to us.

"Look at those fangs and claws! Look how white those teeth are," I said, stunned by the animal's appearance as it bared its teeth yet held a tight grip on the skid.

"This isn't good! We could lose our balance," Sam yelled over the engine noise.

I grew quiet, sensing the seriousness of the situation.

"It could also bite your leg, hamstring you, and then, bye, bye, George!" Tom yelled back to me.

"Why can't we just shoot it?" I asked.

"Can't do that. The kick would throw us into a spiral because we're flying so slow," Sam said. "Plus, it's probably against the law to shoot him on federal land, and I can't reach the shotgun anyhow."

"I got the shotgun right here," Tom said from the front passenger seat. I saw him place his hand on the stock.

We hovered over the wolverine, but with each attempt to shake it off and scare it away, the animal renewed its grasp. Okay, so the creature was only the size of a large dog, but its viciousness gave it the appearance of an unleashed, underworld monster intent on crippling the helicopter and eating us for breakfast.

"If he won't let go, and we begin to lose balance, I'll try to auto-rotate to the ground. Don't leave the copter if that happens. I'll shoot the bastard. I'll have to," Sam said in a dead-calm voice.

After five attempts to land with the wolverine snapping wildly at the skids and twice latching on and vigorously tugging the skids, the wolverine finally ran off to the south. Had we tired it out? I didn't know why it finally left us.

"*That's* something I've never seen before," Tom said, sounding calmer than he probably felt.

"Well, let's give him some space. I'll fly you up north a mile or so. Just follow Disappointment Creek back to camp. But if he's still hot on our trail, I'll take all y'all back to camp," our unruffled pilot said.

After a thorough scan of the scrub and the creek as we slowly flew north, we landed. We climbed down warily and stepped a few feet away from the helicopter in different directions to pee.

"I needed that," Tom said.

Sam took out a pack of Salem Lights and offered them around. I finished mine in record time, my left hand still shaky. I'd never seen Helen smoke before, but it seemed an appropriate response to our situation.

"My pulse is still racing," I said.

"Yup, mine too," Sam said.

"I've got the shotgun," Tom said, taking his gear from the chopper.

I grabbed our daypacks from the helicopter.

"I could kill that son of a bitch," Helen said, taking her pack from me. "No wolverine can get the best of me."

"The kick from firing a shotgun would set you back on your ass, my tiny wife," Tom said, putting an arm around her shoulder.

"Don't you count on it," she smiled, looking up at him.

"I'm just grateful we're here in one piece," I said.

Sam said nothing, but a glance at his calm demeanor indicated to me he could kill a wolverine as soon as look at it, probably barehanded.

When our nerves had finally calmed and all seemed well again, we waved goodbye to Sam, who took off for the safety of Umiat, an outpost on the edge of civilization, but a lot closer to civilization than *we* were.

Although the sweet-smelling landscape, with its rolling hills and alder bushes dotting nearby creeks was among the most alluring I'd seen, I felt too nervous to fully appreciate it.

"What I wouldn't give for a tumbler of Scotch," I said.

"George, tell you what. After dinner, come visit us *chez nous*. I have a flask half full of Chivas hidden away. Let's do er in tonight," Tom said.

I could have kissed him.

* * *

With the exception of confronting the wolverine, Disappointment Creek lived up to its name. It had been named by a prospector who went looking for a pass through the mountains but didn't find one. He probably had to do a lot of backtracking on foot without the advantage of being moved around by helicopter. The creek had been disappointing in the 19th century and it was disappointing now.

"Every time I hear the breeze rustle through the grass and alders, the hairs on the back of my neck stand up again," Helen said.

"That was close, bizarre even," Tom said.

"I haven't even *absorbed* what happened," I added.

Our stretch of Disappointment Creek lay within easy walking distance of low terraces with great views up and down the valley, perfect for spotting game. Although Malcolm had promised us side drainages like these would be teeming with sites, we found nothing.

We sure find a lot of nothing up here sometimes, but we've cheated death again, and that's better.

I reflected on my experience at the Dead Spot. After leaving the nerve-wracking place, Kelly, Lucy, had run right into a fucking grizzly. Our nasty wolverine had left me with the same feeling I'd had then.

After dinner, I ventured over to Helen and Tom's tent for the promised nightcap.

"You know, Georgeie, it's your company that makes the drink taste good, not the other way around," Tom reflected as he poured scotch into my Girl Scout cup.

"Thanks. This stuff is very, very good, and so am I," I answered, anticipating a warm buzz.

"Facing a horrible death by a wild animal makes you savor alcohol, too," Helen said, taking a small, dainty sip out of the bottle.

"And who knew Chivas could taste so smooth in a plastic bottle?" I said.

Tom and I guzzled more than our share until the bottle was empty. We were a lot bigger than Helen, I rationalized.

We laughed, Tom and Helen telling stories about bush Alaska that may have been ever so slightly embellished. One involved Helen being in an outhouse taking a crap and then being surprised by a young black bear who had opened the door with his claws. In a split second, she debated what to do first, finish the crap, scream, or pull up her jeans.

"So, what'd ya do?" I asked.

"I don't remember!" she said.

We laughed so hard, I thought I'd split my pants or at least wet them. When we had finally regained our composure, I hugged them both and walked back to my tent feeling warm from head to toe, not just from the Scotch, but also from the good cheer I'd just shared with Tom and Helen.

* * *

A light fog rolled in during the night, and we slept in the next morning, not starting out until the sun peeked through the haze around noon. We decided to stay together in one group that day for each other's company and to finish the area quickly so we could move to Flora Creek the following day. The day was disappointing, just as yesterday had been, but there were no skirmishes with wildlife. For this I was grateful.

"Let's take both guns today," Tom suggested.

"A big yes to that," said Helen.

"I got really spooked yesterday," I said. "Sorry if I seem jumpy."

"Yeah, you're not the only one," Toni said, "and I wasn't even there."

"Hell, I was born in Alaska and lived in the bush, but even *I* was scared shitless," Tom admitted.

We continued our conversation while climbing a steep hardscrabble slope up to a terrace about mile east of camp. I was so winded when I reached the top that I contemplated quitting smoking. Was I really in such bad shape at twenty-six? I threw down my pack and collapsed on the ground.

"Oh my God, I feel like I've been running uphill carrying a fifty-pound pack trying to outrun our wolverine friend," I gasped.

"Those cigarettes will kill you," Helen said.

"Bite me, Helen. Lots of people smoke up here. Look at Kelly—that mountain goat. All those years hiking through Colorado paid off. I've spent my entire life at sea level lazing around, but I sure feel like I've been growing some muscles since I got here."

"It's all right, George. We loves ya. Smoke?" Tom asked.

"God no."

I pawed through my daypack to find my stash of M&Ms and passed them around. Sharing M&M's always helped no matter the situation and seemed to bring a smile to everyone's faces.

* * *

After too short a rest, we surveyed the terrace, about a mile and a half long, and found a short caribou fence toward the terrace's western end. Not a particularly exciting fence, it consisted of a single short, straight line. We dutifully recorded it, then walked another mile further, where we found three more cairns, isolated from the others.

Helen said, "I've read that single or small groups of cairns could be used by Eskimos to rest things on like sleds."

She grabbed her thirty-meter tape from her daypack, while Tom rooted through his pack, finding a stake and a label to write the site number on. We measured in the cairns from Tom's datum in short order, while I drew the site map and photographed the cairns with some success.

"They could've been boundary markers, too, like where your claim ends and mine begins. You can see Howard Pass and Akuliak, Nigtun and Kiingyak Lakes from here, a primo spot for real estate," Tom interjected, reading the Howard Pass quad map. "I guess a lot of groups could have used this area."

Who could really say why the three cairns were there? The people who piled up the rocks were long gone, and only *they* knew what the piles were really used for. That kind of uncertainty, I realized, was part of archaeology's allure.

I guessed we were now three and a half miles from camp. I was sure my legs would go all rubbery on the way back, but at least the return journey would be mostly downhill.

We had a wonderful meal that night—I fried up a can of bacon, crumbled the bits over spaghetti, and poured melted cheese over my creation. Helen and Tom washed the dishes and I turned in for the night, thinking about my flight to Umiat the following morning.

UMIAT

My time in Umiat was uneventful during my next rotation. There were no giant parties. GSI's booze and cigarette shipment hadn't arrived and Lucy was off falling in love with Corey in one of the hundred or so Quonset huts that populated base camp.

The other ologists on my rotation hiked to the Red Spot several times in pairs or in groups. Although Umiat Mountain was not that far away from the Hilton, no one would venture there alone without bear protection, but couples wouldn't have a problem.

I felt slightly sheepish not wanting to investigate the surrounding area with the others, but, for Christ's sake, all I *did* was explore out in the Pass. I enjoyed Umiat's odd characters and laid-back charm. The place reminded me of backdrops in TV westerns. There were several occasions when I walked down the dirt road from the Hilton to our plywood camp that feeling like Marshall Dillon. I imagined Doc, Chester, and Miss Kitty poking their heads out of the various Quonsets and Wall tents to wish me a pleasant day. I wished for a cowboy hat to tip the brim in their direction.

True, I longed for flirtations and sexual encounters, but on this occasion for a reason I could not fathom, I felt content to blend into the woodwork and just be. Contentment was a new feeling to me, I realized. I had never been completely at ease with the world or with myself. But here, the twenty-four-hour days of bright sunshine, the smell of gasoline, and the whine of the generator made Umiat the perfect place.

I spent most of my time reading in the mess hall and enjoying Dick the Cook's superb field cuisine. I found the sound of his puttering in the kitchen to put meals together for forty or so people comforting. With his whistling and his friendly conversations with mechanics, roustabouts, visiting scientists staying in the Hilton, the Smiths, and the archaeological team, I felt surrounded by security and cheerfulness.

I briefly considered walking over to GSI to see if Skip or Chris had any dope but got a case of the shies. I wasn't that attracted enough to the guys on my rotation to leave the comforts of the mess hall, so I settled back into Michener, happy to drink black coffee, smoke cigarettes, and eat chocolate chip cookies.

Lucy and Corey stampeded into the mess hall late for dinner our second night, their faces flushed red with excitement from love or lust. Lucy sat down next to me and grabbed my hand under the table. She gave me a worried smile and whispered, "I'm in over my head, George."

"I know," I said softly so that no one else could hear me. I patted her hand. "It'll be okay."

Her shoulders sighed with relief. "Thanks, Georgeie."

That's all she needed, just a little reassurance.

I got back to my dinner of pork chops, applesauce, broccoli, and awful candied yams while Lucy turned back to Corey. Jay, sitting across from me, looked at them and rolled his eyes. "Everyone knows," he mouthed with his lips.

"So what?" I mouthed back.

* * *

The next morning, I woke up alone in the Howard Pass tent, got my shit together, and walked down to the Hilton for breakfast. It was a bright, crisp morning with a slight breeze from the southwest, according to the windsock on the tower. Corey and Lucy never showed. When I climbed into the chopper for Howard Pass, Lucy was already there, staring into the distance through the Plexiglas. I thought I saw a little tear escape her eye, but I wasn't sure. The 206 roared to life and we were off.

CAMP 9, ANOTHER STRETCH OF FLORA CREEK

When Lucy and I got back to the field, camp had already been packed up to move to Flora Creek, two miles from its confluence with the Aniuk, near where our first camp had been. Flora Creek felt like coming home minus the cold, rain, and hypothermia.

After our move, Ron said. "When you're finished staring into space, George, would you set up your tent?" He rocked back and forth on his feet a few times as if to emphasize the point.

I started to say something unpleasant, but he interrupted, "I know you had a rough night in Umiat. I can see it in your eyes and lack of coordination."

"Why, thanks, Ron, you ding-dong."

With a snort and a laugh, he walked away, probably to tease someone else.

* * *

After stowing our belongings in our tents and grabbing lunch, the five of us set off to survey some low terraces near camp. Ron, Lucy, and I found a site consisting of two flakes and a delicately flaked, triangular grayish-blue chert point. Lucy was the one to make the discovery, and that evening, she passed the tiny point around.

"Oooh," gushed Ron, "That's an ASTt point or end blade. See how small, flat, and finely made it is? It's probably about 4,000 years old."

"Say again? What's ASTt?" I asked.

"It's the oldest widespread Eskimo culture we know about," Ron said. "Looks like stuff in Siberia. It's known by its real name, Arctic Small Tool tradition, not to be confused with the Arctic Archaeologists' Small Tool tradition." He took a breath. "A row of small points would be attached to a wood or antler shaft and thrown really fast with a spear thrower. One throw could kill a caribou or other critter deader than a doornail. It's all in the Giddings books back at camp."

"Let's see. Pass it over here," Kelly said. She held the diminutive artifact in the palm of her hand. Sure is small. Way cool, too."

"When she passed the point to me, I turned it over a few times in my hand, marveling at the tiny, precise flaking on both sides and the thinness of the object. Had the point found its mark and secured caribou meat for the winter? Did the hunter save the day for his family?

"How the hell could anyone make anything so dainty and deadly?" I asked more or less rhetorically.

"With a lot of patience," Kelly said.

July 26. Moved to Flora Cr, 2 miles from Aniuk. Surveyed low terraces. Find of the day is an ASTt point, very finely chipped. Beautiful. Old. We can see Isikut and Ikhlhuk Mts here. Like coming home. Weather good. A little cold today.

* * *

The next day, the original All-Girl Survey Crew reunited when Kelly, Lucy, and I covered the base of Isikut Mountain, including two quarter-mile long terraces. The weather became warm and buggy after the morning breeze died down. At noon, we ate lunch on one of the terraces. The sun beat down and mosquitoes buzzed, but when the breeze picked up, I felt a distinct, if slight, chill.

Is autumn just around the corner?

Toward the end of the day Kelly said, "You know, since Malcolm left, we've all become a little glum and lethargic."

"*I'm* sure glum," Lucy said.

"I feel shitty that he's gone, but right now, my issue is my fucking feet," I said as I hobbled toward camp.

While I had incipient bunions and my feet lacked arches, it was my narrow heels that bothered me the most. My heels slid up and down in my Sorels with every step, no matter how many pairs of socks I put on in the morning. By the end of a long day, my feet ached.

"George, you walk like an old lady," Kelly said.

"Buzz off. See how you'd like it if you were growing blisters all the time," I countered.

"Now, children. Stop this fussin' and git goin'," Lucy said in a thicker-than-normal drawl, "We'll be back faster than a horny toad hoppin' on a June bug."

"That makes no sense," I said, distracted for a moment.

"I know. I'll keep up with my folksy southern sayins to distract y'all back to camp," Lucy teased.

We resumed our hike. Lucy uttered so many southern aphorisms, most of them made up on the spot, I forgot about my feet completely. My favorite aphorism of the day was "It's rainin' so hard, sounds like a goat pissin' on a flat rock." We laughed loud enough to scare away any harmful creatures.

* * *

Back at camp, I unzipped the mosquito netting at the front of my tent and crawled in. I took off my shoes and socks, rubbing my red feet. Ah, relief. There were blisters coming up on the ball of each foot and on my heels. I dug into my vast supply of moleskin, carefully cutting several pieces with my folding camp scissors. Each foot got three pieces—ball, bunion and heel—then I put on a dry pair of socks and sneakers. My feet actually felt good. Finally able relax, I took out my unread copy of June's *National*

Lampoon and dozed off while reading a P.J. O'Rourke story. Soon, my name was being taken in vain by my campmates as they shouted me to dinner.

I walked outside to brush my teeth sometime after midnight and found myself staring at the western horizon. Camp was quiet. The sun now dipped behind the mountains further with each passing day. Soon, there would be a few minutes of twilight, and later, a little darkness. I looked down at the ground.

Oh my God. I'm casting a shadow!

Melancholy swept over me. I'd have to leave in less than a month.

CAMP 10, DISAPPOINTMENT CREEK

The next day, having found little in the way of artifacts along this stretch of Flora Creek, we packed up for our next move, a different stretch of Disappointment Creek. I had my doubts, and it was a pain in the ass to move so frequently. On the other hand, who would want to stay on Flora Creek when all that was left to survey was tussock fields?

The chopper was late yet again. As the morning stretched into afternoon, we grew bored and restless, not knowing when Al or Sam would make it into camp.

"Let's entertain Sam or Al when they get here. Let's do something weird. Let's surprise them," Kelly said.

Impulsively I said, "How about we put our sleeping bags on over our heads?"

"Even better, let's put our walking sticks up inside them to make us taller. We'll be eight feet tall and the highest feature on the landscape," Ron said.

"And electric blue!" added Helen mischievously.

"A color not known in nature. He'll wonder what he's looking at," Lucy giggled.

We retrieved the sleeping bags from the mound of gear we'd piled up and quickly pulled each one out of its stuff sack and over our heads. I stuck my walking stick inside the sleeping bag and hoisted it up over my head, making sure to unzip the bottom of the zipper so I could see out.

"Eight feet nothing! You're ten feet tall," Kelly laughed.

"You look like a blue banana," Lucy said in amazement.

As if on cue, the whirr of chopper blades could be heard from behind the clouds. Five monstrous blue bananas swayed back and forth, welcoming the helicopter. Sam, on duty that day, seeing this unholy and unnatural sight, circled us slowly, swooping down and back up again three times before finally setting the chopper down. He wore an amused expression on his face. When he jumped out, we had already thrown off our sleeping bags and were convulsing in laughter.

"Howard Pass does it again," he said, and shook his head.

This was a great creative coup. All Ikpikpuk had ever done was moon the helicopter when we'd flown into their camp earlier in the summer. How childish, really. We would never have stooped so low.

I remembered the Ikpikpukkers mooning us earlier in the summer. A disgusting site, the entire crew dropped their pants and bent over. Some asses were large and others small; some were hairy and others smooth. The biggest, hairiest, and roundest had been Ian's.

A gesture of disrespect and defiance as much as giving the finger, mooning also struck me as hysterically funny in the middle of nowhere.

* * *

After our mischief and Toni's return, we moved camp and, because it was so late in the day, Ron decided we might as well settle in and start dinner.

The air had grown hazy and began to smell of smoke again. Before he flew off, Sam told us there were now two large brush fires along the Noatak River.

"How can smoke travel so far and still be so thick?" I asked.

"Well, Georgia, there's really nothin' much to stop the smoke between here and there. The real danger is the tundra catchin' fire," he said softly. "Tundra fires, they travel underground. The fire gets kinda trapped. If the fire gets outta control, it'll smolder, travel under the duff, and surface some other place."

"What if a fire surfaces near us?" I asked. "What do we do?"

Lucy looked alarmed at the prospect of coming face-to-face with a fire.

"We're keepin' an eye on weather reports outta Kobuk and Noatak just like the last time. We'd get you outta here real fast," Sam reassured us. He looked at his shoes in his shy way and took a last drag from his cigarette.

"Thank God for that," Kelly said. "We can always count on you, Sam."

After the 206 flew out with Tom and Helen, Ron called a weather day. It was miserable and, after all, it was after three in the afternoon, almost the cocktail hour.

I retreated to my tent to continue my Michener festival, vowing to visit Colorado in the future while copying his description of the making of a Clovis point into my notebook. After dinner, I relaxed into the book again and was soon asleep, despite the smoky air.

* * *

By the next morning, the smoke had dissipated by for the most part. Ron, Toni, and I surveyed near Flora Creek, finding a couple of nondescript flake scatters.

But Ron's sharp eye saw something more. "Hey, look at this one. This one is a burin. See the burin blow?" Ron asked me.

I studied the small, carefully chipped flake for several seconds before I saw what Ron was talking about. "Yeah, but I forget what a burin is," I said.

"It's like a chisel or engraver, probably used to make grooves in bone or wood or some other soft material. See the edge? You can see where one long, straight flake was struck off, making the edge really sharp and pointed. It's really small like Lucy's ASTt point. See how finely knapped it is? It's probably ASTt also."

"Could you make holes in a shaft for blades and points with that?" I asked, remembering Ron's reaction to Lucy's find.

"Well, sure. Very good, Killer," Ron replied, using my recently bestowed Bitch name.

I hummed on the way back to camp, pleased with myself.

* * *

Just as we returned for the day, we heard the unexpected whine of the chopper's rotors. It was the wrong day for the Jet Ranger to come out to Howard Pass. I looked at my friends quizzically.

Head Honcho Rick jumped out of the helicopter and approached me.

"Your mother called our office phone in Fairbanks, Georgeie. The message I got was that there's someone in your family who's very ill, but I don't have any more information than that. I think you should come back to Umiat with me and call home."

UMIAT, UNEXPECTEDLY

Instantly, a lump came to my throat. My thoughts went to my stepfather. Twenty-five years older than my mother, he was seventy-six and had already survived one heart attack. I imagined a second, more serious one now.

My mother would be in a quiet panic, holding her fears in as best she could. Men die. Men leave. That was her experience and the overwhelming fear she'd passed on to me in words and sometimes in her attitude about the future.

Mom's father had been killed in an automobile accident when she was three, I imagined that pattern would continue with me, killing any future husband and wounding my children for life. I'd had to suppress that since I was a kid. But it was my fate. I knew it.

Mom doted on my stepfather, perhaps thinking about her own father. She coddled him to keep him safe, to prevent another abandonment.

"I'll get my things," I said quietly.

I looked at my friends who had now gathered around me like a family of elephants crowding around a sick young one, showing such feeling and concern some tears trickled down my cheeks. Kelly and Lucy looked upset, their eyes serious and moist.

'I think maybe Doc, that's my stepfather, had another heart attack," I said.

"He'll be okay, George," Lucy said, hugging me.

"Yeah, it's not his time yet. You'll see," Kelly said, stroking my hair.

I could not lose control in front of my friends. My stiff-upper-lip upbringing came to my defense. I regained my composure and gathered the necessary stuff into my daypack. I hugged everyone and flew off in the front seat of the chopper. Sam looked over at me but kept his thoughts to himself.

* * *

The trip took hours, or at least it seemed to. I continued to fight back tears, wiping them away with my bandanna. I stared out of the Plexiglas window into the distance.

Mountains gave way to foothills, foothills to rolling plains, rolling plains to flatland and tundra lakes that extended to the coast. I could see red in the tundra up north. Autumn was coming. The sun would drop behind the mountains for three or four hours each day before the end of August and the temperature would dip below freezing.

Soon, we'd awaken to frost on our tents and on the tundra. Just before our final departure, we would be able to see ptarmigan molting into their winter plumage and foxes changing from red to white. That's what Malcolm had told us to expect, and it sounded beautiful, but it would mean the end of summer.

I'll lose my new family then. Am I going to lose my second father, too?

When the chopper landed, I ran straight for the Hilton. I found OJ's wife, Ellie, and explained my problem.

"Oh, no," she said in a motherly way that had me crying and blowing my nose. "It's okay. It's going to be okay," she said, hugging me, then walking with me to the control tower. "Let's wait until there's no air traffic. Then you can squeeze in a call home. I'll wait and show you how. For them to hear you, you press here. When you want them to speak, you take your hand off the button. You'll be fine."

Several long minutes passed until I got Ellie's go-ahead. She got an operator right away and gave her the New York number. My mother answered the phone and Ellie retreated to the Hilton.

"Mom!" I yelled into the radiophone, remembering to press the button so I could talk and then quickly letting go so she could talk.

"What's wrong? Are you okay?" she asked, her voice crackling over the satellite phone.

"I heard someone was sick. I thought Doc was sick; he might be in the hospital." I yelled.

"He's fine! We're all fine! What made you think anything was wrong?"

I told her about the mysterious phone call to Fairbanks and my being summoned to Umiat. I felt my muscles relax and I breathed a sigh of relief.

"We're all fine," she said again. "Someone made a big mistake. You must have been so worried. That message was for someone else. If your boss was there, I'd read him the riot act," she said, relieved at my safety and angry about the fateful mistake. Anger was her way of expressing fear. I'd learned that a long time ago.

As soon as she'd heard my voice, she must have thought the worst; I was injured. Then her mind would have gone to my stepfather. Was *he* really okay? Then, I guessed she would have thought about her first husband, my late father: *First Ed, now Georgeie.* I didn't know *exactly* what she'd be thinking, but I knew my mother well.

"I don't know what happened, Mom. I thought Doc was in the hospital."

I heard my mother pass the phone.

"Georgeie, you okay?" my stepfather asked, seemingly from the end of a wind tunnel.

"I'm fine, Doc," I said. "How are you?"

"Feeling fine. We're watching the news. Everything seems normal here, but we sure miss you."

"I'm safe and I'm having a great time," I said. This was not going to be a long-distance conversation about bears and hypothermia.

"Uh-huh. Good. Let me give you back to your mother, and don't worry about us," he said, cutting short our part of the conversation. He hated the phone because he took phone calls from customers all day long. At least that was what I thought.

I could see him in my mind's eye looking at my mother quizzically, as if to ask *What the hell was that all about?* I could also see my mother giving him another visual once-over to make sure he was still breathing because he was, after all, seventy-six. Only fifty-one, I knew Mom was not ready to be a widow a second time.

"I'm back, Georgeie," she said.

I tried to tell her how wonderful the north was. "Mom, it's beautiful here. I can't begin to tell you. It's all so new and exciting. I'm making good friends and we're hiking in places no one's ever been before. It will be hard to leave, I think."

There was a pause. I could sense her uncertainty about how to react to what I'd just said. I'm sure she was thinking, *Aren't you coming back?* to herself. Did she just lean her head on one of her hands?

"It's beastly hot," she said instead. "Be glad you're not here. I worry about you every day. Are you really safe?"

"Oh, yeah. I'm with a bunch of really experienced people who look out for me. They call me their tenderfoot."

A chuckle, then "Did you get our care package? Brownies good? Parka all right?"

"The parka is just what I needed and everybody loved the brownies. They were gone in two minutes."

"I had such a tough time finding you a parka in the middle of summer. The Army-Navy man had to climb up into the store's attic to find one. He wasn't happy. Of course I picked orange so you wouldn't get lost up there."

"It's perfect. I danced when I opened the box and saw it," I answered. "Uh-oh. One of the guys is signaling me that there's air traffic in the area. I've got to go now. I love you. See you in September."

"Love you too, Georgeie," Mom said. "Stay safe."

"Bye," I said. "Georgeie over and out."

I set the microphone down on the rickety table, lit a cigarette, inhaled deeply, sighed, and thought I would cry in relief. But I was also pissed off at the project director who'd hauled me into Umiat and scared the piss out of me.

I will throttle the shit out of him if I see him again.

* * *

253

On still-wobbly legs, I walked next door to the Hilton and found Ellie.

"How's things?" she said.

"Everything's fine. It was a false alarm. I don't know what I would have done without you letting me use the radiophone. Fly to Fairbanks?"

She hugged me again and this time, I hugged her back. I blew my nose on my dirty navy bandanna, then wiped my eyes with it, put it back in my jeans pocket, and continued down the corridor to the mess hall. Dick the Cook was washing the dinner dishes and listening to a Doors tape. I poured myself a cup of coffee, slumped onto a bench, and leaned against the wall, all adrenaline having left my body.

"Hungry?" he asked.

"God, yeah," I answered.

"Everything okay?"

"Yeah, things are fine at home, false alarm. How'd you know?"

"Ellie said you were in the control tower making an emergency call. Hey, I got some leftover roast beef with all the trimmings. I'll make up a plate with your name on it, okay?

"Wonderful, Dick. Thanks," I said gratefully.

Dick the Cook quickly heated up some au jus, ladled it on the leftovers, and brought it my way.

"This is great," I said, my voice tired.

"Nothing to it. I've got some chocolate pudding cake left, too. I'll warm up a big piece and put some vanilla ice cream on it. Sound good?"

"Beyond heavenly."

Dick the Cook began to whistle along with The Doors while cleaning the countertops as I continued to relax and unwind. I'd have to spend the night in Umiat since both pilots had logged in too many hours to take me back out, but that would be okay with me.

* * *

After eating as much pudding cake as I could hold, I walked down the dirt road past the Quonsets to our tent camp, breathing much more easily and deeply than I had just two hours before. I felt better, but out of sync. This wasn't my turn to be in Umiat. I'd have to bunk with Tom and Helen. They'd probably shoved the two Howard Pass cots together already and I'd have to sleep on the floor.

I opened the tent door. As predicted, Tom and Helen were reading inside their zipped-together sleeping bags on the cots, looking comfy.

"Hey, George. What are you doing here?" Tom asked, surprised.

"Is everything okay?" Helen said. "You look a little out of it."

"It is now. Rick flew in to Howard Pass and told me there was a call for me from New York. He said it was an emergency," I began.

"Oh, God, George. What happened?" Helen asked.

"Well, it was a false alarm. I thought my stepfather had had a heart attack. He's old and has already had one."

"Oh, Jesus," said Tom.

"But it's okay now. I don't know how Rick got it wrong. He should have double-checked, God damnit. I'm so fucking relieved, but I'd love to smack him," I said, sitting down on the floor. My shoulders sagged under the weight of a burden only recently lifted.

"So happy for you, George, but the wife and I need our privacy so we can, uh, you know? It's not that we don't love you, we do but..."

"You twats. Let me gather up my stuff and find another place."

"Not all the crew tents are populated with couples doing it, you know," Tom said.

"Fine. Yeah, yeah. You turd."

"You're just finding that out now?" Helen laughed.

I grabbed my sleeping bag and walked out, passing the Colville River tent. I didn't know them, really, so I trudged on. Next was the Ikpikpuk tent. I knew those folks. We had flown in and out of their camp a few times and I could at least recognize their faces by sight.

Yeah, I'll bunk with them.

I entered without bothering to knock. Maxie, whom I'd met in Fairbanks, was a fireball from Texas, and had a mouth like a sailor. She sat on the floor reading *Elmer Gantry.*

"What the fuck? Who is this disembodied ghost?"

"Ha ha, it's Gilda Radner. Had to come in to Umiat early," I said, and repeated my story.

"Oh, shit, Georgeie, that's awful. I never liked Rick to begin with—DC bureaucrat that he is. Doesn't know shit from Shinola. Come on in. Gary's around somewhere, but we have an extra cot, so help yourself."

"Thanks, Maxie. It's been a tough day."

"Just put on your jim-jams and take a load off."

A cot had never felt as good, so great was my relief.

* * *

At breakfast the next morning, I shared a table with Donny and Dave from Lookout Ridge. After telling my tale yet again, we got to talking about more run-of-the-mill things.

"We're going to hike over to the Red Spot. Wanna come?" Donny asked.

"Thanks, guys. I'd rather just sit here, drink coffee, and smoke cigarettes. Plus, I walked out there with Preacher John not too long ago. I think I'd rather read," I said, sounding kind of wimpy to myself, but what the hell. I'd been through a pretty harrowing experience.

"What book you readin'?" Dave asked, glancing at me, then looking down through the table to his boots. He plucked an imaginary bug from his shirtsleeve.

"Michener's *Centennial*. We're on a Michener kick out in Howard Pass, although I wouldn't mind reading a Louis L'Amour western novel like Sam reads," I said, gesturing toward the approaching pilot with my chin.

"Sam and I are from the same part of Tennessee," Dave said, making shy conversation.

"Yeah. When we first got to Umiat, I heard you guys talking about the Clinch Mountains and the little towns there," I answered.

"We even know some of the same people," Dave added. He looked intently at the faded Formica tabletop and then motioned Sam to sit down with us. His offer was declined and Sam stood at the end of the table, looking into his coffee cup.

Dave was shy, true, but not as much as Sam. While Dave could hold a conversation and maybe look you in the eye, Sam rarely spoke in social situations. I would never have known about their Tennessee roots had Dave not said something. Sam would have considered this too intimate a detail to tell a woman, and, besides, he might have needed to look beyond his coffee to tell her.

"Well, think I'll go stretch my legs. See you guys," Dave said.

Dave and Donny sauntered out the door and into the Hilton's hallway. Sam was left alone drinking the rest of his coffee. Not wanting to strike up a conversation with a lone woman, or so I suspected, he turned around to study the gigantic series of faded North Alaskan quad maps Scotch-taped together around and over the mess hall doorway, then stepped into the hallway.

I spent the rest of the day in the mess hall, talking to Dick the Cook once in a while, but pretty much ignored anyone else that came in for coffee and a cookie. I was still exhausted and I wanted to keep to myself, more or less.

"Ya know, George, I'm making another chocolate pudding cake tonight so you get to have some two days in a row," he said happily.

Although Dick the Cook was not a pastry chef and couldn't make a Napoleon to save his life, or so he'd told me, his brownie pudding cake was wildly popular. You stuck a fork into a large piece of the delicacy to find a center of mostly liquid chocolate. With a scoop of vanilla ice cream melting into it, I'd almost forget the trauma I'd just experienced.

Dick the Cook's talents were such that at the end of every meal, he was usually rewarded with that compliment of compliments, "good grub, Cookie" from nearly everyone. The phrase spoke even more highly than a belch, an affirmation in its own right. He received many compliments at dinner that night and a significant number of belches.

Pooped, I walked over to the Ikpikpuk tent after dinner, took off my jeans and filthy shirt, got into my sleeping bag, and crashed, falling into a deep sleep without saying a peep to Maxie and Gary.

* * *

The next morning after an early breakfast, I hitched a lift back to Howard Pass with Helen, Tom, and Al. I hadn't forgotten Kelly's challenge of lassoing the handsome pilot. Just thinking about sleeping with Al made my pulse race. I plopped myself into the copilot's seat, leaving Tom and Helen in the cramped back seat like sardines, and made several attempts at conversation.

"See how the tundra's changing color?" I asked.

"Uh-huh," Al replied, not paying me much attention.

Was he playing hard to get, or had he screwed someone the night before, or was he not interested? I remembered the Tootsie Roll Pop he'd sucked on a few rides back and decided I was not yet out of the running.

I took a deep breath and decided to press my luck: "Have you ever had a party in your Quonset?"

"Yeah, I have. Got a great bong," he answered.

"Oh. I don't remember being at a party there," I said, sounding more disinterested than I felt.

"Well, we'll have to fix that, won't we? Maybe have a party of our own."

His response so startled me that I became tongue-tied.

After about five long minutes, he said, "Okay, here we are," as we descended towards the Howard Pass camp.

He handed me the mail with a wink and slowed the rotors so I could jump out. All I could manage was a meek "Sounds nice. Thanks, Al. See ya."

BACK TO DISAPPOINTMENT CREEK

When I jumped out of the chopper, Kelly and Lucy welcomed me back with huge hugs.

"How's Doc?" Kelly asked.

"How's your mom?" Lucy chimed in.

"Everyone's fine," I said. "No one's sick. Holy fuck, I'd like to kill whoever in Fairbanks made such a shitty mistake. I was so rattled; I didn't even think about taking a shower!"

"I wonder who *does* have a sick family member," Toni asked rhetorically, but with concern on her face. "I hope no one died."

"No shit," Ron added. "Who knows about this hell of a fuck up?"

"Sam does. Ellie does—she showed me how to use the radio-phone. I was crying and told her all about it. Dick the Cook, too. Someone told him because he already knew by the time I walked over to the mess hall for coffee. I think all Umiat knows by now. I slept in the Ikpikpuk tent because these guys wanted to screw."

"How uncivilized," Lucy drawled, her nose in the air.

"Too bad none of the crew chiefs were in on rotation. One of them would've told the right person or at least found out what happened." Ron said.

"Well, shit flows uphill and Rick will get some kind of reprimand, I bet," Toni said.

There was a pause in the conversation.

"And, you know what? It's hotter than hell in New York. I'm glad I'm here," I said.

"And so are we," Lucy said.

* * *

The next day, Helen and Tom flew back out on their regularly scheduled flight and we bid Ron and Kelly a fond farewell. Tom claimed that, due to my unscheduled interruption in Umiat, he was still a virgin.

"Shut up, Tom," Helen said, poking him in the ribs through his flannel shirt.

Things being back to normal for everyone, I threw my sleeping bag in my tent and put the usual survey equipment in my daypack to join Lucy and Tom for our next archaeological adventure. We walked three hours to the confluence of the Nigu River with an unnamed stream. The Nigu raged more powerfully than the Aniuk. We found a slow-flowing spot and crossed the river, then found four caribou fences with associated windbreaks and cairns. A huge site, it would take all day to record.

Because we'd walked all morning, we decided to take a break and eat lunch, starting with a large bag of M&Ms. After almost completely devouring the bag, I lit a cigarette and felt completely satisfied.

After mapping and photographing the entire site, we began our trek back home.

When we finally arrived around eight-thirty in the evening, the most wonderful surprise awaited us. We popped our heads in the cook tent to find Malcolm sitting, legs outstretched next to the Coleman stove, stirring a pot of lentils and freeze-dried sausage. His bad ankle was still encased in an ace bandage and sported the same ugly crocheted bootie, but he was there.

"MALCOLM!" the three of us shouted at the same time.

"GUYS!" Malcolm yelled at the top of his voice. He stretched out his arms to encompass the three of us.

Lucy, Tom, and I fell over each other trying to get to him while avoiding his ankle and the Coleman stove.

"Oh, my God! It's too good to be true!" Lucy yelled.

"I can't believe it!" I said, plastering a kiss on his cheek. Tears of happiness and relief came to my eyes.

Our commotion brought Toni over, grinning. She purposely hadn't told us Malcolm was back when we'd checked in on the walkie-talkie earlier in the day, and we sure as shit hadn't heard a chopper land.

"Bwana is back!" she said smiling.

Helen ducked into the tent to join in the happy reunion.

"Yay!" she said, "We're back together safe and sound."

The six of us huddled as close together as humanly possible, hugging one another hysterically laughing; we were *that* ecstatic, and Malcolm seemed beside himself with emotion. "My kids, my little family," he blubbered.

I handed him my trusty bandanna to blow his nose.

* * *

Over lentil soup, pilot bread, and cheese, we listened to Malcolm's tale. We leaned in, hanging on to his every word. On July thirteenth, he'd been flown to Fairbanks.

"I radioed my girlfriend, Viola, to meet my plane and take me directly to the emergency room at Fairbanks Memorial," he began. "The ankle wasn't broken, but I'd sure ripped the shit out of it. The docs bandaged me up, gave me pain pills, and told me to keep my foot elevated and not put weight on it for three weeks, *or else.*

"Today, August second, is three weeks exactly from the accident, and I'm really pushing it to come back so soon. It's still swollen a little, hurts, and I need crutches. I'll hobble around for the next few days and see how it goes. I'm going to stay in camp, rest, and plan our days for us.

"I'm real surprised they let me come back into the field. I had to convince the boss my ankle didn't hurt and I could walk without crutches. That was quite an act I put on, and Jeezus, was I in pain!"

"You know we love you, Malcolm, but maybe you should have stayed in Umiat a few more days before coming back out here," Helen said, sounding a little uneasy.

"I'd rather be here with you guys," Malcolm smiled.

Malcolm could now fit his foot inside his sneaker, although the sneaker was spread wide where laces should've been. I gently touched his foot as a welcome-home gesture. I wondered if it was a good idea for Malcolm to spend his days in camp alone with one good leg and still on pain meds.

"I was home for close to three weeks with Viola. We talked about maybe getting married next summer. Who knows? Maybe we will. Her stash of dope helped the pain a lot. She's a great cook and a phenomenal lover. I was well taken care of. Almost forgot the pain at times."

I tried to remember what three weeks of sex was like, but I didn't think I'd ever had a run like that.

"Viola also has a small collection of porno literature that came in handy."

Lucy and I looked at each other in surprise, right eyebrows cocked. Toni seemed unphased.

"Well, she's from LA," Malcolm explained.

He described a couple of positions in a porno magazine I could hardly picture. They sounded like instructions for putting a packing crate together. I paid strict attention, however, hoping I could use this knowledge sometime in the future.

* * *

My eyes stung with smoke as soon as I stuck my head out of my tent the following morning. It probably came from the wildfire near Noatak Sam had told us about a few days earlier.

In Umiat the day before he returned to us, Malcolm had been made aware of the fire and discussed the situation with OJ who was in regular radio contact with Fairbanks, Kotzebue, Noatak, and Kobuk. "If the smoke gets worse, the helicopter won't be able to find your camp. You may have to worry about smoke inhalation, too," he'd said.

Malcolm related the situation to us over breakfast and warned, "Stay close to Disappointment Creek and keep plenty of water handy. If you have to, you can breathe through water-soaked bandannas. If it gets real bad, come back immediately. If Sam or Al needs to move us, we can camp to the east, or even go back to Umiat."

There was a plus side to the situation. The smoke blocked the sun from beating down too hard on us, and that seemed to keep the bugs at bay.

We were all allowed a late start because of our previous long day. We hesitantly waved goodbye and left Malcolm knitting a pair of Day-Glo orange booties in the cook tent.

We surveyed a large terrace to the north where we found a tent ring and a hearth. Lucy dug a shovel test in the hearth, finding flakes, burned bone, and wood that went down twenty centimeters until she reached permafrost. We photographed the shit out of the hearth since we hadn't seen one that deep before. And why were there unburned flakes in it?

* * *

After recording the site, we called it quits. The smoke was just too disagreeable. When we returned to camp, I filled a pot with water, put it on the stove, and began heating it up for drinks. Malcolm had magically disappeared, probably to his tent to nap.

Once the water boiled, I fixed a cup of cocoa and quietly made my way over to check on him. I peered in. He was reading *Shogun*.

I called his name softly in a singsong voice. "Malcolm... How was your day, Malcolm...?" I said.

"Hi, Georgeie. I slept most of the day," he said, in an equally singsong quiet voice.

I unzipped the tent flap, handing him the cocoa.

"Thanks, Georgeie. I dozed, read a little Giddings, and started a James Clavell novel for fun."

"And you've had the walkie-talkie and the shotgun at your side all day?" I asked.

"Yeah, but I kept the safety on in case I rolled over on it in my sleep."

"That's good! Smart guy," I said. "I'm so happy you're back, Malcolm. I can't tell you," I said, "but first I have to tell you something,"

"Shoot."

I told Malcolm about the phone incident and my unexpected visit to Umiat. He looked pissed.

"Oh my God. How the hell did that happen? I'd love to know who fucked up. But things are okay, you said. Everyone's fine?"

"Uh-huh."

"I'll bring this up with Rick when I go into Umiat next time. We'll get to the bottom of this. I just hope no one else should have gotten that call. I'll find out."

I hugged him then.

He grabbed my hand and said in a serious tone of voice, "You know, there's no place I'd rather be than out here with all of you. Hypothermia or no. Ankle or no. Scary phone calls or no." He gave my hand a squeeze. "That's why I gave you the Most Improved Camper Award. I wasn't sure you were going to make it at the beginning. You seemed lost and scared but look at you now. A real sourdough! Remember the Primus stove and carrying it outside? How bout all the other stuff you've been through?"

I paused. "This is the best thing anyone's ever said to me and the best award I'll ever get. I'd forgotten all about the stove. Tweren't nothin."

"Now, how's about you tackle the Coleman stove again and bring me some hot Tang?" He put his now-empty Melmac cup on the top of his head, signaling he wanted something more to drink.

"Aye aye, boss. I'll put some brandy in it, too."

"You do that, and you'll be promoted to rear admiral."

I scooted out of Malcolm's tent, happy for his trust in me.

By the time I'd reheated the water, Tom and Helen had ambled up to Malcolm's tent. They peered through the mosquito netting, holding steaming cups of cocoa and crowded in with Lucy and Toni who would not leave Malcolm's side.

"Come on in. There's room for everyone," Malcolm said, waving us in. "My kids," he said. "I'm so happy to be back."

"And here's your Tang. No brandy, I'm afraid," I said, entering last.

"That's okay, Admiral George," Malcolm replied.

After recounting the day's finds, Toni asked seriously, "What's next for us, Jefe?"

"Tomorrow, we're moving to Kinyiksukvik, a large lake in Inyorurak Pass. I've seen it from the air a couple of times—it's archaeology heaven—there's a shitload of stuff around the lakeshore. You can see a bunch of house pits and a huge *karigi* from the air. We'll stay there at least a week, maybe ten days. You'll be happy, I guarantee."

"Helen thought it was called Lancy Lake," Tom said. "Or that's what she thought her professor, John Cook, called it. Of course, he was talking about the lanceolate points found in the area. We laughed about that on the pipeline last year."

"Well," Malcolm said, "In honor of Helen and Dr. John, we'll call it Lancy Lake in our notes. By the way, Kinyiksukvik probably means 'place where caribou buy the farm'." He hoisted his Tang in a toast. Helen raised her cup of cocoa to Malcolm.

I like it. Lancy Lake is much easier to pronounce," Lucy said. She raised up her cup of Folgers and clanked it against Malcolm's cocoa.

Lucy and Toni left and came in with Malcolm's dinner. The rest of us took turns getting ours.

Malcolm's excitement over Lancy Lake was palpable. "We'll excavate a test pit inside the humongous stone circle at the north end of the lake—the *karigi*. Lancy Lake may be the mother lode of all sites in this part of the North Slope. And none of the crews have reported seeing anything like it so far, so it's all *ours*." He rubbed his hands together in a gesture of greediness not unlike the carpe bagger/former overseer of Tara in *Gone with the Wind*.

I could hear the actor say, "You owe back taxes, Miss O'Hara! Soon Tara will be all mine!"

"How do you know about the site?" I asked.

"It's been known for a while. It's hard to miss from the air. You'll see a couple of trenches archaeologists left back in the 50s and 60s. But we're the first big team to take a crack at it since then."

As excited as he appeared to be, I could tell Malcolm was also experiencing some anxiety by the way he chewed his beard during our conversation. Tomorrow he would put on both hiking boots and walk across the uneven tundra to the 206 for the first time since the injury. This was no practice walk in sneakers in Umiat; it would be the real thing. Cinching the laces tight, he'd put weight on his bad foot and climb up and into the chopper.

* * *

After dinner, we left Malcolm in peace to read. Back in the cook tent, my interest piqued, I studied Lancy Lake's location on the topo map over another cup of cocoa, and wrote some thoughts about the site in my field book:

Aug 3. Lancy Lake is near the confluence of two rivers, in a pass, on a lake, protected from winds by high mountains, and has many low promontories to use as vantage points. We've found sites in camps just to the north, at Akuliak Lake, and on Fay Creek. We also have caribou fences out the ass all over the place. Inyorurak Pass, not Howard Pass, must be the place to see and be seen in times past. Howard Pass, with its occasional tent ring and caribou fence, is nothing compared with Inyorurak Pass, the center of the prehistoric universe. And Malcolm is back!

After washing the dishes, Lucy and I suggested Malcolm might need encouragement to prepare for the next day's physical test. To relax him into a good night's sleep, she suggested we sing to him while he fell asleep. Around midnight, we strolled over to his tent singing "Lullaby and Goodnight." We sounded rather serene, if not saintly. We linked arms, swaying gently back and forth.

"Thanks, guys," came a tired voice from inside.

The sun had set behind the mountains, allowing a brief glimpse of some of the brightest stars. The air grew chilly as twilight approached, sometime after midnight. But when we woke up, it was bright daylight and the previous night's chill seemed like a dream. For some strange reason, I thought of Homer's *Odyssey*.

When the chopper touched down the next morning, Kelly hopped out with someone new! Frannie came from the Lookout Ridge crew to spend a week with us and Ron had swapped with her.

I remembered Frannie from back in Fairbanks at the beginning of the summer. She lived there with her husband, Jim, and was a grad student at UAF. But what intrigued me about her was not her experiences in Alaska, but her obvious New York accent. She even said "ax" instead of "ask."

We'd had a long and loud conversation that began in Big Ray's, the discount outfitter in Fairbanks, where she'd help me pick out a yellow daypack.

We'd sat next to each other on the bus back to UAF and continued getting to know each other. She'd been born in the shadow of the Empire State Building in a tenement that had been razed a few years before, she told me. Her family had then retired to Hoboken, NJ, home of Frank Sinatra.

Retired to Hoboken? Who would do that?

"I'm from Westchester County," I'd said.

"One of those blue bloods, huh? While you were swimming at the country club, I was playing hopscotch on the sidewalk in front of our tenement."

"You dumb shit," I'd said, using a term of endearment reserved for New York friends, "My stepfather is Jewish. We're not allowed in any of those clubs, and even if some brave Christian sponsored him, he'd never join."

"We're blue-collar Catholics. Papists, they call us," she'd muttered. "We'd be outcasts in your silver-spoon neck of the woods, Jewish or not, but I guess we can be friends."

Unfortunately, a more in-depth reacquaintance would have to await my return from Umiat.

Malcolm limped over to the chopper with his faithful scout of the day, Tom. He had claimed dibs on being first over to Kiniyksukvik with our fearless leader.

Reaching up and grabbing the floor of the helicopter, Malcolm placed a foot first on the skid, then on the strut. Shifting his weight fully onto the weak ankle, he pulled himself up slowly. Toni, Al, and Tom stood behind him in case he needed a boost. An expression of concern, then relief, crossed Malcolm's face.

Phew!" he exclaimed and waved his arms around in a mock celebration after catching his balance.

"Yippee!" Lucy shouted.

"Good going, Malcolm," Al said.

"Hi, Al," he answered, grabbing the seat as he climbed into the chopper, using both arms and his good leg, then turned himself over in the seat. We clapped and whistled, stuffed the chopper full of gear, carefully protecting his bad leg with sleeping bags and pads.

Tom climbed in behind him. When the rotors picked up speed, we turned away from the wind, then turned back to see Malcolm and Tom flying over us, waving formally, like British royals.

Lucy and I were the last to fly, but we were going to Umiat, the land of milk and honey.

UMIAT

This rotation would be much more goal-oriented than the last one because I had an exciting mission—to honor the pledge I'd made to Kelly about sleeping with Al.

As luck would have it, Al said he'd have a party in his Quonset hut the second night of my rotation. The usual suspects—archaeologists, GSI, the roustabouts, Dick the Cook, the Smiths—were all invited.

While we were getting our dirty clothes ready for one more turn in the bottom of the shower, I reminded Lucy of my promise to Kelly. She remembered the conversation and agreed I should go after Al.

"Take that young'un for a ride he'll never forget; right up into the stratosphere," she cooed.

Although Al's poor treatment of Lynne had occurred over six weeks before, we agreed that revenge was still necessary. More importantly, I hadn't gotten laid yet and the summer was almost over. Tom had Helen; Malcolm had been to Fairbanks and stayed with Viola; Lucy and Corey had begun coupling. Now, it was my turn.

* * *

The following day, after lunch and my second shower, I bumped into Ellie Smith in the Hilton's hallway.

"Oops," I said, "I'm sorry. I should watch where I'm going."

"No harm done, Georgeie," she replied. "Say, would you help me unload my laundry and carry it to our room?"

"Sure," I said, happy to be of use.

Four huge dryers formed the heart of the laundry room. Two of them rattled and squeaked as they spun. The room, tucked away between the mess hall and the lavatory, seemed hotter than hell, although it functioned as a cozy game room in winter, Ellie told me.

We reached into two of the dryers and lifted out armfuls of clothing. There were gobs of T-shirts and briefs, an unknown number of white socks, and a few of Ellie's nylon panties in the first dryer. I sorted the socks and tossed them into her laundry basket. The second dryer, full of Carhartts, flannel work shirts, and bandannas, more than filled another basket.

"Some days, all I do is laundry for OJ, the kids, and me," she said while we walked back to their quarters at the far end of the Hilton, past Dick the Cook's domain. We set the basket on the bed and began to unload the laundry, sorting clothing into piles.

"How you like it up here, Georgeie?" she asked, folding a faded plaid shirt and putting it on the top of the stack of other carefully folded shirts.

"I feel like I've been here forever," I said, "and yet I feel like I just got here. Everything's so new and exciting, but it's also getting kind of familiar now. I can't imagine going back east at the end of the month. It will be so bloody hot in DC, and probably in New York and Connecticut, too."

Other thoughts were too painful to articulate. At grad school no one would know about Killer Bitch or the Blue Bananas. There would be no destroilets, no freeze-dried carrots, no helicopters, no shotguns, and no grizzlies. I'd lose what I'd had here.

"Yeah, it'll be hot back there," Ellie said. She paused. "I'll probably go to Oregon in the fall once the summer season winds down. Winter is tough everywhere, but up here it's brutal. No use dressing up, putting on lipstick, trying to look like a woman. You put on your insulated pants, your bunny boots, expedition gloves, and your parka with a scarf tied around your face beneath a fur hat, go outside and hope you don't get frostbite. And there's not that much to do sometimes. I've read almost every book in the library— I'll be reading your Michener books this winter. Something to look forward to."

She wore a distinctly sad expression on her face as she talked. I sensed she had more to say, so I kept quiet.

"OJ and I have had a rough time of it. It's tough being wife to him and mother to the boys. He doesn't understand I need companionship, someone to talk to. With him and the boys, it's all about radios, cars, and planes. Sometimes I get so frustrated, I don't know what to do with myself. It's not as if I can go for a long walk on the tundra in December. My life is old trailers, destroilets, laundry, generators, and weather reports. I may not be appreciated by the men, but I keep this place running."

"Hey, most of us think you're the soul of this place," I said, trying to be comforting, but not intrusive.

I felt bad for Ellie and didn't know what else to say. I really didn't know her well and would have never guessed she was discontent because she always wore a smile.

"Thanks for listening," she said. "I love OJ, but it's tough living with a man who flies off every other day in little planes that look like they're made of aluminum foil held together with duct tape. I worry. And Jay and Ray are following in their father's footsteps. I need a break, a change of scenery. Today, I'd really like to soak in a tub and read. No interruptions, either. But we don't have a tub. Maybe I'll lie on a beach in Hawaii for part of the winter."

Jay interrupted us by stomping into the room.

"Hey, Ma," he said. "I need a new pair of work gloves so I can finish the tune-up on the truck parked out front.

Feeling a little in the way at this familial exchange, I said, "Well, I'd better go and see what's going on back at the ranch. Bye, Ellie. Bye, Jay."

Ellie had already turned away and was rummaging through a drawer in the chest nearest the door. She stuck out her hand in a goodbye wave.

"Jay," I heard her say, sounding irked, "I don't know why you can't keep track of your things. I can't go down to Sonny's Surplus and get you another supply of work gloves, you know."

"Oh, Ma," came the response as I pushed open the front door of the Hilton and headed back to the tent camp.

* * *

In the wall tent, I found a note from Lucy scrawled on the back of an envelope saying she was with Corey and would see me at dinner or else at the party. I turned the envelope over. It was addressed to Lucy with a return address from Athens, Georgia. The handwriting was feminine—her mother, I guessed.

I dumped Kelly's duffel full of makeup, shoes, and clothes on the floor. There was a long, flowered skirt, clogs, sandals, a pair of high boots, sparkly knee socks, a pink sweater, lacy underwear, even a bottle of cologne. I grabbed her cream-colored sweater with a blue and brown stripe around the V-neck collar. I sat down on my cot and opened the makeup bag to find everything I needed— mascara, blusher, and lipstick. There were plenty of extras, too— eyeliner, an eyelash curler, tweezers, false eyelashes, and foundation that was too light for my now-tanned skin. I would have looked like Dracula had I put it on.

I pawed through my own meager supply of things and retrieved my last pair of fairly clean khakis, always reserved for a night on the town in Umiat. I'd have to think about footwear—all I had was my Sorels and a pair of muddy sneakers. Kelly's feet were way too small for me. I could not cram my size nines into those sixes. I settled on the sneakers.

With my wardrobe picked out, I grabbed my copy of *Hawaii* and headed down to the mess hall for dinner. I found a seat across from Corey, Lucy, and Preacher John. After claiming my space, I sauntered up to the salad line and took a no thank you helping of rather oldish lettuce, radishes tinged with brown, canned garbanzo beans, and Day-Glo orange French dressing.

The main event was stuffed pork chops that covered the plate and looked like they had been cut from a pig weighing 1,000 pounds. Dick the Cook had placed the contents of a large can of applesauce in a plastic bowl that was supposed to look like cut glass. He had lovingly sprinkled cinnamon on top. There were steam trays of broccoli and cauliflower, potatoes au gratin, and light brown gravy. For dessert, he had pulled several cheesecakes out of his walk-in freezer and was now pouring canned blueberry filling over them.

"If you don't want cheesecake," he said, "There's chocolate ice cream and chocolate sauce, too."

* * *

Sam sat down next to Preacher John, kitty-korner from me. He was planning this winter's trip to Costa Rica. I couldn't really imagine Sam lying on a beach, making conversation with women. He wasn't much of a reader, either, except for his Louis L'Amour novels, so I couldn't picture him lying by a pool reading Shakespeare, Michener, or even Perry Mason books. Instead, I pictured him sitting on a shaded porch, tall drink in hand, looking out to sea and listening to the waves. I decided to ask him a few questions about his trip.

"How long will you stay there?" I asked.

"Oh, probably six months or so," came the slow reply. "I'll go down in November, mebbe come back in April."

What will you do for all that time?" I pressed.

"Oh, nothin' much. Just relax, I guess."

I knew further probing would be useless. I'd never find out how Sam spent his time in Costa Rica, but that was okay.

* * *

After dinner, I retreated to the Howard Pass tent. Now was the time to doll myself up. I put on my khakis and slipped Kelly's sweater over my head. I headed over to Al's Quonset feeling almost feminine, despite the dirty sneakers. Maybe the pink lipstick would make up for them.

All the usual suspects were already there, laughing, talking, drinking, and passing around a bong. Jay and Ray were enjoying some booze, even though Ellie had forbidden them to fraternize with us. The archaeologists on my rotation and a few of the GSI folks busily munched popcorn and potato chips. Lucy and Corey, notably absent, had likely found themselves a love nest in which to while away the hours.

I struck up a conversation with Leslie and Chris. Leslie was going back to Indiana U in the fall to finish her MA in anthropology. She doubted she'd ever come back to Alaska because she liked the Great Plains.

"Still," she said, "I had to come up and see for myself what Alaska was like."

"I think most of us had to come up to see what it was like," Chris said. "Kansas is going to look pretty dull to me now."

He was headed to the Lower 48 in a few weeks to see his sixty-something parents who lived a trailer park.

"Sixty's almost ancient," he said. Chris, at thirty-five, seemed ancient to me.

Al was sitting on his makeshift double bed talking to Preacher John and Linda. He caught my eye, smiled, and held my gaze. If I was ever going to make my move, now was the time.

I walked over and sat at the foot of the bed, hearing springs squeak underneath me.

"How'd you like flying over the clouds with me yesterday, New York?" he asked.

"That was fabulous. It was like being high," I answered.

"Well, here, take a hit off the bong and let's get you up there again," he said, looking at me intently and ignoring Linda and Preacher John.

We chatted about Alaska and generally engaged in small talk. After a while, I noticed the party had started to thin out a bit. In the distance, I could hear wall tent doors slamming shut and people yelling good night to one another. Al was talking about going back to Homer for a while to chill, then hopping a flight to Mexico to catch up with a special friend.

Although I was slightly stoned and very tired, I pretended to listen with rapt attention. I made a shallow comment about the interesting life he led. At this point, he leaned forward, grabbed both my arms, and kissed me. When he pulled back, he looked at me as intensely as he had no doubt done with Lynne, Carol, and countless others.

The last people at the party must have decided this was probably a good time to split and did so hurriedly. I leaned into Al and kissed him back. In a matter of seconds, our clothing was on the floor and we were on each other with a passion I'd rarely experienced. The combination of the marijuana high and Al's enthusiasm made the sex incredible. I think it lasted for at least an hour, but in my condition, I wasn't sure. When it was finally over, I fell back on the bed, drenched in sweat.

"How'd you like that?" he asked.

I managed a low purr. Rounds two and three were equally thrilling and gymnastic, but drowsiness overcame me and I fell asleep in the crook of Al's arm.

* * *

The next sound I heard was Lucy's voice yelling outside Al's Quonset:

"Georgeie! Get dressed! Chopper's gonna leave. You already missed breakfast! I got your stuff. Hurry!" she yelled.

"Holy Mother of God!" I screeched.

I sat bolt upright, blinked a few times, saw Al lying next to me, kissed him quickly, and threw my clothes on.

He called after me, "So long, New York! It was great!"

I only had time to yell "Bye" before dashing outside.

In the front seat next to Sam, I blushed with shame, staring at my hands in my lap until I fell back to sleep.

CAMP 11, KINYIKSUKVIK

Still high when we landed at Lancy Lake, I slid fluidly out of the helicopter.

"What's a matter, George? You look like a zombie," Toni said while offloading the 206.

Managing to stand upright with Lucy's help, I motioned my women friend over in while putting my finger to my lips in a "shh" sign.

"Well," I bragged, "I did it. I fucked Al. That's why I'm so tired. His hashish is the most amazing stuff. I almost missed the chopper; Lucy had to come find me. We screwed all night. I've officially gotten back at Carol for Lynne."

I swayed on my feet and thought I might fall down in front of my comrades.

There was a short, stunned silence as my friends took this in, then Lucy, Helen, Kelly, and Frannie patted me on the back. "Way to go, Killer!" they said.

"My hero," Kelly said. "I knew you could do it."

Toni looked at the ground, then at me, and back down at the ground.

In her soft Texas drawl she said, "Well, I've been sleeping with him all summer."

"What? You didn't tell us?" I asked, stunned.

We did a collective double take, mouths opened wide.

"I guess I'm just not used to talking about my sex life like y'all do."

"Oh," I said, feeling Toni had not been forthcoming with us. I felt obligated to give an explanation. "This all started after Al dumped Lynne for Carol, and Kelly said she thought some kind of revenge was called for, so she nominated me to get back at him. She dared me and I couldn't resist."

I still couldn't defend the logic, but I stuck by my story.

"Okay, I get it, I think," Toni said, her face puzzled. "I don't mind, George. He's not my boyfriend or anything. I'll still sleep with him. He's so good. Can't bear to pass him up. Well, see you ladies in a couple days."

She climbed into the back seat of the chopper.

With that, Lucy helped me to my tent where I fell asleep. Malcolm had not noticed anything amiss. He got into the chopper without ever knowing of my daring-do.

I'm told I remained comatose all day. At some point, I smelled food and dragged myself over to the cook tent and received a round of applause. Frannie designated me the State Vegetable of Alaska while I gluttonously ate two full servings of freeze-dried chili and a handful of pilot bread with peanut butter.

While washing dishes after dinner, I told the women of Howard Pass I'd expected a far greater reaction from Toni when I confessed my sin. Maybe she just thought of Al as a convenient screw. The four of us were left to guess how many women Al had really slept with so far, and who would be next. "I want a crack at him," Kelly said, exhaling cigarette smoke through her nostrils.

I'm so horny I could bite something," Frannie said, "but I'll be back home in a week or so, so I can handle it."

"I don't think he's my type, and making love with Corey is the best," Lucy said, "but if we were all weathered in for days on end and Al flew in on the chopper, well. I don't know. Maybe..."

"Maxie on Ikpikpuk is so horny she can't even look at a tube of hand cream without her teeth chattering. She walks around Umiat like she's in heat," Helen said.

After I retreated to my tent for the night, I listed past, present, and potential bedmates for Al on the inside back over of my field notebook in extremely light pencil. I vowed to remember where the untitled list was so I could erase it before turning in the notebook at the end of the season. I mentioned nothing of this in my official entry for the day, and I lied about my condition:

Aug 4. Felt sick when I got off the chopper from Umiat. Was it something?

I ate? No work for me today. Slept all day. A few days left to write up Lancy Lake. I'll be as right as rain tomorrow.

* * *

We explored Lancy Lake for part of the next day. I thought we could have spent many more days there, but because our time was now limited, we'd have to sample a small fraction of what we saw. Frannie, Helen, and Tom, Alaskans all, thought there were eight distinct concentrations of house pits and cache pits.

"I see that. Let's run this by Malcolm when he comes back," Tom said.

"Uh-huh. I think I see what you're saying. Yeah, there're like empty places between the concentrations," I said.

"Yup," Helen said shielding her face from the rain with her hand. "I vote we pack it in. The rain is getting worse."

"The wind is blowing something horrible," *Frannie* said, putting up the hood on her raincoat. "Only idiots would work in shit like this."

The weather, now turned rainy and cool, made many full workdays uncertain. Twilight came earlier and earlier. On the next weather day, I took advantage of the downtime by reading more archaeology and continuing Hawaii, but I couldn't read until the wee hours of the morning like I had in June because it was too dark.

Snug in my sleeping bag one snowy morning, I looked out of my south-facing tent in wonderment to see the entire site before me covered with a dusting of snow.

I contemplated my near-term future as it loomed ever closer. Loss: that's all it was. I'd leave the field for good on August nineteenth, and on the twenty-second, I'd be on a plane for Fairbanks. The following day, I'd fly to DC, say goodbye to my college friends, and, a week later, fly to New York to say goodbye to my parents as they headed south.

I remembered that my mother had taken me on a road trip to Florida when I was five, right after my father died. We stayed with one of her best friends, whom I hadn't met before. I liked her and her little wire-haired fox terrier. The dog's name was Tecky, short for Technical Sergeant. I didn't know what that meant, but Tecky and I became best friends. I hadn't associated my father's death with Florida until that night. I hated Florida, and now I knew why.

"It's one big elephants' graveyard," I mumbled out loud.

The timing couldn't be worse. I'd move from DC to Connecticut just as they were moving south. I would start a completely new life in grad school. So, there I'd be:

No safety net.

No Malcolm and gang.

No DC pals.

No parents.

No dog.

Alone.

I had to be at UConn by the second of September to register for classes. Could I transition that fast? Could I transition at all?

Here I was in the middle of a wilderness, terrifying a short while ago, but now a refuge. This wild place had a rhythm, one I'd adapted to during my short stay. The landscape had embraced me and I had become a part of it.

I had also become part of a team that depended on one another. Bonding with them was a significant gift. The old voice telling me to be independent and keep my emotional distance was fading. As long as we had each other's backs, I'd be fine.

But who will have my back when I leave?

* * *

The next day, the Jet Ranger reappeared despite bad weather. Malcolm and Toni were back and we began to strategize about tackling the site. We gathered for the usual lunch of pilot bread heaped high with goodies, then walked south through a multitude of house pits. Malcolm noted several distinct concentrations of them, most seemed to be three or four feet across and excavated a few inches into the ground. Their smaller equivalents, storage or cache pits, averaged about four feet across. Malcolm called these groupings localities, meaning they seemed to be distinct physically from one another but were obviously part of the same huge site.

They were fairly close to one another and it looked like there were paths connecting them. I wondered if each grouping represented a different family or a different neighborhood.

"Jeez, there must be forty house pits here," I said when we stopped at the grouping nearest to camp.

"Look at all this recent stuff strewn around," Lucy said. There were cans with bullet holes, rifle shells, a pair of men's long underwear, canvas fragments, and a couple pieces of an old stove.

"Looks like this part of the site has been occupied like forever," Kelly said.

"And see all the caribou bone," I said, pointing to a thin scatter strewn across the ground near my feet. Some bones carried cut marks, indications of butchering.

"And there are some flakes nearby, next to this house pit," Frannie said.

"These are winter house pits," said Malcolm as we continued to the south end of the lake. He leaned on his walking stick. "See, they're dug into the ground, I'd say about two feet, and so are their entrance tunnels. They all face south or east. And there must be 100 cache pits here. Maybe this end of Lancy Lake was the winter village, and up near where we're camped was the summer village, where the house pits are shallow and don't have tunnels."

"Hot damn," I said. "You said Lancy Lake would be the best, and it is."

Malcolm was beginning to limp—it was time to wrap things up for the day. We turned around and began the half mile or so back to camp and the spectacular ring of boulders. The karigi looked to be fifteen feet across, much larger than any of the house pits, and had one well-defined entrance or gap in the boulder ring. Someone had put a trench through it years before.

"I'll check my pile of articles to see who was here when I get back to my tent," Malcolm said. He slowly picked his way around the boulder ring leaning on the rocks with one hand for support.

The *karigi* and its mysteries so entranced us, we decided to sit inside it and get high. I lit a joint and passed it around. Toni helped Malcolm find a comfortable sitting position. Hoping for inspiration or a vision, we inhaled deeply.

Clouds swirled overhead while we stayed in the same spot—it was as if our little band in the karigi was the center of the universe and everything moved around us. In the sunshine of the late afternoon, it was warm enough to lie back on the ground. I took off my heavy sweater. The bugs were gone for the year. The brief frost we'd had the night before ensured that.

Time stood still, or did it? The cool breeze and sinking sun meant fall; the tundra was already turning a fiery red. I'd be leaving in two weeks. I pushed melancholy thoughts aside, stared at an elephant-shaped cloud, and passed the joint to Frannie.

Eventually, we got up and dusted ourselves off for the short walk back to the cook tent. Because Malcolm's ankle was throbbing, Toni got on his bad side, put an arm around him, and the two of them walked over together. We sang the chorus from a sea chantey to urge Toni and Malcolm on:

Heave away, my bully, bully boys;
Heave away, haul away;
Heave away and don't you make no noise;
We're bound away for Australia.

The sudden sight of a large grizzly bear on the flanks of the closest mountain as we reached Malcolm's tent stopped us in our tracks. We stood together, forming a giant animal as we'd been taught.

"Yo, bear! Go away!" Toni yelled, having spotted him first about a quarter of a mile away.

We easily determined which direction the bear was headed because the sun illuminated his large, honey-colored behind as he ambled up a terrace at the base of Isikut Mountain. The bear paid us no attention, seemed content to wander, and was soon out of sight. We sang a chorus of "The Bear Went Over the Mountain" to urge the bear on his way.

The bear went over the mountain;
The bear went over the mountain;
The bear went over the mountain;
To see what he could see.

We didn't see that particular bear again.

* * *

After dinner in the cook tent, Malcolm hobbled back to his own tent, with Toni at his side. Toni, Lucy, and Kelly left the cook tent to catch up on field notes and mend rips in various items of clothing, leaving Frannie and I in the cook tent drinking tea and Tang.

"I got a personal question to ax you," she said.

"Yeah, what?"

"Do you always come when you have sex?"

Stunned, I paused at her frankness before answering, "No, do you?"

"Un uh. I've always wanted to ax someone that question and you seemed like you'd answer it. My husband and I have a great sex life, but I have nothing to compare it with because I was a virgin when I got married, Cat'lic that I was."

Frannie wasn't shy telling me about the frequency of their screwing and the stamina of her husband. I was astonished at her candor. I had a few tales of my own but had never considered going into such great detail with someone I'd just recently met.

Who gives a shit? We're sitting here in a tent in the middle of nowhere. Who's gonna know?

"The first time I got it from behind was in my shower, I almost saw the face of God. Jerry could go for hours. When we went out for breakfast the next morning, the shit made me pay," I said.

"He should have paid you!" Frannie said, then paused. "I didn't mean that the way it sounded."

I regaled her with more tales of lovers, positions, and penis size into the wee hours of the morning, and she continued describing Jim's lovemaking in excruciating detail.

"I like it doggy style," she said. "It's so nasty."

"Oh, yeah. Makes you feel dominated, and of course that's what they like. And I'll tell you something; I did it with Al that way, too. We screwed several times."

"Jeez, I hope you didn't hurt him—he's our pilot!"

"You know I did it because he dumped Lynne for Carol. She was heartbroken, so this is revenge."

"I don't see how that helps Lynne."

"Kelly said it would and I believe her."

We stepped out into the crisp night air, with only a glimmer of sun coming from behind the mountains. I realized I was aroused.

I loved listening to Frannie speak in her New York nasal accent. I realized I missed the East, although not enough to leave the tundra behind sooner than planned. I thought of the City, of chestnuts actually roasting on an open fire, skyscrapers soaring, taxi cabs honking their horns. These were a few of the things I missed. And DC? No New York accents, but people from all corners of the planet, living among cherry blossoms and landmarks that I knew and loved.

Like the asshole buddies we'd become, we pitched our tents next to each other. We were in the middle of a conversation when we crawled into our respective homes away from home.

"Your New York accent is thicker than mine," she screamed in her softest voice.

"You bitch, that's not true. Who else says *ax* instead of ask? That would be you," I hollered back.

"Pipe down, you two!" Tom said from the other side of camp. "You're not that interesting."

I found my own accent became thicker when we were together, but the general consensus among the crew was Frannie sounded as if she and I were from different planets. She brought back memories of the tall buildings, honking taxis, and smell of the City in the world I'd left behind. The Nigu River was not the City, but we were in the prettiest part of the Brooks Range, and even the two New Yorkers were content. We could look out of our tents and see the sun sparkling on the lake. True, snow inched down the mountain slopes every day, but the setting was as close to perfect as I'd ever seen. It was like a fancy summer camp, and Malcolm was our camp counselor.

* * *

The next morning, Malcolm decided we should tackle Locality Two, the supposed archaeological jackpot. We got a late start because of wet autumn weather. I didn't want to leave the warmth of my sleeping bag to venture out into fog and rain, and I imagine no one else did either. On the other hand, Locality Two beckoned.

The locality occupied a large gravel terrace near the lakeshore. There were over forty tent rings, a bunch of house pits and cache pits, several hearths with microblades inside them, worked bone, and flakes scattered randomly in and around the structures. And that was just what we could easily see in our initial walk over. Locality Two would be a bitch to test because there were so many features. It struck me as the middle of the site, its density reminiscent of the area around Forty-Second Street and Fifth Avenue in New York City.

I passed my analogy on to Frannie because I thought she'd understand it. She called me an ass and said I didn't know shit from Shinola. "It's more like Greenwich Village, you fool; it's not on a north-south grid like midtown."

I was about to stick my tongue out at her when Malcolm limped over.

"Put in a meter square next to that house pit, Lieutenant Georgeie," he said, pointing toward a flattish piece of ground near one of them.

"Yes, sir!" I answered, excited to dig an entire square meter of earth. Who knew what I'd find?

"Frannie and Lucy, I need you at Locality Five. We'll leave Toni, Georgeie, and Kelly at Locality Two right now," Malcolm said.

Lucy and Frannie followed Malcolm over to Locality Five to begin measuring in features, leaving me to ponder the square I was about to begin. Like Frannie and Lucy had done, I laid out the square with stakes and string, making sure the sides would be at right angles with each other with the help of my six-meter tape. Kelly and Toni put in a dateline and a baseline, then Toni stood at features and artifacts. They noted distance and bearing of each pit while I carefully excavated my square.

I dug slowly over the next two days, finding neither artifacts nor stratigraphy, just brown dirt. I motioned Malcolm over and bitched about my empty square.

"George, don't think of it as an empty square; there's a reason why there's nothing there, and we don't know what it is yet," Malcolm said, perusing the square. "When we draw the final site map this winter, we'll be able to see where there's lots of stuff, and where there's hardly any stuff—it's the pattern, not the number of artifacts."

"Oh," I said, "I get it. I mean, there could be a lot of reasons why there's nothing in my square, like maybe someone put a piece of hide down here to flint knap, then flung the leftover stuff some other place. I guess finding nothing is important, too."

"That's my smart little camper," Malcolm said, and patted me on the head.

* * *

We toiled away recording Lancy Lake over the next few days. Each feature was mapped and photographed, and at least one square meter was excavated in every locality. The site map would reveal some of Kinyiksukvik's intricate secrets, but other secrets might never be discovered. Maybe the localities were neighborhoods, the idea I was fondest of, or maybe some were occupied at different times or different seasons. We might not reveal all of the secrets at Lancy Lake, but based on our work, future investigators might unlock more of Kinyiksukvik's treasures.

The high point for me was drawing the *karigi*—the location of our vision-seeking a few days earlier. I measured each separate boulder and carefully refigured the numbers to the appropriate scale for my notebook. I wanted to get every detail just right. So fascinating did I find the site that when Malcolm called off the next day's work due to snow, I read archaeology texts all day, only taking short breaks only to shoot the shit in the cook tent.

The next day, I began transferring distances and bearings of the eight different concentrations. There was a multitude of features— house pits, cache pits, hearths, and tent rings, with caribou fences and hunting blinds in the areas farthest out from the lake. I knew the map would take at least two days to draw.

I looked out of my tent that evening and admired our Day-Glo pink flagging tape wafting in the light breeze at the approximate center of each concentration.

How the fuck are we going to record all this before the end of the summer?

I wrote about the benefits, unrelated to archaeology, of this incredible site and its setting in my notes:

Aug 11. Because the site is clustered around the lake, the entire crew can work on it together and we'll actually be in sight of each other. Don't have to walk far—maybe we could get an extra hour of sleep. We can yell for each other if we find something cool, or if someone sees another bear or a wolverine.

Christ, I hope not!

* * *

When Tom and Helen returned, I finished mapping Locality One, the smallest of all of the concentrations. It occupied a small but distinct knoll and consisted of six structures, possibly a house pit and several cache pits. It would be a piece of cake to investigate and record.

As we got out our survey gear to record dimensions of the area, Lucy, looking down at the ground next to her daypack yelled, "Hey, look at this," picking up a flat object.

"What's that you got there, Miss Lucy?" Malcolm said.

"Look!" she said.

She held half of the bottom of an oval wooden container, smooth and flat, having been worked to a uniform thickness.

"Wow," Toni said, taking the bowl fragment from her and feeling its smoothness before passing it to Malcolm.

"Cool! This is the first wooden artifact we've found all summer," Malcolm said. "Good job, Lucy. Go write that sucker up."

"Aye aye, Captain Malcolm," she replied.

* * *

Malcolm decided it was time to finish Locality Two and wrap things up. From what I could gather, there were several different time periods represented. There was modern stuff, like canvas, tin cans, and Blazo cans, meaning someone had camped there recently. But the house and cache pits could be 100 to 500, perhaps even 1,000 years old. Some looked like the stones had been placed there yesterday, and others were covered with moss and lichens.

We also saw various colors of chert and a piece of highly prized obsidian.

"Like I said so long ago, there isn't any obsidian around here," Malcolm said as we gathered around a flake scatter, "so it's probably from the Koyukuk area. There's obsidian all over Alaska but it only comes from a few places. Okay, enough yapping on my part. Frannie, put in a one-meter test pit next to one of the house pits in Locality Six. Lucy, do the same in Locality Four "

I watched as Frannie measured out her square with stakes and string, making sure the sides were at right angles to one other. We shot the shit while I smoked a cigarette.

"Why does Malcolm want a test pit here?" I asked.

Frannie started out seriously: "Don't know, but he'll probably put one in every locality, that's my guess. There's lots of info here and plain old shovel tests won't tell us much. Plus, the fucking entrenching tools will break your back."

"Oh, yeah, I remember," I said, thinking of the shitty khaki-green shovels we had.

"See, you measure in each artifact you find in your test pit by distance from the north and east walls and by depth. Your six-meter tape and line level are your best friends. Of course, you'll have to stop thinking about sex for half a minute."

"Fuck off, Frannie."

"Never mind. Then, you can locate the square on the site map by measuring distance and bearing of the northeast corner from the locality datum. Well, you'll be doing that, I guess. Tedious work, but kinda fun, too.

"Look at all this fire-cracked rock twenty centimeters below the surface," she continued. "Must be a hearth nearby."

"I get that, but what critter is this?" I asked, pointing at several bones at the same level.

"Caribou, you fool! Think of all the caribou fences around here. You gotta think the people stood behind each *inuksuk* and drove the animals into the lake here."

"Duh, of course. I'll take a photo of the square."

"Put this arrow in the photo and have it pointing north."

I took the wooden scale with centimeters painted on it, took the shot with no major difficulty, then ambled over to Lucy's square to see what she was finding. She had gone through the duff and was now troweling through the brown soil, already elbow-deep. I peered down into the hole. No permafrost, no fire-cracked rock here, but pottery fragments were appearing in the bottom of the square. Lucy dutifully measured the position of each one, drew them in her notebook, and continued digging.

"Hey, pottery fragments," Malcolm said as he walked over. "The pottery up north stinks. There's nothing much to use for temper, like, there's no wood. All they got is feathers and pebbles to keep it together. They call this 'Barrow crudware.' Useless shit."

About forty centimeters down, a stone projectile point appeared in Lucy's square.

"Malcolm!" she yelled with excitement, her right arm and most of her face covered with dirt. Malcolm hobbled over to Lucy. The rest of us followed.

The brown chert point was nearly complete, long and pointed like a lance, and diamond-shaped in cross section—a true "Lancy Lake" point.

"Could be up to 4,000 years old, when Eskimos were in the area. I don't think it's an Athabaskan point. Nope, I think it's Eskimo," Malcolm said, turning the artifact over in his hand.

He examined the point carefully. I took it from Malcolm's hand to admire the precise flaking, then handed it to Lucy to record its position and label a bag for it.

There were several layers of charcoal interspersed with layers of soil, an indication of several occupations. I got down on my hands and knees and stuck my head into the pit and saw the various levels of different charcoal.

"This is so exciting!" I said, then yelled down into Lucy's pit, "Do you know how filthy you are? You're gonna have to burn those clothes."

Lucy kept her head down in the pit and didn't look up. I heard a muffled "I don't care" drift upwards.

"I think I'll take a radiocarbon sample. We have enough in the budget to send five or six samples to the Smithsonian Institution," Malcolm said, scratching his head through his wool cap. "Georgeie, would you go get me some tinfoil?"

"Sure," I said. I got up and walked over to the bleached and ragged blue tarp. Not knowing how much he'd need, or why he needed it, I brought the whole roll.

"Now put your cigarette out. The smoke will contaminate the sample," Malcolm said, wiping his trowel on his pants and, with Tom's help, lowering himself into a kneeling position.

I gently stubbed out my smoke and put it in my down vest pocket so I could smoke the rest later.

He took a piece from the roll of tinfoil and shaped it into a cone with the narrow end folded up so none of the charcoal would fall out of the bottom.

"Guess I'll take a sample from the concentration of charcoal nearest to the point. The two could be associated and we might get a more accurate date for the point," he mumbled.

With the sharp end of his trowel, he dug out some of the charcoal from the wall of the test pit and gently placed it in the tinfoil funnel, then folded the top into a neat envelope.

"See, you want a large enough sample to be able to measure the percent of carbon remaining in the charcoal," Malcolm said, a satisfied look on his face. "Okie dokie, that's that. Lucy, label a paper bag and put the sample in it? Don't take it out of the tinfoil. And Georgeie, draw all four soil profiles and the current bottom of the square. Let Kelly photograph it, okay? You're better at drawing and Kelly understands the camera better."

And the fucking Brunton compass, too.

I got down on the ground, stretched out on my side, and reached over to the far wall, outlining the different soils with the tip of my trowel. I repeated this exercise three more times. I drew the profiles in pencil on the graph paper section in my notebook. They looked good to me.

* * *

Cold, gray autumn was in the air with ever more frequent rain and snow showers. After a morning getting dirty while working in the rain and mud, Malcolm called a weather day. Tom, Helen, and I stayed in the cook tent after lunch, drinking cocoa and eating peanuts. I listened as my friends described Fairbanks life.

"In midwinter, the sun rises after eleven a.m. and sets before one p.m.," Tom said.

"And snow falls from September to May," Helen added.

That sounded really shitty to me and my face must have indicated disbelief. "But," Frannie said, "in the summer, the sun doesn't set until after midnight, rises around two in the morning but it can still get up to 100 degrees."

"And we have thunderstorms, too," Helen said.

"You're shitting me," I said, incredulous.

Gradually, our talk of weather changed to gossip about grad students and faculty in the anthro department at UAF. I listened intently to tales of preeminent Arctic scholars whose names I'd only seen in print—messy divorces, student liaisons, and fluid sexual identities abounded.

"They sound nuts," I said. "I'm going back to my tent to read. *Hawaii* is calling to me."

I was up to the chapter about Father Damien and the leper colony on Molokai. A little while later, Frannie "knocked" on my tent flap and invited herself in.

"Hey, Killer," she said, her blue eyes twinkling, "Mind if I come in?"

"Nah."

Frannie was happy in Alaska, she said, but missed New York, even though she frequently flew back to see her family. We talked about our mutual fondness for the sleek Chrysler Building and Grand Central Station with the constellations on its ceiling.

"We're going to be lifelong friends, I know it," she said, "even though you're a snot from Westchester."

"And you're a low-life hoodlum from Manhattan," I answered.

We laughed. I hoped I would ultimately become a hybrid of two worlds, the wilderness and the city, as comfortable in a tent as in an apartment building, something Frannie had already achieved.

* * *

You know," Malcolm said when the Jet Ranger flew in the next day, "this is the last time we'll all be together."

He was right, I realized with a sharp intake of breath. Ron had rejoined us and Frannie was about to leave. We would now fly to Umiat by twos and stay there. Helen and Tom would be the first to go. Another two would fly out two days after that. The crew would be reunited in Umiat by the twenty-first, give or take a day. It would take extra flying hours to get all four crews back in the next few days, but Al and Sam would do it. The season was winding down.

We ran to get our cameras and give them to Sam and Frannie to take pictures of our hardy band. We posed in front of the beautiful, dark mountains with a vast reach of tundra sweeping down in front of us. The sky, cloudy in spots, held patches of blue and sunlight showed on the redness of the tundra behind us. Malcolm, Kelly, Ron and Tom made up the back row. Malcolm and Tom struck cool poses in their sunglasses. Kelly squeezed tried to look professional, a field notebook in her hand, while Ron, in his thick glasses and bright orange survey vest, looked kind of goofy. Helen, smallest of us all, stood in front of Tom, her parka zipped up to the top because she was always cold.

I got down in front of Malcolm and smiled. Toni, still holding onto her topo map and staring directly ahead, kneeled down next to me, while Lucy kneeled and brushed her bangs out of her eyes. The guys had full beards by this point in the summer, and the women had wild hair, but we looked happy, determined, and somewhat clean. The shutters clicked.

It was a family portrait, so obviously a family.

After the big photo shoot, we hugged Frannie goodbye. I hollered after her, "Don't do anything I wouldn't do, bitch." She flipped me off and promised to make my life miserable the last few nights we'd be together in Umiat. I missed her already, but Kelly would return with Ron, and that was okay, too.

But before we got in another abbreviated workday, Ron had a tale to tell.

The next two days were part survey, part packing things away, and part napping during the rainier moments out in Howard Pass.

"A chopper flew into Umiat yesterday with two US Senators," he said, excitement in his voice. "Udall and Seiberling are up here touring the petroleum reserve, so we decided to welcome them! Umiat is decorated in their honor. The door to the supply tent now says 'Mo Udalled here.' A door on one of the destroilets in the Hilton said 'Mo shat here,' but OJ washed it off."

"Jeez, I miss all the good stuff!" Helen laughed, pretending to pout.

"Jay and Marty built Mo an altar of Spam, Sunny Jim, and Dak bacon cans. Lynne and Dave carefully excavated a single, perfect tussock and placed it lovingly behind the altar for effect," Kelly added. "We had a brief ceremony, including hymns and prayers, and afterwards the usual wild party."

"Christ Almighty," I guffawed.

"Also, I think Marty got laid," Ron said, "but I don't know who the lucky gal was because by the time he staggered into our tent by mistake, we were all loaded and nobody knew much of anything."

I began to miss Tom and Helen right away; I even missed their conjugal red and white tent. But I missed Frannie even more.

CAMP 12, NIGU RIVER

We moved to the Nigu River camp after recording as much as possible at Lancy Lake in the time we had. There would be other expeditions, I was sure of it.

The next two days were part survey, part packing things away, and part napping during the rainier moments out in Howard Pass. Nigu River camp was a let down from Lancy Lake.

We laughed at the tale of Umiat going wild once again.

Malcolm became melancholy. He missed Viola; that much was obvious, because he kept bringing her up in conversations having nothing to do with her. His ankle still hurt and he had to walk carefully on the uneven ground, always using his hiking stick. He slugged back a few aspirin every day and, once in a while, a pain pill.

* * *

The next day, Lucy, Malcolm, and I surveyed an area just to the west of the river. Malcolm's ankle was still achy and slightly swollen, so we walked at a leisurely pace and he made good use of his walking stick. We stopped to write up several caribou fences and an enigmatic single cairn, giving Malcolm a chance to rest and rub his right ankle.

It was Lucy who first spotted the big honey-colored grizz on the far side of Inyorurak Creek.

"Hey, look," she said, pointing to the bear.

"I think he's far enough away that he might not see us," Malcolm said quietly.

We walked a little farther north and sat down to eat lunch, sitting in a circle, and keeping our eyes peeled, just in case.

"Uh oh," Malcolm said, finishing his second piece of pilot bread, "The bear just recrossed the creek. See? He's moving in our general direction. I think we should head back to camp."

As he spoke, the grizz headed south along the terrace. He stopped and stood on his hind legs by the cairn we'd just recorded. While I'd become somewhat used to bears over the summer, I didn't like the look of a bear rearing up and sniffing the air about a half a football field's distance from us.

"I bet he smells us," Lucy said, eyes trained on our furry friend.

"You're right," Malcolm said. "And now he's between us and camp."

We gathered close to each other at Malcolm's urging, stood tall, waved our arms, and began yelling "Yo Bear! We're really *BIG* and we're going to bite you!"

The grizz rocked back and forth on his hind legs and cocked his head to look at us from different angles, still sniffing the air. I could easily see his face and his breath from that distance. He backed off slowly, finally turned around, and sauntered past the cairn away from us.

"Thank God," Malcolm sighed, "I won't miss brown bears at all when we leave here."

We sat and watched the bear for a while as he headed north. Our yelling had attracted the other survey team who called us on the radio. Only a quarter of a mile or so away from each other, and easily visible in our bright red and orange DayGlo clothes, we waved and told the other team we were walking back to camp.

"Hey. Be on the lookout for a grizz. He's headed north on your side of the Nigu. We're headed in. You guys should pack it in, too," Malcolm said into the walkie-talkie.

"Headed in. Toni, over and out."

"But leave the radio on, just in case!" Malcolm yelled. "Malcolm, clear."

* * *

When we got back, I walked over to the disintegrating tarp to throw away some garbage. As I bent over to lift the corner of the tarp, I saw a second bear, darker than the first, walking along the riverbank headed towards camp. I felt the hair on the back of my neck rise.

"Hey! Bear! Another one!" I yelled, running towards the cook tent.

The three of us gathered to watch the second bear approach from the south. The first bear, having dropped down to the river, headed toward camp from the north. Although they were both on the opposite bank of the Nigu, it did not escape my attention they could easily cross the river and charge us in less than a minute. I watched as the two bears neared each other, heads down, looking for ground squirrels or voles.

"Holy shit," Lucy said, "You don't see stuff like this every day. Two bears!"

"Thank God we have the loaded shotgun," I whispered. The closer the bears got to us and to each other, the softer we spoke and the more nervous I became. My palms sweated inside my glove liners.

"Okay, gang, let's stand close together again," Malcolm said calmly.

We gathered together and made a cacophonous clatter for the second time in less than two hours, blowing our bear whistles and beating on pots and pans I'd grabbed from under the old tarp. I didn't know if it was our noise or whether the two bears saw each other at the same time, but suddenly they turned tail and sped away from each other.

"What just happened?" I asked.

"Did they scare each other?" Lucy asked.

"I don't have a fucking clue," Malcolm answered.

"Jesus, Joseph, and Mary," I added.

Just then, screams emanated from the radio—bear number one had sped past the other team at close range. We could hear yells, whistles, and bells all at the same time.

You guys okay?" Malcolm yelled into the radio.

"Yeah, but that was close! What did ya do to that poor bear?" Ron yelled back, "And thanks for sending him our way!"

"Scared the shit out of him, I guess," Malcolm said. "Now get your asses back here on the double."

"Aye aye, General, Sir," Ron said. "Over, out, and everything else."

I watched the team high up on the slope, brightly colored ants on the giant red landscape, pick up their packs and work their way down to the river.

In about five minutes, both bears had disappeared and the six of us were reunited. Malcolm, Lucy, and I hugged Toni, Kelly, and

Ron. Malcolm considered posting bear watch for the night, but by the end of the evening, after we had sat for several hours in an outward-facing circle, musk-ox style, without spotting anything, he decided it wasn't necessary.

"We've scared *all* the bears around here so badly with our noise and our stinky human smell," he said, "I don't think they'll be back tonight."

* * *

Standing next to the river, Kelly asked me, "So, tell me more about Al. Was it really good?"

"Al? Oh, yeah," I said. "Lots of stamina. We screwed three times. I felt like I was in a coma afterwards, and you know I did it for Lynne, and you dared me to do it, too, remember?"

"Oh, yeah, I remember. Well, congratulations, George. I can't imagine you had any doubts you could snag him."

"Well," I said, "I can be little shy, but this had everything going in my favor. There was booze. There was pot. It was a dare, so I screwed his brains out. Your makeup and the sweater helped me look just right. I can't believe Toni's been sleeping with him all along!"

"You think he'd sleep with me, too?"

"Of course! You're gorgeous! Just one toss of those auburn curls and a bat of those eyelashes and he'd be putty in your hands! Everyone lusts after you, Kelly."

"Oh, sure. Not *everyone!* Jim's gone and I'm horny, but I still have time to work on Al. And you still want that your dreamboat at Ikpikpuk, don't you?"

"Yup, I do. I'm sure there's something there, but he's married," I sighed. We stamped out our butts, then put them in our jeans pockets, and dove into our tents to retrieve our daypacks for an afternoon of surveying.

* * *

Malcolm, Toni, and I walked to the west, finding and recording yet another caribou fence. These strange, exotic structures, so fascinating just a few short weeks ago, now felt commonplace, even dull. I longed for a flake scatter with bright green chert and reddish jasper flakes, or even a cache pit. But that day, recording another row of *inuksuks* was my lot.

Sitting on my butt on the tundra and smoking a Marlboro, mountains surrounded me, their peaks showing new snow. The splash of a glacially fed stream punctuated the silence. I felt lucky to inhabit the vast, unspoiled tundra, and decided I had nothing to bitch about. I drew the best damn diagram of any caribou fence I'd done, knowing it would be among my last in this splendid world.

The following day, Lucy, Toni, and I walked north for two and a half miles, finding still more fences.

This must have been like the Chicago Stockyards or something, I drew each cairn as realistically as possible, as if I were one of the Wyeths. I'd be gone soon, but the *inuksuks* would remain, their stories told only in photos and illustrations.

At the end of the day, the light-colored grizz made a brief reappearance. We stood together, yelled, and stared him down. I'd like to think he backed off quickly because he recognized our voices and aroma from the other day, but I couldn't be sure. We waved the bear goodbye:

"Bye, bear. Don't forget to write," Lucy shouted.

"Don't let the door hit you in the ass," Malcolm yelled.

"Bye bye, Pooh Bear," Toni said softly.

We watched as Pooh wandered up a side drainage, then watched for another half hour or so to make sure he'd left the area.

Rain began to pelt us, dampening our spirits along with the tundra. We broke out our rain gear and continued trudging homeward. We'd also started carrying our down vests with us because of the increasing cold. Cold and dry felt okay, but cold and wet was a bummer.

Just as the wind picked up, I caught a glimpse of a shiny something on the ground ahead of me.

"Hey," I yelled, "here's something that's not a caribou fence— a jasper flake. Yippee, skippy!"

We dropped to our hands and knees and I lit a smoke, knowing a nicotine jolt would warm me up temporarily.

"Hey, y'all," Toni said, "a projectile point. Really cool, too."

I bent down and grabbed a point with a tang on the distal end. It reminded me of a hook. "Ooh, what's this? Maybe Northern Archaic? Could be four to six thousand years old!" I proclaimed.

"Over here! A striped biface!" Lucy crowed.

Another great find. I ventured a guess that it was a preform for a Lancy Lake point. I felt so smart—a Doctor of Arctic Archaeology in the making. But the weather grew colder and wetter, sleet stinging our faces. We wrote up the site even faster than Lucy and I had written up the Dead Spot, collected the points, quickly stuffed them in labeled coin envelopes, and put them in our packs. After I finished the simplest of site maps, we dead-headed back to camp.

* * *

The aroma of chili grew strong as we neared home. I looked into the cook tent to see Kelly putting the finishing touches on dinner. Drops of rain ran off the end of my nose.

"Smells heavenly, Kelly," I said.

"Even freeze-dried chili smells good after a day in the rain," she said.

"Wait 'til you see what we found!" I said.

"Go change out of your wet clothes first and hurry back," Malcolm ordered.

"Yes, sir," I said and crisply saluted him.

In my tent, I shivered and goosebumps came up on my arms. I put on my dry plaid flannel shirt topped with my red down vest, then walked back over to the cook tent with the artifact bags.

"Look at our tanged biface," I said to the gang once I was inside the warmth of the cook tent. "Northern Archaic, don't you think, Malcolm?"

He shook a finger at me and said, "Ach, you are wrong zees time, my little friend!"

"What, then?"

"Arctic Small Tool tradition, maybe from Choris times. If it was a Northern Archaic point, it would probably be notched, not tanged."

I feigned great disappointment and grief, threatening to commit hara-kiri with it.

"No you won't!" Malcolm quipped, "You'll change its wear patterns. Someone studying this years from now will struggle with the fact that microscopic remnants of down and wool are sticking to it along with traces of blood. Take this kitchen knife and kill yourself if you have to but fill out the paperwork first." He handed me the knife Kelly had used to dice an onion.

"Well, okay, I've changed my mind." I said, "I'll just clean up the dishes after dinner instead."

"Good choice," Malcolm said as he passed the point over to Kelly and Ron, who hadn't seen it yet, then to Toni, Lucy, and me for another look. Ron grabbed the rest of the artifact bags and pulled out our other goodies for show and tell.

"Well, look at all these. This is quite a haul and that point is so cool," Malcolm declared.

"The force is strong in you, young Skywalker," Ron said to me.

* * *

After our freeze-dried beef and rice had been eaten and I'd washed our dirty dishes in the river, Ron and I took a big plastic bag of garbage away from camp, cleared a space on the ground, dumped the trash, and started a bonfire under clearing skies. The prohibitions against open fires had been lifted after recent bear encounters. We'd been shipping our garbage back to Umiat all summer long but could no longer take chances with aromatic garbage in camp.

Howard Pass wasn't alone in contending with bear problems, or so we'd heard through the Umiat gossip grapevine. Lookout Ridge had recently endured two all-night standoffs with multiple bears. The entire crew stood guard each time, banding together, yelling, and banging pots, pans, utensils, whatever. On several occasions, shots had to be fired into the air, and once there had been a close enough call that Mitch, the crew leader, had contemplated shooting one of them.

But no one wanted to shoot a bear. They were beautiful creatures—sleek, powerful, and noble. No shots were fired, but we heard that the Lookout Ridge crew continued to have encounters until their last day in the field.

I sprinkled the pile of garbage and willow branches with a little Blazo and lit it with my Bic. Soon, the flames rose to waist high. It was ten in the evening and getting colder in the gathering darkness. We stared into the fire, warming our fronts, our hands stretched toward the flame.

After the fire died down, we stayed to make sure no embers were left and used the ends of our walking sticks to put the tin can remains and other non-burnables back into the garbage bag. After we'd worked at it for a while, I looked at him and sighed.

"Feels strange Tom and Helen won't be back," Ron said.

"Well, *I* don't want to leave," I said. "I've never experienced such contentment in spite of all the danger out here."

Ron, not usually not much for philosophical chitchat, admitted he felt the same way, not only this year, but at the end of *every* summer on the pipeline.

"You have so much fun, face so many perils, and discover so much, all at the same time. Everything else seems irrelevant and unimportant when you get back. Civilization seems too big and too fast. You'll want to hold on to this life for as long as possible," he said, pushing the last of the burned tin cans into the garbage bag, "and you will." Ron leaned on his walking stick and scanned the horizon.

"You won't be overwhelmed for long. You'll get into your new routine at grad school. You'll have your stories and your memories.

Plus, you're going to study with Uncle Mikey. He's an old field hand himself, and he'll understand you're bummed. He'll cut you a few days' slack. Trust me."

I nodded silently as we walked back to camp, grateful for his insight, but still feeling down.

* * *

"Let's inventory our shit this morning," Malcolm said glumly after breakfast the next day. It's raining and we might as well do something useful."

Such light rain had never stopped us before, but Malcolm seemed preoccupied, so I didn't ask why he made the decision. We spent the day inspecting survey gear, cameras, and compasses, cleaning and repairing them as necessary. I volunteered to consolidate the remaining food boxes and burn the empties. Had we really survived on freeze-dried crap, cans of Spam, and jars of peanut butter for almost three months?

While breaking down the boxes, I found the last case of M&Ms, opened it, and took out a package. Okay, so they weren't the peanut kind, but they'd do. I remembered someone saying no matter how good or bad food tasted in the field, you could always find something food-related to complain about, because eating was so important to morale and wellbeing. I wolfed down the M&Ms in about a minute and only thought about sharing them after they were gone.

I could see Malcolm and Lucy just upslope from me rolling out empty tents, shaking them in the breeze to get all the twigs, lichens, mud, and cigarette butts out, then putting the now-empty ones back in their tent bags. Such a mundane activity—I'd never see it again.

The six of us burned the trash after dinner, warming our hands over the fire while the sun disappeared. I'd only have one more sunset out in Howard Pass. I tried to inhale the entire scene— sights, smells, smells—into my nostrils without exhaling.

On my final day, Malcolm decreed some of us could survey to the west while others would finish our inventory.

"Please, Malcolm, the All-Girl Survey Crew wants a last crack at working together," Kelly said.

"Okay, but be careful out there with the bruins," Malcolm said, wagging a finger to emphasize his point.

Just before lunch, lazily surveying to the west, finding a lone cairn about four feet high, constructed of weathered lichen-covered rocks. We walked around it, admiring its perfect construction. I started drawing the feature, then noticed adjacent patches of bare ground the exact size of the rocks comprising the cairn.

"What's the deal here?" Kelly asked.

On the cairn's north side, Lucy noticed a piece of paper sticking out from between two rocks about halfway up. She tugged at it and out slipped a piece of Rite-in-the-Rain paper folded in half. It read "Fooled you! Tom!"

"Well, you booger," I said, considering all options for revenge.

Kelly suggested dumping out his Dr. Bronner's shampoo and putting cooking oil in the bottle once we got back to town.

"I'd do that," I said. "Serves him right."

* * *

A mile further, we found two caribou fences running the length of an unvegetated terrace.

I flung my daypack on the ground and rummaged around for some peanut butter and pilot bread. "Ugh. I'm so hungry. Anybody else want lunch?"

"Oh, yeah, I do," agreed Kelly. "The site can wait."

After munching, Lucy talked excitedly about her Dad's visit and how they were going to hike in Mt. McKinley National Park. I wrapped my elbows around my knees, looked at the end of my cigarette, and watched as the smoke curled into the sky.

Kelly, leaning back on her elbows, legs outstretched, stared into the middle distance beyond her boots. Just then, she looked beautiful with her red hair and blue eyes silhouetted in the Arctic sun, beautiful, vulnerable, and lost. Perhaps listening to Lucy talk about her father had stirred up memories for her as it had for me.

The memory of my father's death was still a shroud, usually folded and stored away in the back of my mind, but ready to unfold and envelop me when triggered by an event. The image of Lucy and her father enjoying an experience didn't help, especially since I'd thought my stepfather was dying or dead earlier in the summer. I thought Kelly might be thinking about her father, too. I could tell by her silence and her faraway look.

Lucy must have read our faces. She changed the subject abruptly. "Maybe I'll go back to the University of Georgia in the fall," she said. "What about you guys?"

I brightened, thinking about starting my PhD program at UConn. "I've always loved school," I said. "My parents are afraid I'm becoming a full-time student. I can't wait to hear Uncle Mikey's talks about the intricacies of the temporal bone, his favorite part of the skull."

"What's so interesting about the temporal bone?" Kelly asked.

"I don't know yet. When I find out, I'll tell you," I answered.

"Sounds weird to me," Lucy laughed.

"I don't know what I want to do right now," Kelly said. "Maybe take some time off before grad school. Gotta save some money and decide if I like Alaska stuff or stick with the southwest. It's so much fun here. Maybe I'll stay up north. I don't know."

"But maybe now we should think about recording this site. It's pretty big. It's going to take fucking forever to map, let alone write up," I said.

We got up and broke out our gear. Measuring the length of each fence, as well as the distance and orientation between each cairn, took six long hours. The site demanded extra time to record because of all the outlying windbreaks and other features situated near the cairns. As much as I was growing to love the wilderness and the thrill of discovery, I found recording several caribou fences seemed a tad tedious.

"I bet this is an important site. I bet there's shit loads beneath the surface. You can see where ground squirrels have carried up some flakes when they made their hidey-holes. I could write my MA thesis on it," Kelly said.

"Leaning towards studying Alaska, then?" Lucy asked.

"Don't know yet. Well, maybe," Kelly answered.

"It's cool up here, I'll grant you that," I said, "but Jesus H. Christ, my feet are ready to hike back to camp. It's a long way home and it's after five anyway."

The three of us toddled back to camp, singing "Hi-ho, hi-ho, it's home from work we go." On the way, I lit a cigarette, and then felt a sharp pain in my crotch. An ember had blown off the end of my cigarette, burned a hole next to my jeans zipper, and was now burning through my underwear headed for my pubic hair.

"Ow, what the fuck?" I cried.

Lucy, seeing the smoke, poured water from her canteen on my pants as I hopped up and down.

"Shit," I shouted. "These jeans are practically new! How will I ever show my face in town with a hole in the crotch?"

"Give me a break, George. You will, and you'll be happy to," Kelly.

"Hah!" I said. "Of course, you're right."

We laughed on the way back to camp, even though I felt gloomy because I'd be leaving.

Seeing my expression, Kelly said, "George, don't forget you have one more giant to kill and his name starts with an I. Focus on that!"

"Yeah, George," Lucy said. "Maybe you'll strike gold again."

I perked up immediately.

* * *

That final evening in camp, I longed to stay, and I longed to go. We'd all be together in Umiat, but our little band was already breaking up.

We lit a fire, burned the garbage, and sang all the folk songs we could remember, our faces reflected in the heat and light. I felt conflicted, uncertain, but excited about my new life at UConn, and missing my friends already. I went back to my tent for the night.

Aug 19. Not an exciting day. Some survey. Everything is winding down. Crew has started to go into Umiat for good. Getting cold/dark at night. It's almost over.

Bears around so burned garbage and sang songs around campfire.

* * *

The following morning, I struck my tent and heard the familiar whirr of the chopper. I put a last couple of sentences in my field notes:

Aug 20. Want to stay here. Have learned so much. Is going back east like losing my freedom? Nothing else to say except this has been an astonishing and extraordinary summer.

Thanks, guys. Thanks, Uncle Malcolm.

The chopper landed and Al cut the motor. He helped us throw some extra stuff on board, including many unopened bags of loathsome freeze-dried vegetables. I strapped my daypack to the skids, turned to Malcolm, Kelly, Toni, and Ron, and enveloped them in bear hugs. I thought about the final episode of *The Mary Tyler Moore Show* when everyone hugged each other. I could even hear the music.

Malcolm hugged me saying, "Hey, I'll see you in Umiat, probably tomorrow. Maybe even tonight. There's still time. We'll have some more fun before you go."

Again, I felt like crying. Kelly wiped tears from her face.

Malcolm said, "Listen, Georgeie and Lucy, make sure the Howard Pass tent is spic-and-span by the time I get to Umiat. I'm counting on you!"

"Yes, your worship," Lucy said and bowed.

A last hug and we were in the air, looking down on the four small and lonely looking people below. Al pointed the chopper northeast, and a moment later, camp was lost from view.

* * *

I felt down but had something big to look forward to. In a couple of days, maybe tomorrow, Ian would come in from Ikpikpuk. I had almost forgotten his handsome face and laughing eyes, but I quickly remembered. I knew we'd sing together. Would sparks fly, our harmonies blending as if we'd been on each other's wavelength for years? Despite red flags, my quickening pulse and racing thoughts bathed my brain in a cocoon of anticipatory lust.

What could happen? So what if he's handsome? He's married—I just want to sing with him, that's all.

But, Christ, he was so good-looking and so unbelievably funny. I tried to take my mind off my impending encounter with Ian to focus on the autumn tundra.

Next to Al in the front seat, I tried to make small talk. We hadn't chatted since our night of wild, frantic sex. Words escaped me. *How's the weather?* came to mind, but I thought anything would sound stupid at this point. I wanted to tell him I'd enjoyed the sex and that, even though we wouldn't see each other again, I liked him, but I felt nauseated at this treackly thought and said nothing.

The truth was, I had slept with him on a dare and a bet. It had been great, athletic sex, but it could have been anyone. I was certain he felt the same way. The Girls of Howard Pass had officially lost track of how many women he'd slept with that summer, even though I had attempted a list. I was a notch on his belt, nothing more. And there was no way of telling whether he knew he was a notch in mine, too.

"Tundra's turning red. Pretty, huh?" I said lamely.

Al nodded. "Uh-huh."

Lucy, in the back seat, was silent the whole way, adding nothing to the conversation, purposefully, I thought, just to make me squirm.

UMIAT, THE LAST TIME

As we approached Umiat, I noticed the ceaseless bustle that had descended on base camp due to the end-of-summer population boom. Umiat resembled a giant ant farm buzzing with frantic activity. More planes than usual flew in and out of the airstrip, taking scientists and their equipment home for the year.

I entered the Howard Pass tent and found heaps of Tom and Helen's belongings strewn across the floor. Usually, Lucy and I found the tent empty when visiting Umiat. Missing from the huge mess were sleeping bags, but no Tom and Helen—they, had no doubt, already found an empty Quonset to cohabit.

"I don't want to sleep on a cot again." Lucy said flatly, looking around our wall tent. "Pretty soon, we'll all be back and the place will be crowded."

"Let's find another place with some privacy. And these cots are gross anyway. What do you care anyway? You'll be shacked up in a World War II vintage love nest with Corey," I teased.

"Yeah, hope so. He'll be in later today. So nervous! Can't wait to see him. Heart's going pitty pat. What's gonna happen, George?"

"Don't worry. You'll be fine in your hideaway, and I bet you already have one, but before you two start screwing, help me find a decent Quonset for the rest of us girls. How bad can a World War II mattress be after sleeping on the ground since June? And even if the bedsteads are rusty, that's okay because I got a tetanus shot before I came up this summer," I said, ready for our Quonset-inspecting adventure. I wanted a decent one that didn't smell of mold.

What we found, however, was far better than what we had anticipated, a fairly new-looking trailer near our tent camp but far enough away for privacy. Lucy opened the door and found the unit empty and clean, with two sets of bunk beds. A stone's throw from GSI and close to the Umiat Hilton, we wouldn't even have to use the shitty latrine near our wall tent camp.

"We'd better ask first," she said.

With high hopes, we walked over to the GSI bunkhouse, entering without knocking. The Moody Blues blared loudly:

Timothy Leary's dead; no, no, he's outside, looking in.

"Hello! Who's here?" I asked, my eyes trying to adjust to the relative darkness.

"We are. C'mon in," came Skip's familiar voice. He and Chris were playing cards and drinking bottles of Heineken.

Skip said, "Hey, gals, back at last, I see. Make yourself to home. Wanna drink?"

"No, too early for my champagne, but we have a favor to ask you," Lucy began.

"Anything you want," Skip answered, a faint blush creeping into his cheeks.

"May we use that nice, cozy, empty trailer to sleep in for a couple of nights, just us Howard Pass girls?" she said, batting her eyelashes.

I wanted to roll my eyes at her conniving behavior, but I wanted a nice bed to sleep in, too.

"Why, sure, ladies, it's all yours," Chris said, grinning.

Skip smiled and nodded his agreement.

"Thanks, guys. Maybe we'll invite you over for a party later on," I said in my coyest possible voice, trying to mimic Lucy's drawl.

Both men grinned. Chris scratched his head and looked back at the cards in his hand, looked up again, and said vacantly, "Where's my manners? How bout some hash?"

"That's mighty nice of y'all, but now we need to grab our stuff. See you in a while," Lucy said, again emphasizing her drawl as we headed out the door.

The trailer would be a fine home, certainly more comfortable than the stupid old plywood tent camp, and close to the showers and Dick the Cook's food. We resolved to save spaces for Kelly and Frannie when they got in from the field.

The thought of possibly spending the night with Ian somewhere else crossed my mind. So handsome. So sexy. Uncertainty and insecurity penetrated my now usually confident primitive brain. My pulse quickened. What would happen when he came in? *Hold on, Georgeie. Nothing's gonna happen. Stop it.*

I decided not to share my anticipation with Lucy because I felt kind of stupid about the whole thing.

* * *

After we'd moved our stuff down to the trailer, Lucy and I gathered our soap and towels and headed for the showers. First, we looked in on Dick the Cook and grabbed cups of coffee.

"Hi, girls. You can't see the cake yet, "he said. "I still need to decorate it, but it's too hot yet."

"What cake? What's the occasion?" I asked.

"Why, *you* guys," he said, picking his teeth with a toothpick. "Day after tomorrow will our last night together. Some of you guys go out the next morning. Gotta celebrate."

"Yeah, I go out first," I said glumly.

"Funny how this weird place gets under your skin," he said. "Some days I hate it here and some days I love it. Some days I can't wait to leave and some days I think I'd never leave because it's my home."

"But you've got the kids and Sheree to think about," I ventured.

"That's why I'm excited now—I'm going in two weeks. Be gone until after Thanksgiving," he said, a grin on his face.

He danced a couple of waltzing steps with an imaginary partner.

True love. Must be nice. I'd be lucky to find a guy like Dick the Cook, gentle and thoughtful, even kind of good-looking with those big blue eyes. And he can turn a can of lima beans and stale saltines into a gourmet feast.

"What kind of cake, Dick?" Lucy asked.

"Can't tell you, but tonight, by popular demand, my famous chocolate pudding cake will take center stage," he answered.

That was what I wanted to hear.

* * *

We left Dick the Cook to his chores, showered, and headed back towards our new digs. On the way, Linda intercepted us and asked us to join the food inventory chain gang. I knew Linda rarely had the chance to leave Umiat and I thought she was one of the least recognized people on the project, stuck in a dull job. So of course we dropped our things off in the trailer and followed her.

"Did Al ever take you up in the chopper?" I asked.

"Yeah. He let me go out on a mail run to Lookout Ridge with him. It was, how can I put it, gorgeous? Splendid?" she answered.

"Both of those things," Lucy said.

"You guys have had it rough all summer flying around."

"Yup, for sure," I said.

"Right now, you two can tally all the freeze-dried food coming in from the field. Put all the main courses in one box, vegetables in another box, well, you get the picture," she said.

This was an okay assignment—indoors and out of the wind and cold. I could pick up some gossip, too. Dave and Maxie from Ikpikpuk were counting tins of butter, sardines, and strawberry jam, while Tom and Helen, our own dynamic duo, inventoried boxes of Kimwipes, tissues, and food. There was a vast amount of oatmeal, Cream of Wheat, and Krusteaz pancake mix left over after almost three months in the field. The mountain of freeze-dried vegetables stacked behind some cots dwarfed this pile. There was enough freeze-dried corn to feed all the chickens in the Lower 48.

As Dave placed another can of butter into a box, he looked over at us and said, "I won't even touch the freeze-dried vegetables through my work gloves. I think they're radioactive."

A chorus of laughter ensued.

Conversations about where our lives were headed filled the air. While Debbie was excited to be seeing her husband soon, and Dave was looking forward to the Tennessee hills, a general air of melancholy spread through the supply tent. Even the more seasoned members of the crews who had several years of Alaska field experience under their belts looked bummed out. The North Slope had to be the most isolated, remote place on the planet most of us had ever seen, and most of us had loved it.

* * *

That evening, Lucy and I entered the mess hall packed with more returning crewmembers and the several regulars that kept Umiat running. An overflow crowd stood in the hall.

"Tomorrow, you guys will have to eat in shifts," Dick the Cook said to Lookout Ridge Mitch, the only crew chief who'd made it back so far. "You're killing me! I can't cook that fast," he moaned.

Mitch took charge and announced that Howard Pass and Ikpikpuk would eat together, at seven, eleven, and five, and Lookout Ridge and Colville River would eat afterwards, at eight, twelve, and six.

"But," Dick the Cook said, "on our last night, we'll all eat cake together at seven o'clock! Standing room only."

"Hey, I *like* that idea!" a familiar voice said.

I turned towards the door to see Malcolm coming into the room, quickly followed by Kelly, Ron, Maxie, and Ian. How could Al and Sam have flown the entire Ikpikpuk and Howard Pass crews back in one day? They must have flown non-stop. I was flabbergasted.

Colville River and Lookout Ridge wouldn't completely rejoin us until the following day. I wondered who Mitch had left in charge out at Lookout Ridge—he struck me as someone who had to be in control all the time. My guess was, however, whoever had been designated Chief-For-A-Day, the crew would sleep late, eat chocolate, survey for an hour or two, inventory leftover supplies, get high, and consume a large dinner devoid of freeze-dried vegetables.

I wanted to hug my Howard Pass comrades, but Ian's presence stopped me. He looked at me intensely and with no small amount of longing. I wanted to run to him but lost my nerve. Nothing had happened yet. Maybe nothing would.

Mitch acknowledged fellow crew chiefs Ian and Malcolm, then continued outlining the plan of attack. "Everyone will be back towards dinner time tomorrow, including the rest of my crew and Andy's boat crew on the Colville. Those of you who were invent-torying supplies and food will have plenty more to do once everyone else arrives. All tarps, Coleman stoves, shotguns, cameras, and compasses will have to be counted, inspected and cleaned. Freeze-dried vegetables will be conveniently forgotten or obediently packed up for next summer. Other crewmembers will either muck out the latrine near the tent camp or clean up trash around Umiat. We've been guests here all summer," he concluded. "Let's do our best to clean up Umiat—leave it the way we found it."

This comment caused the normally quiet Sam to say in a rather loud but genteel voice, "Cleanin' up Umiat is like stickin' a ruby up a goat's ass."

Everyone roared. Mitch was a little taken aback but had to admit that cleanin' up Umiat *was* just what Sam said it was. Malcolm laughed so hard, I thought he'd bust a gut. Ian, who had been staring at me, lost his composure, bent over, and guffawed loudly.

"Now, people," Mitch said, "I know how funny that sounds, but we've got to leave Umiat in a better state than we found it in."

Despite this admonition, titters and giggles were slow to die. Ian winked at me.

329

Then, Rick got up and put the ultimate kibosh on my evening: "Good ideas, Mitch. I want to meet with the crew chiefs tonight and figure out in more detail the plan ahead for this winter and, if we're lucky, a second field season. We'll fill in Andy when Colville River gets back." He crossed his fingers. "Tomorrow is time enough to party."

Well, there go my chances of getting lucky tonight.

* * *

After dinner, I told Kelly about our new digs.

"Far out! Killer, you're the greatest," she said, "Let's check out this wonderful trailer."

We walked over to our new digs.

"Wow! A real bed," Kelly said, a smile on her face. "Look, there's even a mirror. I can't wait to lay my head down on that nice pillow,"

The trailer had passed muster.

"But wait a sec," I said. "Where's Toni? She got back, didn't she?"

"Yeah, she's here," Kelly said, "And if you can't figure out where she is, why don't you check out Al's Quonset?"

"Duh," I said. "I bet she's being well taken care of, so let's go hang out at GSI and see what's going on."

"I wonder if the Howard Pass crew will *really* be reunited," Kelly mused. "Tom and Helen, Corey and Lucy, and Toni and Al are all off doing the horizontal cha-cha in the Quonsets somewhere."

"So, it's just you, me, Ron, Malcolm, and, of course, Frannie, who aren't fornicating," I said. "I really want to see Lucy and give her a hug good-bye. And Tom and Helen, too, and even Toni."

"C'mon, lets break out some makeup and break hearts at GSI," Kelly said, putting an end to gossip.

* * *

When the three of us arrived at GSI, Chris welcomed us and offered us paper cups for our favorite booze. I poured myself a scotch. Kelly chose tequila.

Skip ambled over. "Ladies, wait til you see what I brewed for tomorrow night," he said, a proud smile on his face.

"What?" I asked.

"Moonshine," he answered. "One batch is made with raisins, the other batch

with canned fruit cocktail. She's been sittin' in the sun for a few days. I just have to skim er one more time and she'll be ready for tomorrow night."

Skim what? Is that shit drinkable?

We shot the shit with Chris and Skip for a while, then I wandered back to the trailer and made it a fairly early night.

When I crawled into my sleeping bag with one hand curled around *Hawaii*, my thoughts turned to the following night when I'd see Ian. Way too excited about being with him, I tried to distract myself with thoughts about going to grad school, but that didn't work. I could only see Ian's brown eyes and beard. He had a nice chest, too, beneath his khaki shirt. In fact, he had a nice everything. His distinctive loud voice gave orders and told jokes equally well. I found his alpha male take-charge personality incredibly sexy.

Best of all, he could sing and so could I. Our duets back in the dorm at UAF had electrified me. I'd never the chance to sing my favorite songs with anyone else. Hell, all I did was sing them out loud by myself in my DC apartment and pretend I had a partner to sing them

* * *

I resumed my supply tent duties the next morning after breakfast. Denied Frannie's company—she'd been assigned to cleanup detail—I listened to conversations around me. Kelly sat next to me counting cutlery and Melmac cups.

Our part of Umiat had become a boomtown, just like the beginning of the summer when we'd all flown north together. Every time the chopper brought in more crewmembers, it stayed on the ground for a scant five minutes and lifted off again. Finally, all four crews were back. Excited greetings and the sounds of the plywood doors opening and slamming shut again filled the air. The tent camp had completely recolonized, not unlike a beehive. The ant farm analogy was too tame.

I heard Ian's voice long before I saw him. He and Gary had stopped outside the supply tent where they stood talking about getting field notes together and packing up artifacts. I couldn't resist. Putting down my magic marker, I got up and walked outside.

"Hey, Ian, we have a rendezvous this evening," I said, surprising myself with my boldness. I grinned at him.

He spun around, ignoring Gary, looked at me, and doffed his fedora, a smile spreading across his face. "Ma'am, it will be my pleasure to rendezvous with you whenever you say!" He gave me a bear hug, lifting me off the ground. "Georgeie, I've been thinkin' about ya. I'm glad to see ya," he whispered in my ear.

I felt a soft kiss on my neck. Stunned, I staggered back a couple of steps. I smiled again, ecstatic at the thought of singing with him later, and just feeling happy in general. He comforted and disturbed me at the same time. I had it bad and as the saying goes "that ain't never good."

* * *

After steaming-hot showers, we applied Kelly's mascara and blush to our tanned faces, giggling into the latrine mirror. A guy entered to use the destroilets and did a double take—young women in makeup was an uncommon sight in Umiat.

"You know, when I got picked up at the Fairbanks airport in June, I asked the guy from the U what Alaska would be like for a whole summer. You know what he said?" I asked.

"What?"

"He said, 'You'll have the time of your life but you'll look twenty years older when you leave.'"

"He was right, huh?"

"Well, I still recognize myself, but I've never looked quite this weathered," I answered.

We finished primping and then walked down to the mess hall. We got coffee, sat down, and lit up. Dick the Cook was standing in the back doorway, looking off to the east, letting the autumn breeze cool him off a little. He'd just finished baking an industrial-sized apple cobbler and his face and apron were covered with flour. I could smell the cobbler. It made my nose quiver.

"Kelly, I've got something to tell you," I said.

"What?"

I leaned over so Dick the Cook wouldn't overhear my confession. "I want Ian so bad I think I'm gonna pop."

"Take it easy, George. Take a deep breath."

"We're going to sing together at GSI tonight. We sang in Fairbanks before we all flew up here, and it was powerful, like we were connected deep inside."

"Singing isn't fucking. Chill."

"Yeah, but I really want him, and if I feel that electricity, I'm going for it," I said, "but he's married. We'd be committing adultery."

"Just be careful, George, and remember, I love you no matter what."

For the one hundredth time that summer, I gave Kelly a hug. What would I do without her to help run my life that fall?

* * *

That evening, the sun hid behind the clouds and the air grew cold. I wore my parka walking to dinner, then to the GSI party. By then, Frannie had found us and moved her stuff from the Lookout Ridge tent to our trailer and declared it "Otay!" Her idea of fashion in the cold was an ugly pink crocheted hat a friend in Fairbanks had made for her.

"That's hideous, Frannie," I said.

"Sucks, I know," she answered.

Suddenly, a hand grabbed my shoulder and a loud voice said, "Ready for tonight, gal?" Ian's eyes danced in excitement and expectation. Out of the corner of my eye, *Frannie* indicated her distaste for Ian by rolling her eyes and shaking her head.

I caught Ian's buoyant mood immediately and asked, "Where's the instruments?"

"At GSI," he replied.

"Can't wait," I said, a slight quaver in my voice. "See you in a while."

Ian ran ahead while Frannie and I continued at a leisurely pace. She waited until Ian was out of earshot, then turned to me. "You're nuts," she said.

* * *

Frannie and I, along with a throng of happy partiers, pushed into GSI at about the same time. I found Ian just inside the front door, drinking a *Scotch* and holding up the bar. My heart skipped several beats before I said, "You want something really good? There's two kinds of moonshine, one made from raisins and one made from canned fruit cocktail."

"No shit, really?" he said loudly, "Why, Jesus, I've had a lot of stuff in my day, but that's new to me!"

He set his Scotch on a table nearby and we headed over to Skip.

"Raisin or fruit cocktail?" Skip asked, ever the host.

"Believe I'll try the raisin moonshine," Ian said.

"And for the little lady?" Skip asked, looking at me.

"I've been waiting for the fruit cocktail moonshine for a while now," I said, smiling in anticipation.

"Moonshine for two!" Skip said, reaching behind the counter for the two jugs. He poured me a Dixie cup full of a clearish yet pulpy liquid.

"Bottoms up!" I said enthusiastically.

Whoever coined the expression "white lightning" wasn't kidding. The stuff burned all the way down.

"This must be what Sterno tastes like," I said. My nose began to run immediately. I sniffled, wiped my nose on my sleeve and coughed, "Great stuff! How's the raisin kind, Ian?"

"Holy mother of God!" was all he could wheeze.

We shambled over to the sofa and sat down to recover. "Won't Get Fooled Again" blared from the eight-track. I watched as Skip offered the moonshine to his guests and observed various reactions. Skip had apparently grown up on moonshine. He sipped his creation with pride. His buddy, Chris, on the other hand, refused to drink any. I guess he knew better.

Soon, GSI was packed. All of Umiat was there, even Ellie for a short time. Sam grabbed some bourbon and ice and headed over in our direction, fiddle in hand, and stood quietly next to the Naugahyde sofa. Ian tuned one of the guitars. He asked me what I'd like to sing first.

"Let's see. How about "Old Blue"?" I asked.

"Okay, here goes."

He started strumming the intro. We looked at each other, hitting the first note on time and in pitch. I had to look down at my shoes to concentrate and not stare at Ian's face, but I could feel his eyes on me.

I sang as I looked up, "*Had an old dog, and his name was Blue...*"

Sam caught the melody and accompanied us on fiddle. Several people stopped their conversations to listen and some began to sing along. At the end, we got a round of applause and hugged each other. We sang through most of the evening, reveling in our harmonies. Sam accompanied us on either the banjo, guitar, or fiddle, depending on the song. He kept his saw, a strictly a solo instrument, for a finale. Preacher John strummed the other available guitar.

Some of the partygoers moved outside for a while because a group of guys had gotten the brilliant idea of setting fire to the old telephone pole closest to the latrine.

"This hasn't been used since World War II, so it's got to be sacrificed," someone said.

"Down she comes! Get the Blazo!" someone else shouted.

A great fire lit up the dark, end-of-summer sky. People lined up on either side of the pole to warm themselves and yell obscenities at the air. I could see Corey and Lucy a little way down from me, arms around each other, kissing. I saw Tom passing a joint to Helen, who passed it on to someone from Colville River.

Al was noticeably absent, as was Toni. Ross was so drunk he fell down on the ground. Ron sank to his knees and threw up, and Malcolm walked around in a stupor.

"Oh God, oh God, oh God," he mumbled.

Kelly, Frannie, and I grabbed him by the shoulders and told him about our trailer.

"So that's where you guys are! Thanks so much, you bitches! You leave me and Ron alone in the Howard Pass tent. You know how much he farts. Thanks so much. You are all banished from Uncle Malcolm's kingdom," he said, swaying back and forth.

"Awwww, you'll see Viola the day after tomorrow, so I don't feel sorry for you," I said. "C'mon, we'll show you our palace."

We left the telephone pole to show Malcolm our digs.

"Christ, I have to pee," Frannie said. She dropped her pants near our trailer. Kelly and I, full of alcohol, squatted in sisterly solidarity in front of Malcolm.

"That's the most disgusting thing I've ever seen. Stop!" he yelled. He stumbled back towards GSI, holding his head in his hands as if he'd gouged out his eyes like Oedipus. The three of us zipped up and laughed. I was barely aware of what I was doing, and Malcolm never *did* get to see our happy hideaway. He'd fled the scene.

Back at GSI, I poured myself a Scotch and returned to the sofa and the guitar. I was getting tired and the party was breaking up. Sam was still there, though, and I asked him to play the fiddle while I sang "Faded Love," a quiet song and one of my favorites. Halfway through, Ian sauntered over from the bar, joined me on the sofa, and began to harmonize.

There it was again—that spark, that rush of adrenaline. We finished the song. I leaned back into the sofa. Ian looked at me and told me I was prettier now than when he'd met me. He put his fedora on my head. All summer long, I had wanted his hat as much as the man wearing it. I lit a smoke and relaxed further into the sofa.

Ian leaned over to me and whispered, "Why don't you go get your stuff, Georgeie, and let's us go take a shower at the Hilton."

I wasn't entirely sure that was what he said, but, on the other hand, I *was* sure. I feigned nonchalance. We agreed to meet outside the all-girl trailer. I went to my bunk and grabbed my toothbrush, towel, and just to be on the safe side, my diaphragm. If taking a shower meant sex, I wanted to be prepared, like the Girl Scouts had taught me in my teens. On the other hand, I'd be horrified if it *didn't* mean sex and Ian saw the diaphragm in my bag of toiletries.

When I got outside, he was there, towel thrown over his shoulder, whistling "Darcy Farrow," a favorite of mine. I started to sing,

Where the Truckee runs down through the Carson Valley plain,
There lived a maiden, Darcy Farrow was her name...

By the time we'd finished the song, we'd reached the Hilton, arms flung around each other. No one was up. It was quiet as a still day on the tundra. We headed toward the latrine. Any fogginess caused by alcohol and dope had evaporated during our walk.

Without a moment's hesitation, Ian walked up on the shower platform and closed the curtain behind him. I followed him after ducking into a stall to insert my diaphragm. Unable to stand the suspense any longer, I stepped up onto the shower platform, closed the curtain, and began to undress. Ian's clothes lay in a heap on the wooden floor. I stuck my hand in his shower to test the water temperature. He pulled me in immediately, grabbing me while my back was to him and began to lather me up.

Oh my God, this is really happening. I want this.

Carried away in a dizzying flood of lust, I turned around and kissed him hard. The water beat down on us as we embraced. The muscles on his lean body were exquisitely defined and the hair on his chest made me almost faint dead away. I felt his hardness against me but never having made love in a shower, didn't know what to do. He lifted me off my feet. I wrapped my legs around him and grabbed the top of the shower compartment with my left hand, putting my right hand around his shoulder.

I moaned softly, not wanting to wake the Smiths, Dick the Cook, or any visiting scientist who might be a light sleeper. I pulled back my head to look at him. His was one of the most intense gazes I'd ever seen. He looked into my eyes and thrust harder. When we were done, he set me down on my feet. We stood embracing each other under the pelting water. Practically out of breath and in a stupor, convoluted emotions flooded my brain. A lump rose in my throat.

I just had sex with a married man. What have I done?

What did adultery mean up here? I had been attracted to Ian since I'd first seen him and created the fantasy that if he weren't married, we'd end up together. I was in way over my head and I knew it. I reached over and turned up the water temperature and let it massage the back of my neck while he kissed me softly.

"You like it awful hot, don't you?" he said.

My arms still encircled him as I felt his body go limp. He hit the ground with a thud, his ankle falling through a space between the shower and the platform next to it. Alarmed, I kneeled down and took his head in my hands. Here I was naked in a shower at the Umiat Hilton with a married man wearing a wedding ring who happened to be one of the bosses, and he had just fainted. I hoped he hadn't broken his foot.

I called Ian's name softly and gently slapped his face until he started to come to. As white as a sheet, he got up with my help.

"I heard you hate coffee, but you and I are going to get dressed, walk down to the mess hall, and I am going to see that you drink a couple of cups," I said.

He sighed. We kissed softly, got dressed in slow motion, and walked down the hall, arms around each other, not saying a word.

"Sit down, Ian" I said. I poured us coffee. "You've got to drink it," I said, resting the palm of my hand gently on his back, then walked around the table and sat across from him.

He began to drink his coffee. I was silent, still thinking about having just made love to a married man.

"You okay?" he finally asked, apparently sensing my quiet discomfort. He touched my arm gently.

Instead of replying with a long explanation of what I was feeling, I just said, "Yep."

"Good," he said, "Let's go find us an empty Quonset hut and stay together tonight." He sighed again and stared into his coffee cup.

We walked back toward the girls-only trailer in silence. When we reached it, I went in, tripped over a backpack, and found my sleeping bag on the bunk.

Frannie woke up. "Georgeie, is that you?"

"Yeah," I replied, "I'm taking my sleeping bag and going elsewhere."

"Huh?" she said.

"See you tomorrow," I replied.

Ian and I found an unoccupied Quonset nearby, cold and dank, but a love nest just the same. We opened our sleeping bags, lying on one and putting the other one over us. We made love again, slowly and gently. This time, I kept two pairs of wool socks on and wrapped my arms and legs around him. Afterwards, I put my head on his chest and soon fell asleep after the most erotic, exotic night of my life.

* * *

I woke up slightly disoriented and cold because my ass hung outside my sleeping bag.

Huh? Where am I?

When I felt the warmth of Ian's chest and heard his rhythmical breathing, I remembered. His right hand grabbed my left arm in his sleep. He shifted slightly, turned his face toward me, and lightly kissed my forehead. He began to rouse.

"Good mornin', darlin'," he said softly, kissing my face.

All I could manage was a contented sigh. It had all come back to me. I had wanted this man for so long, but now that I had him, what should I do with him?

Wordlessly, he spread my thighs with his knees and entered me again while nuzzling my neck. I felt open, vulnerable, and willing. He kissed my face, my ears, my nose, and my neck as we made love. When he felt me come, he grabbed me tighter, and yelled in what I thought way too loud a voice, "Thank you, Jesus!"

After he came, we quickly disengaged. While I was content to lie in bed and replay the last half hour in my mind over and over, hoping for a repeat performance, Ian had moved quickly beyond the afterglow phase and into the giddy-up phase.

"Gotta get up!" he said. "Gotta go to work! Gotta muck out the latrine today! Gotta supervise getting rid of all that old shit! C'mon, girl! Chop-chop! Get a move on. C'mon!"

I was not a morning person as everyone on the Howard Pass crew had come to appreciate. But I had never woken up at Ikpikpuk so Ian had no way of knowing what a slug I was in the morning, and I had no idea what a go-getter he was. I waited while he put on his long johns, jeans, boots, flannel shirt, and down vest.

"Okay, I'm right behind you," I lied. He sat back down on the bed, looked at me and stroked my hair.

"That was special," he said. He kissed me tenderly, then literally bounded out of the Quonset.

I lay in the tangle of sleeping bags and clothing for a full five minutes. I would have stayed there even longer, but I needed to pee, catch breakfast, and do some work. I had no idea what time it was. My watch had stopped.

What will people think? I worried. *Should I avoid him? Should I grab his hand, or pretend nothing happened? I don't have a fucking clue.*

Luck was with me that morning in one sense. When I went around the side of the Quonset, no one was there and I could pee without being seen. I next headed down to the Hilton and entered the mess hall. Breakfast was over but there was some leftover bacon on a plate and several partial loaves of bread. I put rye bread in the toaster, poured a cup of coffee, buttered some toast, and put several slices of bacon on it. I folded over my sandwich, sat down at a table, and stared out the window.

"Hey, George, late night?" It was Dick the Cook.

"I guess so," I answered.

"Hey, why the long face? You bummed?" he asked.

"Yeah, I guess," I answered.

"So, what happened? Wanna talk about it?" Dick the Cook drew closer.

"No, Dick, not really. Thanks, though. I just got too close to someone last night and I shouldn't have."

"Don't feel bad," he said, sitting down across from me with his own cup of coffee. "Weird shit happens up here. Whatever it was, it's probably okay. You'll be fine. Nothing wrong with getting close to someone up here. People need that. It happens. Happens to most of us, me included. It may become one of your fondest memories," he said soothingly. He paused pouring water in the coffee urn for the next refill, reached across the table, grabbed my hand, and gave it a squeeze.

"Thanks, Dick," I said, feeling emotional. Instead of crying, I sighed and said, "I guess I better go do something today. See ya later."

"Chin up, George, you'll see. You'll be fine. You know I'm jealous, don't you?" he said, swallowing his last gulp of coffee.

His kindness meant everything to me at the moment.

* * *

I walked back towards our tent camp to continue inventorying food and whatever else needed to be sorted. On the way, I'd have to pass our new latrine where Ian was overseeing a handful of aromatic colleagues dressed in rain gear. About ten guys had been conscripted to muck it out under Ian's direction. I saw Ian in his yellow rain gear spattered with brown. He saw me and smiled.

"Hi, stranger, having fun?" I asked.

"More than I can tell you, Georgeie. Talk to you later." He winked at me. The ice was broken. Good.

I passed three or four groups of fellow archaeologists with garbage bags on my way to the supply tent. They were on the making-Umiat-look-good detail. I heard "Hi, George" from several friends but felt too preoccupied to respond, except with a half-hearted wave.

In the supply tent, inventory duty had resumed. Carol, Colville Jay, and Kelly were labeling boxes and putting the remaining flagging tape, duct tape, graph paper, and pencils into discrete piles. Helen had been assigned to take all the Coleman stoves apart for inspection and cleaning. She sat cross-legged on the wood floor reassembling them.

I continued stuffing different categories of freeze-dried food into duffels. If there were to be a second season for the project, as was now rumored, we would *all* sign a petition against the frigging freeze-dried vegetables, the corn especially.

I took a piece of paper and a pencil to write down a list of tolerable freeze-dried food versus intolerable ones. I also noted what fresh foods we'd been able to use, at least for the first part of the summer, and compiled a list of suggestions for the least noxious freeze-dried food. My choices amounted to beef stroganoff and chili, period. I suggested we do away with all freeze-dried vegetables. They weren't food, didn't stay inside anyone long enough to provide nutrition, and certainly were never digested.

Real onions, garlic, carrots, and potatoes would probably stay good for most of the summer. Malcolm's insistence on taking Tillamook cheese in the field in five-pound blocks had proven very popular. Peanut butter (chunky), pilot bread, jam, canned bacon, breakfast bars, real maple syrup and pancake mix were essentials. More spices and Tabasco sauce would liven things up. I finished my master list, proud of my contribution, and took it back to the Howard Pass tent where Malcolm was lying on a cot, writing notes with his foot elevated on his daypack.

"Malcolm," I said, "I have a present for you—a list of what I think was good grub out there and what sucked."

"Why thanks, George," he said, and glanced at the list.

"*No* freeze-dried vegetables? None at all?" he asked.

"The only thing I can think to do with them is string them together in a necklace either before or after they're eaten," I said.

"Okay, well, I'll keep this and deal with it this winter. Thanks. You know, I don't envy you leaving tomorrow then flying all the way back to DC the day after," he said.

"I don't even want to think about it. Malcolm, I want to stay in Alaska this winter," I said pitifully.

"I know, George, but you'll come back next year. I know you will. Looks like there may be a second season; at least that's what Rick told me over breakfast. This summer was a big winner—over 200 sites."

"Wow, a second season? Think how much more experienced I'll be! No longer a cheechako. I am so excited!" It was just as if he'd told me it was Christmas.

"Yeah, I'd hire you again. You're great and look at where you came from. You didn't know anything that first week. You had no experience, but you watched, you pitched in, you learned. But now, you've got a chance to study with Uncle Mikey and begin making a name for yourself. I'll say I knew her when."

"Screw Uncle Mikey. He sounds nuts," I responded petulantly.

"Georgeie, my dear friend, give it a chance and let me know what's what," he said, sucking on the end of a pen.

"And there's something else, Malcolm," I said, looking down at my boots, "I had sex with Ian last night. Oh, Malcolm, I like him so much. I didn't mean for it to happen. Oh, man. He's married. What am I going to do?" I asked, feeling guilty as hell again.

"Don't blame yourself. Happens a lot in the field. Almost a rite of passage. The situations you get into out here—they're so extreme, so out there. Sometimes it's really life and death, and you take comfort in your friends in many ways."

He reached up and grabbed my hand. "Now, Georgeie, go finish up what you were doing over there and walk me down to the

Hilton for dinner. I may need to lean on your arm for the last little bit," he said.

"Okay, great. But I'm kind of afraid Ian will sit with us and I'll turn beet red," I said, looking at my boots.

"Georgeie, you can handle anything. Now, go on and come back and get me in a few," Malcolm called after me as I left the tent.

When the inventory was complete for the day, a half an hour later, Malcolm and I started our walk. He leaned on his walking stick for support. Maxie, Colville Jay, Ross, Tom and Helen, Kelly, and Ron joined us.

"Hey, Malcolm, wait up," Ian said, catching up to us. I didn't look at him. He and Malcolm talked about the day. Malcolm, of course, had been on light duty because of his ankle, while Ian had mucked out the latrine.

"I already threw out my rain gear," he said, "I don't think it will ever smell normal again."

"That was dumb. You could have put them in the washing machine a few times."

"Too late. After three showers, I feel somewhat clean," he said, turning to look at me at the word shower. "Say, Georgeie, how's your day?"

"Great, Ian. Although I only had time for one shower, it was quite a satisfying one," I teased.

"I'll bet it was," he said, and returned to talking with Malcolm about having to do some paperwork. Malcolm showed no reaction to our banter about showers.

* * *

Later, I took Kelly aside and whispered to her why I hadn't woken up in the trailer that morning. Her eyes got big.

She said in a soft voice, "Maxie says he's been going nuts lately. You probably saved his sanity. You did him a favor!"

"Probably a big one," I said awkwardly.

Kelly was right. Towards the end of the summer, most people had been going slightly nuts, or so I'd heard. Malcolm had a theory that every field season was just one day too long, no matter how short or long the season was. You started to anticipate going home. You got tired of pumping a stove to brew coffee in the morning. Living in a tent lost its allure. You started to bicker with your tent mate, if you had one. You wanted to go home. Malcolm's theory sounded right on the money to me, except I didn't want to go home, and I wasn't sure I was going to have a real one for quite a while. A shitty little dorm room, I guessed.

As much as I was ready to leave, dress in normal clothes, look in a mirror, sit in a chair with a back, and drink a carbonated soda, I also wanted to stay in the land of destroilets and grizzly bears. I didn't want to leave this life behind, but I kind of missed my East Coast life, too.

* * *

At dinner, I sat between Malcolm and Kelly. Preacher John took a seat next to Kelly. Ian sat opposite me, making me sit up very straight. Malcolm and Ian talked about the upcoming winter, analyzing artifacts, and writing the report. They were also discussing the inevitability of moving from Fairbanks to Anchorage to set up a new office and lab. During a lull in the conversation, Ian looked at me across the table and said, "How ya doin', gal?"

"Fine," I said, "Got mixed feelings about going out tomorrow."

"I know," he said, "But we'll sing tonight, make more music. It'll be good."

He looked at me as if he was in a daze.

The whole world must know we're screwing.

"Al," I brazenly asked our always-hunky pilot as he walked by, "where's the party tonight?"

"The supply tent. GSI's still cleanin' up after last night and some of the guys are hungover," he said, paying me little attention. Maybe he'd bagged his next trophy, but so what? I had someone far better.

"Hey, look at that," Ross said, turning his attention to a nearby commotion.

Kelly and I turned around to see Dick the Cook placing his highly anticipated sheet cake on the first table so everyone could gather around it. He carefully lifted a layer of waxed paper off the icing. The paper had been carefully supported with toothpicks to preserve his artwork. People who were waiting in the hallway crowded in to get a glimpse of his magnum opus.

"Voila," he said with pride.

There were "oohs" and "aahs" and "let me sees" from around the room. An Arctic scene covered the top of the cake. Sitting on green tundra was a blue Jet Ranger, faithfully reproduced in detail, serial number included. In large letters over the chopper were piped in black NORTH SLOPE ALASKA ARCHAEOLOGY ADVENTURE 1977. To the left of the chopper in smaller green letters was written HOWARD PASS and IKPIKPUK RIVER. To the right, LOOKOUT RIDGE and COLVILLE RIVER were similarly written. Pink icing rose in curlicues around the edges.

"I think Rick, your noble leader, should cut the first slice," Dick the Cook said.

He handed the cake knife to Rick, who declared the field season a success because we'd found so many new sites. He thanked us all, said he'd never forget this summer, and attempted humor when he mentioned how wonderful it was that no one had died. Although there were howls of laughter, Rick's pronouncement rang true. Malcolm had come close to doing himself in, as had I, and someone on the Lookout Ridge crew could easily have suffered a fatal bear mauling.

Rick sliced into the cake, revealing three layers of chocolate. A round of applause followed, along with hoots and screams.

"Cut the damn cake!" someone yelled.

Most of us stuffed ourselves with two helpings of the wonderful dessert. If thirds had been available, I would have had another slice.

"Thanks, Dick," I said after my two slices. "Thanks for the cake. It was real good."

Dick the Cook hugged me and told me he'd miss our talks.

"Me, too," I answered and slunk towards the door, sniffling back tears.

But I looked at Ian over my shoulder and smiled. I had magically gotten over any guilty feelings I'd had. Maybe our tryst *would* become one of my best memories but I'd be leaving him behind. Hell, I'd be leaving everyone.

* * *

On the walk back to the trailer, I questioned my decision to go to Uconn, but what would I do if I stayed in Anchorage? Ian was spoken for. His wife and kids were moving up sometime during the winter. There was no future with him, despite our attraction. I had no doubt he loved his wife and adored his children. So there I'd be, no job and lusting after a man I couldn't have.

But, I'd have tonight. I'd make the most out of it, then say goodbye to Ian, Malcolm, the Howard Pass crew, and everyone else, the following day.

I reached our trailer. Frannie and Kelly were inside. Even though I knew Frannie wouldn't approve, I told my New York bud about my adventure, including the fainting episode in the shower. She looked at me and quipped, "Now I know why they call you Killer Bitch."

"I really like him, Frannie. What am I gonna do?" I said, feeling helpless.

She put an arm around me. "But he's obnoxious! You're an ass, you know? Why couldn't you pick Ross or Dave?" she asked.

"I don't know," I answered. "I'm an idiot."

"Don't be too hard on Georgeie," Kelly said, coming to my defense.

"Yeah, yeah, I know," Frannie said, engrossed in her novel.

Kelly and I primped for the hootenanny. She chose a pink shade of lipstick and I chose hot red to match my increasingly lusty mood.

"How do I look?" I said.

"You look beautiful in an Arctic Killer Bitch kind of way," she said, picking a piece of lint off my sweater.

"And you, as always, are Feisty Bitch personified."

Arm in arm, we proceeded to the supply tent. Beer already flowed and someone passed a joint around. I made my way over to the cot where Sam, Preacher John and Ian were tuning up.

I said to Sam, "It's my last night. Will you play something on the saw for me?" "I'd be honored, Georgia."

Ian asked Sam, "You still think cleaning up Umiat's like sticking a ruby up a goat's ass?"

"Uh-huh. Just because some trash got picked up don't change nothin'. It's still the ass end of the world."

Our last party was more mellow than lively. A telephone pole had already been sacrificed and fried. People were terrifically hungover from the night before; some faces were positively gray. More than anything, people seemed content to talk with their crewmates enjoying last-minute conversations.

About twenty of us were flying out at noon the following day. Ian and I sang more of our favorite songs that night—"Summer Wages," "Mr. Bojangles," "Hobo's Lullaby." Toward the end of the evening when people started to retire to their tents or Quonsets, Ian asked me, "Do you know "Texas Rangers"?"

Of course I did. It was one of my favorite songs, a chilling lament sung a capella, I'd long fantasized about singing with someone. We looked intently at each other, took a breath, and started to sing,

> *Come all you Texas Rangers;*
> *Wherever you may be;*
> *I'll tell you of some troubles*
> *That happened unto me...*

We hit every note on the money. The ten or so people still in the room stopped talking and listened. Someone said, "I didn't know they could sing like that!"

We were in a world of our own where all that mattered were words and harmony. We did not look away from each other's gaze until we finished the dirge, holding the last note for emphasis. Stunned silence turned to enthusiastic applause and a few whoops. We hugged each other.

"Christ Almighty," Maxie said. "Who knew y'all had such talent?"

After a brief instrumental on the saw to close the evening and hugs among various partygoers, Ian and I made our way out of the supply tent, arms wrapped around each other, not hiding our relationship. We headed back to our Quonset, quickly undressed and got under the sleeping bags. All of my body parts touched all of his body parts in an effort to keep out the cold. I could see my breath.

"You sad, George?" Ian whispered.

"Yeah, uh huh," I said.

I really didn't feel like saying anything else. What was the use?

"Tonight, we have each other, darlin'," Ian said, kissing my face. "Just concentrate on that."

I did. I was quickly and effortlessly caught up in our passion which was about as sweet as any I'd ever experienced.

* * *

"Georgeie! Get your lazy ass out of bed! The plane's here! You got fifteen minutes!" Frannie yelled into our row of Quonsets.

I could hear her approach about three doors down and by the time she got to ours, I was wide awake. Ian and I convulsed in laughter.

"I'm coming!" I answered. Obviously, we had overslept. We hurriedly dressed and looked at each other. So, this was goodbye.

"Shit. I got to go down to the Hilton. Give me a hug goodbye, Georgeie," Ian said.

I didn't know what to say, so I said nothing. I hugged him and we kissed for the last time.

"I'll always remember this," he said.

All I could manage was "Me, too."

He turned around and stepped outside. I could hear his footsteps crunching on the gravel. The sound grew gradually fainter. I thought I would cry but didn't want to look heartsick and give the whole thing away completely in case one or two people hadn't picked up on our affair.

I walked down to the Hilton, alone, looking at the reddish tundra surrounding Umiat for the last time. The dinged-up old DC-3 that had brought me up was ready to take me back to Fairbanks. One of my pals had put my belongings into the middle of a pile of stuff going out on the first plane. She had done me this favor, probably knowing how bummed I'd be.

I can't get on, I thought.

My only consolation was that Frannie was going out on the same plane. I'd stick with her and spend the night at her house. She'd look after me.

I felt like someone had died. Was it the old me? I felt like I was going to a funeral and likely looked it, too. I wore a totally ashen, somber look on my face.

I opened the door of the Hilton and went into the mess hall. The DC-3 had brought in a load of mail. Ian stood in the middle of the room handing out the last letters from home. A letter from his wife, I supposed, stuck out of his shirt pocket. I looked at the floor.

Ray poked me in the side and said, "Hey, George, you hear the news?"

"What news?"

"Elvis Presley died."

"No shit?"

"No shit."

The news fit my mood. Hadn't Don McLean written about the day the music died just a few years earlier?

* * *

"Hey, folks, chop-chop! Plane's leaving. Gonna miss you," OJ said.

By the time I got outside, a blur of people were getting on board the DC-3. I had to hug everyone goodbye. I gave Malcolm a special hug and told him he meant the world to me. I told him I'd be good and make him proud at school.

"You better! Uncle Malcolm's counting on you!"

I hugged Kelly and Lucy, my dearest friends. We cried on each other's shoulders.

"What am I going to do without you guys?" I said.

The three of us sniveled and embraced for too short a time.

I reached Ian last. We embraced each other for what seemed like an eternity but was only a few seconds.

"Think of me, darlin'," he said. I nodded. No words came. I didn't want to cry again, so I let go, turned around, ran over to the plane, and hopped on. I turned to wave, then found the one open seat.

Jay Smith shut the door and the propellers began to spin.

PART II
AFTERWARDS

WASHINGTON DC, 1993

I rounded the corner into the hospital corridor, heart pounding. I told myself it didn't matter how Malcolm looked; I would kiss him on the cheek because he was still my friend, not the cancer he had.

The hospital smelled of disinfectant that masked odors of death and decay. Bright, cold, sterile lights in the halls brought into focus minute details of things I did not want to see. I had never been this afraid of anything. I'd braved bears, injuries, and wolverines in Alaska, but coming face-to-face with a dying friend was far worse.

I entered Malcolm's room. I saw my friend, shrunken by cancer, sitting propped up amid a pile of pillows on a hospital bed. Various tubes snaked from his arms and from under his hospital gown. He was skeletal but recognizable. I held his gaze for a moment and gently kissed him. My husband and I sat down on the couch. On a chair next to us sat Alice, Malcolm's wife. She gave us a tired smile.

Malcolm's liver was failing. You could tell by his color. Even the whites of his eyes were yellow. Malcolm's death was near, although we still hoped for a miracle.

Alice broke the silence: "Malcolm, look who's here—it's Georgeie and Alan, all the way from Alaska."

Malcolm smiled. "I'm proud of you, Dr. Georgeie."

I had finally finished my PhD and defended my dissertation about the prehistoric Inupiat of Barrow, Alaska a few days before. I had been so nervous about this rite of passage I'd developed a cold and then laryngitis just before the flight east. I considered not visiting Malcolm, using my cold as an excuse. But I knew I had to see him to honor our long-standing friendship. My remaining cough and sniffles weren't going to matter in the long run. There was no way around it. I couldn't chicken out.

* * *

Malcolm had migrated from California to Alaska in the early 70s and worked as an archaeologist for years. But, by the late 80s, long after we'd worked together, he'd had his fill of long, dark winters and isolation. He met Alice at a conference, fell in love, left Alaska behind, and moved in with her in DC where I'd gone to college, and a place I still call home no matter where I'm living.

We reminisced. He said, "Someone should excavate that complex site at Lancy Lake—you remember that one, of course, the one with all the localities, and the *karigi*?"

"Yeah," I said. "We could have spent the entire summer there. I bet there's hundreds of MA theses and PhD dissertations there. I kinda wish I could do it myself, but a second dissertation? This one almost killed me."

We talked about the site for a while, then gossiped about our friends in Alaska, but I think we both knew he would never get up north again.

He began to look tired and mentioned that Alice was looking forward to dinner with Alan and me.

"She needs a break," he said.

I kissed Malcolm a second time, squeezed his hand, and said we'd have a good dinner gossiping about him. I didn't look back as we left the room.

* * *

At dinner, my focus turned to Alice, about to become a widow and suffering with that knowledge. Throughout the barely touched meal, she talked about Malcolm's treatments, his reactions, and his general physical deterioration. I had never been exposed to such an intimate level of detail about the process of dying. I listened and remained focused on her despite my discomfort.

I'd always weathered death and dying mechanically, remembering the deceased intellectually in somber conversation. A stiff upper lip was expected, even demanded. When my father died, I wasn't allowed to be involved in any ritual involving his passing. I didn't even miss a day from school. From that point on, I appeared to be a happy, if aloof, kid. Inside, I felt an incredible sadness and a fear of the future. I had mourned quietly for decades without realizing it.

In Malcolm's hospital room, long-suppressed dread resurfaced. But, because he was not family, the old family rules did not apply. I felt physically raw. I had to keep myself together during the chaos of feelings.

This is about Malcolm, not about you. He needs you. You can't shrink away.

ANCHORAGE, ALASKA, 1993

A gorgeous spring day in Anchorage, I began to unpack from my trip back East. Tonight, I'd put my dirty clothes in the wash and sort the stuff I'd brought home from my dissertation defense—notes, the dissertation draft, ideas from my committee, a copy of the page signed by my committee accepting the dissertation.

I had a little editing to do, but I was now officially Dr. Georgeie. The degree was in the bag. That evening, I'd been treated to a celebratory dinner of lamb at my advisor's home. He said I had done well, even though I had been mortified at my performance.

The phone rang as I finished stuffing the laundry in the washing machine. My friend Susan said, "There's no good way to say this, Georgeie, but Malcolm died a couple of hours ago. Alice just called me."

I could not speak. I had heard the words. I had even believed them. I could not speak.

"After you left, he seemed to be improving, but then a couple of days ago, he went into a coma," Susan continued. "Alice was with him."

She waited for a response, but hearing nothing on my end, she continued. "He's going to be cremated and his ashes scattered up here in Katmai National Park. Alice will come up here in about a month. It's up to us to plan a party, or a wake, or something."

I cleared my throat. "We'll have the wake here at our house and invite all our archaeo friends."

"Well, let's talk about it later," Susan said, "We're both upset. Talk soon. Bye."

"Bye."

I choked on tears as I put the phone down and let myself cry while my mind wandered. I was grateful I'd visited with Malcolm in the hospital back East. He was one of the first to know I was a full-fledged PhD. He had known me when. Our connection was as easy the last time I saw him as it had been the first time. I thought about the Howard Pass Eight. One of us was gone now; the circle was no longer unbroken.

* * *

I returned to Alaska in 1978 and worked for Malcolm again, then went on to other fun and risky archaeological adventures. Alaska burrowed more deeply under my skin with each passing summer. Alan and I finally moved up to live year-round in 1982.

Malcolm, on the other hand, had tired of Alaska, moved back East sometime in the late 80s, married Alice, and begun a new career as a conservative-looking businessman. How ironic. One thing I was sure of, however. Alaska was imprinted permanently on all of us who were there that summer.

I stared at the picture cube containing our crew photo. I looked at the seasoned group of confident explorers, all in our twenties, tested by adversity, and ready to rely on one another for our lives. The tundra provided a striking backdrop.

My first summer up north transformed me. Before 1977, I'd never been out West, never camped out, pitched a tent, seen a bear except in a zoo, or relied on friends for protection and wellbeing. I became part of a group whose whole was far larger than the sum of its parts.

I had grown stronger and more vulnerable at the same time. Strong and vulnerable actually went together—it was a revelation.

PORTLAND, OREGON, TODAY

Sometimes I tell Malcolm about my adventures, ones he's missed. I tell him about the time I flew to Prudhoe Bay and then down the pipeline to Fairbanks in a chopper, seeing some of our old haunts from the air. I tell him about how I got weathered in on Little Diomede Island for a week. I tell him things pretty much look the same on the Slope—the stone *karigi* and all the caribou fences at Lancy Lake are still there.

I tell him about the current escapades of the crewmates I've kept track of. Kelly lived around the world, had two sons, and returned to Colorado. Lucy got married and is chair of the Anthro Department at a major university. Ron still lives in Alaska and has worked for the government ever since our summer together. Ian retired a few years ago, or so I heard. Frannie and I are still asshole buddies. Her husband died a couple of years ago. We get together when I'm in Alaska or she's down here, and we laugh like idiots, even though she's in the beginning stage of dementia. The others? I don't know. Tom and Helen probably still teach in the bush and have kiddies of their own. Toni? No idea. I wonder what she's doing.

Me? I finally retired from the government in DC after working with Indian Tribes across the country for a decade. Now I live in Portland, easy flights to Alaska and DC.

Malcolm never answers me when I talk to him, but I think if he hears me, he must enjoy my tales. I can even tell him the same story over and over and he doesn't mind.

Malcolm saved my life in 1977 by making sure I'd survive on the North Slope of Alaska. He saved me again in 1993 when he let me come close to his illness and continue the long journey to confront my fears.

I am eternally grateful.

ABOUT THE AUTHOR

GEORGEIE REYNOLDS has been hooked on Alaska since she first experienced the North Slope in 1977. Enchanted with the north, she moved to Anchorage in 1982 to continue her career as an archaeologist and stayed for many years. She has traveled north to Utqiagvik, south to Metlakatla, east to Eagle Village, and west to Attu and Saint Lawrence Island.

While living in Alaska, she completed her PhD in Anthropology at the State University of New York at Binghamton. Her dissertation focused on the proto-historic Inupiat of Utqiagvik (Barrow) Alaska.

Georgeie now writes about her many exploits and her cherished comrades from her home in Portland OR, halfway between Alaska and DC, her two favorite places.

She says, "Alaska has been the most important influence on my life and will always be with me."

Made in the USA
Columbia, SC
15 November 2021

48992378R00207